STUDENT SOLUTIONS MANUAL

Lindsay Packer
College of Charleston

Fundamentals of
STATISTICS

Michael Sullivan, III

PEARSON
Prentice
Hall

Upper Saddle River, NJ 07458

Editor-in-Chief: Sally Yagan
Acquisitions Editor: Petra Recter
Supplement Editor: Joanne Wendelken
Assistant Managing Editor: John Matthews
Production Editor: Donna Crilly
Supplement Cover Manager: Paul Gourhan
Supplement Cover Designer: Joanne Alexandris
Manufacturing Buyer: Ilene Kahn

© 2005 Pearson Education, Inc.
Pearson Prentice Hall
Pearson Education, Inc.
Upper Saddle River, NJ 07458

Pearson Prentice Hall® is a trademark of Pearson Education, Inc.

The author and publisher of this book have used their best efforts in preparing this book. These efforts include the development, research, and testing of the theories and programs to determine their effectiveness. The author and publisher make no warranty of any kind, expressed or implied, with regard to these programs or the documentation contained in this book. The author and publisher shall not be liable in any event for incidental or consequential damages in connection with, or arising out of, the furnishing, performance, or use of these programs.

Printed in the United States of America

10 9 8 7 6 5 4

ISBN 0-13-146787-5

Pearson Education Ltd., *London*
Pearson Education Australia Pty. Ltd., *Sydney*
Pearson Education Singapore, Pte. Ltd.
Pearson Education North Asia Ltd., *Hong Kong*
Pearson Education Canada, Inc., *Toronto*
Pearson Educación de Mexico, S.A. de C.V.
Pearson Education—Japan, *Tokyo*
Pearson Education Malaysia, Pte. Ltd.

Table of Contents

Chapter 1. Data Collection

1.1 Introduction to the Practice of Statistics

1.1 Concepts and Vocabulary

1. Statistics is the science of collecting, organizing, summarizing and analyzing information in order to draw conclusions.

3. Descriptive statistics consists of organizing and summarizing information. Inferential statistics consists of generalizing results from a sample to the population, and measuring the reliability of those results.

5. A qualitative variable classifies individuals based on some attribute or characteristic. Some examples are gender, zip codes, class (freshman, sophomore etc) and ethnicity. A quantitative variable is a numerical variable on which arithmetic operations can be sensibly performed. Some examples are temperature, height, blood pressure and life expectancy.

1.1 Exercises: Skill Building

1. Qualitative.   3. Quantitative.   5. Quantitative.   7. Quantitative.

9. Qualitative.   11. Discrete.   13. Continuous.   15. Continuous.

17. Discrete.   19. Continuous.

21. The population consists of all adult residents of the United States aged 18 years or older. The members of this population are the individuals. The sample consists of the 1019 adult residents contacted by the Gallup Organization.

23. The population consists of all soybean plants grown by this farmer. The individuals are the individual soybean plants. The sample consists of the 100 plants randomly selected by the farmer.

1.1 Exercises: Applying the Concepts

25. (a) To determine the genetic and non-genetic factors to structural brain abnormalities on schizophrenia.
  (b) The sample consisted of 58 pairs of twins (29 with schizophrenia, and 29 healthy).
  (c) The study would have calculated average brain volumes in the two groups of subjects. They found that brain volumes were 2.2% smaller in the schizophrenic patients.
  (d) An increased genetic risk to develop schizophrenia is related to reduced brain growth early in life.

27. (a) To determine whether there is a relationship between music cognition and cognitions pertaining to abstract operations such as mathematical or spatial reasoning.
  (b) The sample consisted of 36 college students.
  (c) The researchers calculated the mean scores of these students on a spatial reasoning test, taken both after the students had listened to Mozart, and after the students had sat in silence. The mean scores were 119, after listening to Mozart, and 110 after listening to silence.
  (d) Subjects perform better on abstract/spatial reasoning tests after listening to Mozart.

29. (a) To determine what percentage of households had been victimized by crime in the preceding year.
  (b) The sample consisted of the households of 1012 adults, aged 18 years or older.
  (c) The researchers calculated the percentage of these households that had been victimized by crime in the preceding 12 months. It was 24%.
  (d) Gallup News Service concluded that 24% of all households had been victimized by crime in the preceding year.

31. The individuals are the five students in Michael Sullivan's business calculus course. The variables are gender (qualitative), age (quantitative, continuous) and number of siblings (quantitative, discrete). The data for these variables are: F, M, F etc for gender; 19, 19, 19 etc for age; and 1, 1, 2 etc for number of siblings.

33. The individuals are the five states. The variables are age for driver's license (quantitative, continuous), blood alcohol concentration limit (quantitative, continuous), mandatory belt-use law seating positions (qualitative), and maximum allowable speed limit in 1999 (quantitative, continuous). The data are: 16, 18 etc for age for driver's license; 0.08, 0.08 etc for blood alcohol concentration limit; front, front etc for mandatory belt-use law seating positions; and 70, 65 etc for maximum allowable speed limit in 1999.

1.2 Observational Studies; Simple Random Sampling

1.2 Concepts and Vocabulary

1. An observational study uses data obtained by studying individuals in a sample without trying to manipulate or influence the variable(s) of interest. In a designed experiment, a treatment is applied to the individuals in a sample in order to isolate the effects of the treatment on a response variable. Observational studies are appropriate where the control of certain variables is either impossible or unethical. Designed experiments are appropriate when it is possible to control certain variables and this is necessary for the study (for example to establish causation).

3. Sampling is used in statistics because it can be prohibitively expensive or impossible to obtain census data.

1.2 Exercises: Applying the Concepts

1. Observational study.   3. Experiment.   5. Observational study.

7. Observational study.   9. Experiment.   11. Observational study.

13. **(a)** All possible samples of size two, selected without replacement, are:

Graham, Murkowski	Graham, Kyl	Graham, Baucus	Graham, Conrad	Murkowski, Kyl
Murkowski, Baucus	Murkowski, Conrad	Kyl, Baucus	Kyl, Conrad	Baucus, Conrad

   (b) If the members are selected at random, then there is a one in ten (or 10%) chance of these two being selected.

15. **(a)** Answers will vary.   **(b)** Answers will vary.

17. **(a)** Number each student in the list of registered students, from 1 to 19,935. Generate 25 random numbers, without repetition, between 1 and 19,935 using a random number generator or table. Select the 25 students with these numbers.
    (b) Answers will vary.

1.3 Other Types of Sampling

1.3 Concepts and Vocabulary

1. Stratified random sampling may be appropriate if the population of interest can be divided into groups or strata that are homogeneous (or similar) in some way.

3. Convenience samples are typically selected in a nonrandom manner (such as self-selection) and this makes it impossible to quantify the likely margin of error in statistics calculated from those samples. Convenience samples may also be self-selected, which will frequently result in sample bias.

1.3 Exercises: Basic Skills

1. Systematic.   3. Cluster.   5. Simple random.   7. Cluster.

9. Convenience.

1.3 Exercises: Applying the Concepts

11. Answers will vary. One design would be a stratified random sample, with two strata being rail commuters and those who do not commute by rail, as these two groups each might be fairly homogeneous in their reactions to the proposal.

13. Answers will vary. One design would be a cluster sample, with the clusters being city blocks. Randomly select city blocks and survey every household in the selected blocks.

15. Answers will vary. Since the company already has a list (frame) of 6,600 individuals with high cholesterol, a simple random sample would be an appropriate design.

17. (a) $N = 4502$, $n = 50$, $4502/50 = 90.04$ $\therefore k = 90$.
    (b) Randomly select a number between 1 and 90. Suppose that we select 15. Then the individuals to be surveyed will be the 15th, 105th, 195th, 285th and so on up to the 4425th employee on the company list.

1.4 Sources of Errors in Sampling

1.4 Concepts and Vocabulary

1. The population may be very large (for example the population of the United States), making it difficult to obtain a complete frame, and the population may change frequently (for example the voter roll), making it difficult to keep the frame up to date.

3. A closed question is one in which the respondent must choose one from a list of prescribed responses. An open question is one in which the respondent is free to choose his or her own response.

5. A talented interviewer will be able to elicit truthful responses even to sensitive questions.

7. A pro is that the interviewer is more likely to find the individual at home at this time. A con is that many individuals will be irritated at having their dinner interrupted and will refuse to respond.

9. Open questions allow respondents to give answers that more accurately reflect their true opinions. However, if there are too many distinct answers, then the results may be difficult to use. Closed questions limit the responses and so the results are easier to analyze. However, the choices do not always allow the respondent to answer as he or she would wish.

1.4 Exercises: Skill Building

1. **(a)** Flawed sampling method.
    (b) A simple random sample would be a good choice of sampling method as the vice president would have access to a list of all students.

3. **(a)** Flawed survey due to a poorly worded question.
    (b) The survey should inform the respondent of the current penalty for selling a gun illegally and the question should be worded as: "Do you approve or disapprove of harsher penalties for individuals who sell guns illegally?" The order of "approve" and "disapprove" should be switched from one individual to the next.

5. **(a)** Flawed survey. If a foreign language is the primary language in a household, then the head of the household might not be able to respond to the question.
    (b) A better design would be to use personal or telephone interviews.

7. **(a)** Flawed survey because the students are unlikely to give honest answers if their teacher is administering the survey.
   (b) An impartial party should administer the survey in order to increase the rate of truthful responses.

9. It is very likely that the order of these two questions will affect the response to B. Either B could be asked first, or the order of the two questions could be switched at random.

1.5 The Design of Experiments

1.5 Concepts and Vocabulary

1. **(a)** An experimental unit is a person or object to which a treatment is applied.
   (b) A treatment is a condition applied to an experimental unit.
   (c) A response variable is a variable that measures a response of interest to the experimenter.
   (d) A predictor variable measures a factor that might affect a response variable.
   (e) A double-blind experiment is one in which neither the subject nor the experimenter knows what treatment is being administered to the subject.
   (f) A placebo is an innocuous treatment, such as a sugar pill, administered to a subject in a manner indistinguishable from an actual treatment.
   (g) Confounding occurs when the effect of two predictor variables on a response variable cannot be distinguished.

1.5 Exercises: Applying the Concepts

1. **(a)** Achievement test score.
   (b) Method of teaching. Two levels.
   (c) School district, grade level and teacher.
   (d) By selecting students from a single school district.
   (e) Completely randomized design.
   (f) The 500 students.

(g)

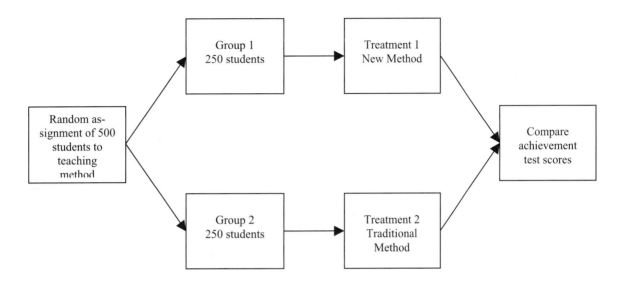

3. **(a)** Occurrence of prostate cancer.
    (b) Weekly consumption of tomatoes. Three levels.
    (c) Age, eating habits and other lifestyle variables.
    (d) Completely randomized design.
    (e) The 600 males aged 30 years.
    (f)

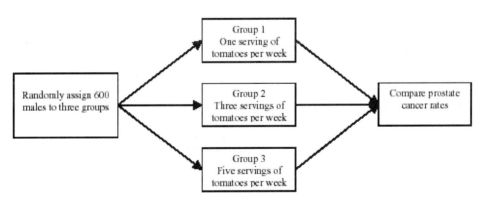

5. **(a)** Weight difference before and after space flight.
    (b) Space flight.
    (c) Matched pairs.
    (d)

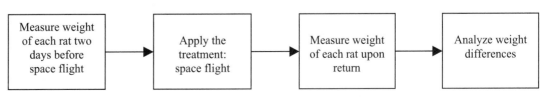

7. **(a)** Hair counts.
   (b) Medication. Two levels (Propecia or placebo).
   (c) Completely randomized design.
   (d)

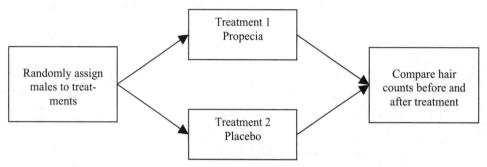

9. Answers will vary. The experimental units would be people who work out. Some factors to take into account might be age, gender, and physical condition prior to exercising (such as weight, blood pressure etc). A matched pairs design would be the best way to control for these factors. The response variable would be the change in lung capacity from before to after the exercise regimen.

11. **(a)** Completely randomized.   **(b)** Answers will vary.

Chapter 1 Review Exercises

1. Statistics is the science of collecting, organizing, summarizing and analyzing information in order to draw conclusions.

3. A sample is a subset of the population.

5. In a designed experiment, a treatment is applied to the individuals in a sample in order to isolate the effects of the treatment on the response variable.

7. Errors in sampling consist of sampling error (the error resulting from using sample data to estimate a characteristic of an entire population) and non-sampling error (from poor sampling design). Sampling error can be quantified by using the theory of probability. Some common non-sampling errors are non-response, which can be ameliorated by call-back or incentives, and poorly worded questions, which can be avoided by careful survey design.

9. Qualitative.

11. Quantitative, continuous.

13. Quantitative, discrete.

15. Observational study.

17. Observational study.

19. Systematic.

21. Stratified.

23. Answers will vary.

25. Answers will vary.

27. (a) Score on the Hamilton Rating Scale for Depression.
(b) Group. Two levels (psychotherapy or no treatment).
(c) Age and medical history are two, neither of which is controlled.
(d) Completely randomized design.
(e) The 120 women with postpartum depression.
(f)

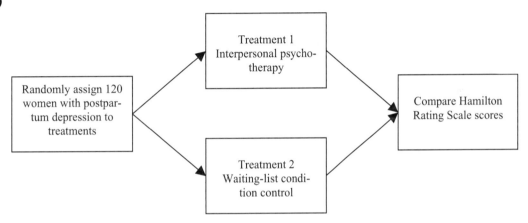

29. (a) Lymphocyte count.
(b) Space flight.
(c) Matched pairs.
(d) The four members of Skylab.
(e)

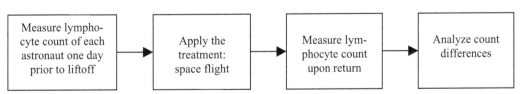

31. In a matched pairs design, experimental units are paired based on some common characteristic. One of each pair is assigned at random to each of two treatments, and the difference between the pairs is analyzed. In a completely randomized design, each experimental unit is randomly assigned to one of the treatments, and no attempt is made to compare individual units receiving different treatments—only the two (or more) treatment groups as a whole are compared.

Chapter 2. Organizing and Summarizing Data

2.1 Organizing Qualitative Data

2.1 Concepts and Vocabulary

1. Raw data are the data as originally collected, before they have been organized.

3. A Pareto chart is a bar chart with bars drawn in order of decreasing frequency or relative frequency.

5. Pareto charts emphasize those observations with the higher frequencies or relative frequencies.

2.1 Exercises: Basic Skills

1. **(a)** 34–52.   **(b)** 18–33.   **(c)** 27%.

3. **(a)** United States.   **(b)** $\approx$ 18 million.

5. **(a)** 447,927
    (b) Total votes cast $= 49,922,623 + 49,659,871 + \ldots + 98,226 = 103,268,793$
        Gore: $49,922,623 / 103,268,793 = 48.3\%$
        Bush: $49,659,871 / 103,268,793 = 48.1\%$
    (c) Nader: $2,756,008 / 103,268,793 = 2.7\%$. No.

7. **(a)** 16%.   **(b)** Natural gas.   **(c)** LPG.
    (d) The shift of population towards the southern states.
    (e) The oil crises that drove up the price of heating oil in the past.

2.1 Exercises: Applying the Concepts

9. **(a)** Total receipts $= 1009.5 + 234.7 + 691.5 + 111.2 = 2046.9$
        Relative frequency of individual income tax $= 1009.5 / 2046.9 = 0.4932$ and so on.

Source of income	Relative Frequency
Individual Income Tax and Tax Withholdings	0.4932
Corporate Income Taxes	0.1147
Social Insurance and Retirement Receipts	0.3378
Excise, Estate and Gift Taxes, Customs, and Miscellaneous Receipts	0.0543

(b) 49.32%.

(c)

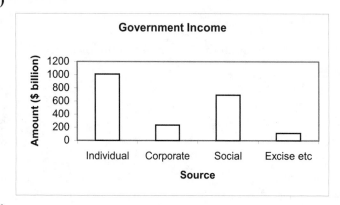

(d)

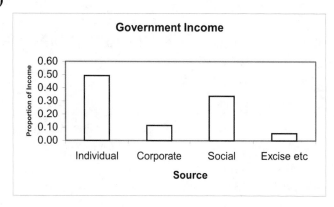

(e)

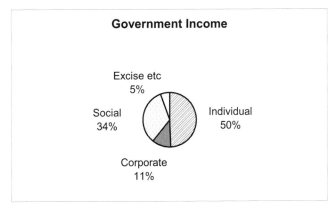

11. (a) Total students surveyed $= 125 + 324 + 552 + 1257 + 2518 = 4776$

Relative frequency of "never" $= 125 / 4776 = 0.0262$ and so on.

Response	Relative Frequency
Never	0.0262
Rarely	0.0678
Sometimes	0.1156
Most of the time	0.2632
Always	0.5272

(b) 52.72%   **(c)** $2.62 + 6.78 = 9.40\%$

(d)

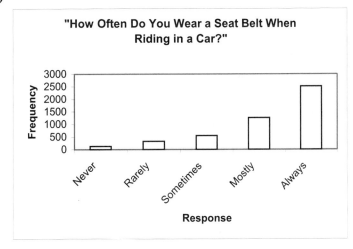

(e)

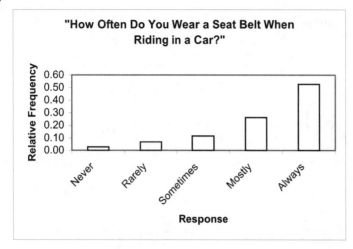

(f)

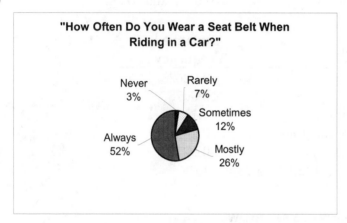

13. (a) Total foreign $= 4772 + 8364 + 840 + 180 + 15472 + 836 = 30464$ (thousand)

Relative frequency for Europe $= 4772 / 30464 = 0.1566$ and so on.

Region	Relative Frequency
Europe	0.1566
Asia	0.2746
Africa	0.0276
Oceania	0.0059
Latin America	0.5079
North America	0.0274

(b) 2.76%

(c)

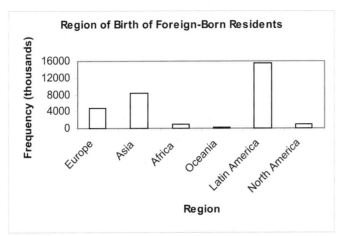

(d)

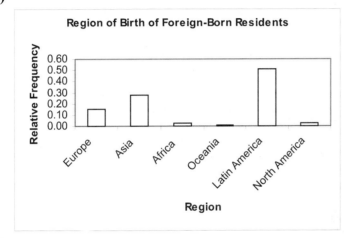

(e)

15. (a) Relative frequency of not HS graduate (male) $= 16.6/100.0 = 0.1660$ and so on.

Educational Attainment	Relative Frequency
Not a HS graduate	0.1660
High school graduate	0.3180
College, no degree	0.1710
Associate's degree	0.0700
Bachelor's degree	0.1790
Advanced degree	0.0960

(b) Relative frequency of not HS graduate (female) $= 16.6/100.1 = 0.1658$ and so on.

Educational Attainment	Relative Frequency
Not a HS graduate	0.1658
High school graduate	0.3477
College, no degree	0.1748
Associate's degree	0.0799
Bachelor's degree	0.1618
Advanced degree	0.0699

(c)

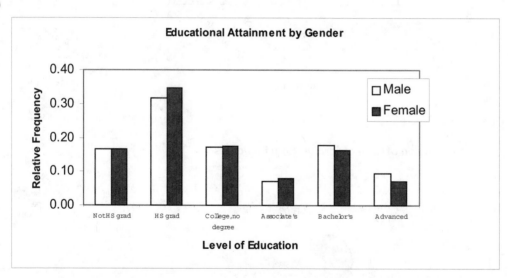

(d) In 1999, a higher percentage of males than females attained bachelor's and advanced degrees. Conjectures will vary.

17. (a) Total number of launches in 1995 $= 32 + 27 + 2 + 11 + 2 + 1 = 75$.
Relative frequency of launches by FSU in 1995 $= 32/75 = 0.4267$ and so on.
Total number of launches in 1998 $= 24 + 34 + 2 + 11 + 6 + 0 = 77$.
Relative frequency of launches by FSU in 1998 $= 24/77 = 0.3117$ and so on.

Country	Relative Frequencies	
	1995	**1998**
Former Soviet Union	0.4267	0.3117
USA	0.3600	0.4416
Japan	0.0267	0.0260
Europe	0.1467	0.1429
China	0.0267	0.0779
Israel	0.0133	0.0000

(b)

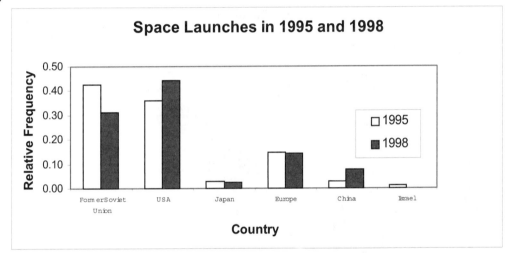

(c) Most striking are the decrease in launches by the Former Soviet Union (due to budget cuts), the increase in launches by the United States and the increase by China.

19. (a) & (b) Total number of voters polled $= 14 + 25 + 1 = 40$.
Relative frequency of Bush voters $= 14/40 = 0.350$ and so on.

Candidate	Frequency	Relative Frequency
Bush	14	0.350
Gore	25	0.625
Nader	1	0.025

(c)

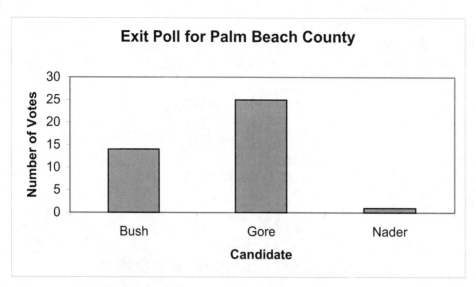

(d)

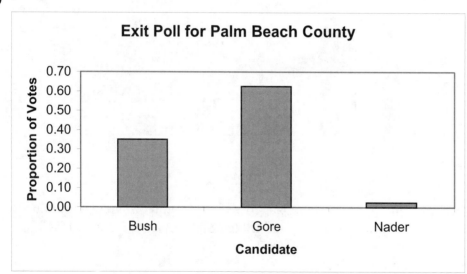

(e)

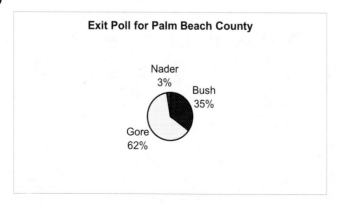

(f) It would appear that Gore is the likely winner of Palm Beach County. If George W. Bush were the winner then you might rightly conclude that a sample of size 40 is too small to give a reliable indication of the outcome of the election in Palm Beach County. A sample of size 100 would give more information about the outcome of the election. However, even a sample of 100 will not give a reliable prediction.

21. (a) & (b) Total players sampled $= 36$.

Relative frequency of pitchers $= 12/36 = 0.3333$ and so on.

Position	Frequency	Relative Frequency
Pitcher	12	0.3333
Catcher	2	0.0556
First Base	7	0.1944
Third Base	2	0.0556
Shortstop	2	0.0556
Center Field	5	0.1389
Right Field	6	0.1667

(c) Pitcher.

(d) Second base and left field because neither makes the list of highest paid positions.

(e)

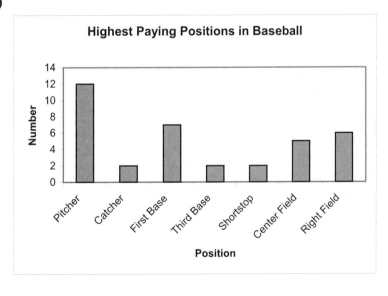

(f)

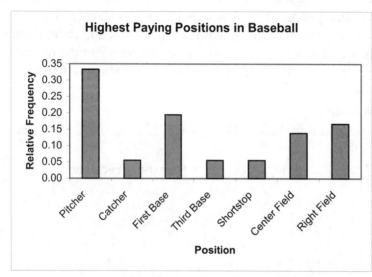

(g)

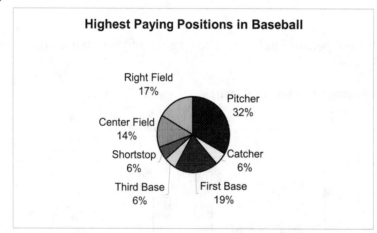

2.2 Organizing Quantitative Data I

2.2 Concepts and Vocabulary

1. We have already seen that the pattern of a distribution is the same, whether we look at frequencies or relative frequencies. However, in statistics we will often use data from a sample to guide us to conclusions about the larger population from which the sample is drawn. (This is called inferential statistics.) The actual frequencies for a sample do not, by themselves, give much useful information about the population, but the relative frequencies for the sample data will usually be similar to the relative frequencies for the population.

3. Not all the class widths are the same.

5. Time series are data measuring the value of a variable at different points in time.

2.2 Exercises: Basic Skills

1. (a) 8   **(b)** 2   **(c)** 15   **(d)** $15/100 = 15\%$ **(e)** Bell-shaped.

3. (a) Total frequency $= 2+3+13+42+58+40+31+8+2+1 = 200.$
   (b) 10
   (c)

IQ Score (class)	Frequency
60–69	2
70–79	3
80–89	13
90–99	42
100–109	58
110–119	40
120–129	31
130–139	8
140–149	2
150–159	1

   (d) 100–109   **(e)** 150–159
   (f) $31/200 = 0.155$ **(g)** Bell-shaped.

2.2 Exercises: Applying the Concepts

5. (a) Total frequency $= 16+18+12+3+1 = 50.$
        Relative frequency of 0 children $= 16/50 = 0.32$ and so on.

Number of Children Under Five	Relative Frequency
0	0.32
1	0.36
2	0.24
3	0.06
4	0.02

   (b) 0.24 or 24%   **(c)** $0.36+0.24 = 0.60$ or 60%

7. 10, 11, 14, 21, 24, 24, 27, 29, 33, 35, 35, 35, 37, 37, 38, 40, 40, 41, 42, 46, 46, 48, 49, 49, 53, 53, 55, 58, 61, 62

9. (a) 4   **(b)** Lower limits: 25, 35, 45, 55 Upper limits: 34, 44, 54, 64   **(c)** 10

11. (a) 6   **(c)** 10
  (b) Lower limits: 50, 60, 70, 80, 90, 100
      Upper limits: 59, 69, 79, 89, 99, 109

13. (a) Total frequency $= 29.3 + 37.0 + 30.4 + 19.5 = 116.2$.
      Relative frequency for $25 - 34 \; = 29.3 / 116.2 = 0.2522$ and so on.

Age	Relative Frequency
25–34	0.2522
35–44	0.3184
45–54	0.2616
55–64	0.1678

(b)

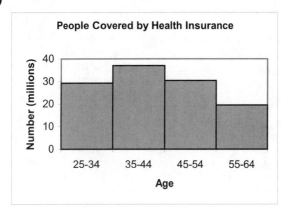

(c)

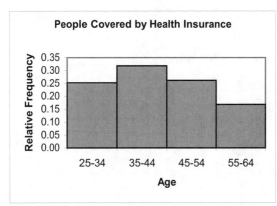

      25.22% are 25–34 years old; $25.22 + 31.84 = 57.06\%$ are 44 years or younger.

15. (a) Total frequency $= 1 + 308 + 1519 + 1626 + 503 + 11 = 3968$.
      Relative frequency of $50 - 59° \; = 1 / 3968 = 0.0003$ and so on.

Temperature	Relative Frequency
50–59°	0.0003
60–69°	0.0776
70–79°	0.3828
80–89°	0.4098
90–99°	0.1268
100–109°	0.0028

(b)

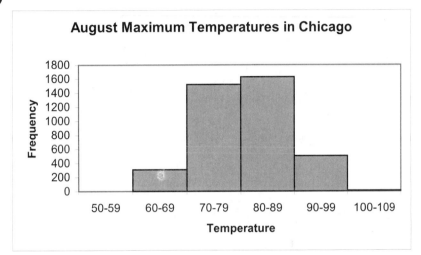

(c)

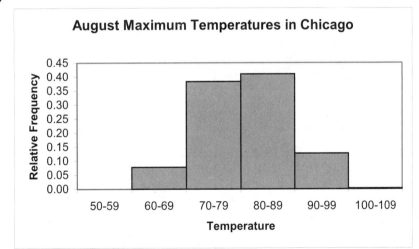

38.28% had a temperature of 70–79°; $0.03 + 7.76 + 38.28 = 46.07\%$ had a temperature of 79° or less.

17. (a) & (b)   Relative frequency of 3 customers waiting $= 2/40 = 0.050$ and so on.

Number of Customers	Frequency	Relative Frequency
3	2	0.050
4	3	0.075
5	3	0.075
6	5	0.125
7	4	0.100
8	8	0.200
9	4	0.100
10	4	0.100
11	4	0.100
12	0	0.000
13	2	0.050
14	1	0.025

(c) $10.0 + 10.0 + 0.0 + 5.0 + 2.5 = 27.5\%.$

(d) $5.0 + 7.5 + 7.5 = 20.0\%.$

(e)

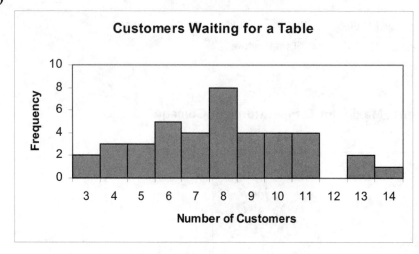

(f)

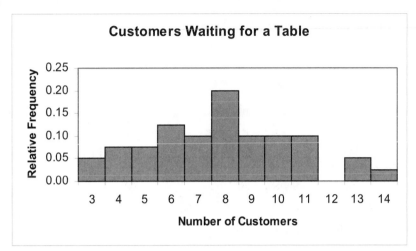

(g) More or less bell-shaped.

19. (a) & (b) Total number of data points $= 25$.

Relative frequency of $160 - 169.99 = 1/25 = 0.04$ and so on.

Tensile Strength	Frequency	Relative Frequency
160–170	1	0.04
170–180	1	0.04
180–190	4	0.16
190–200	1	0.04
200–210	9	0.36
210–220	6	0.24
220–230	1	0.04
230–240	1	0.04
240–250	1	0.04
Total	25	1.00

(c)

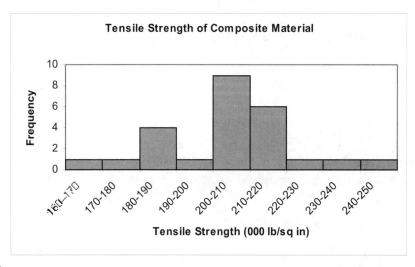

(d)

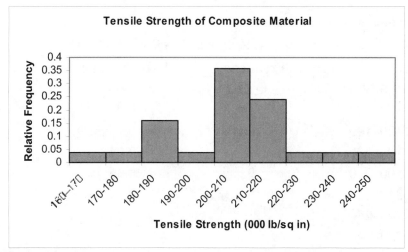

(e) Symmetric

(f)

Tensile Strength	Frequency	Relative Frequency
160–175	2	0.08
175–190	4	0.16
190–205	5	0.20
205–220	11	0.44
220–235	2	0.08
235–250	1	0.04
Total	25	1.00

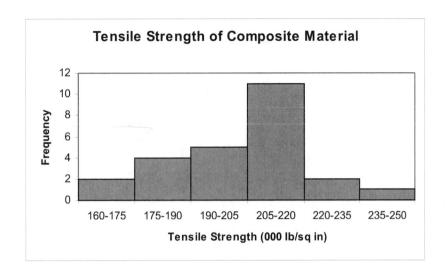

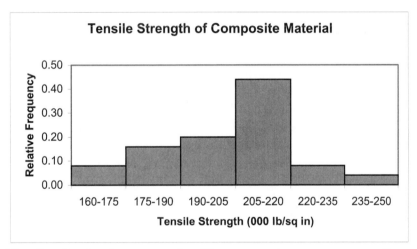

The distribution is symmetric. The pattern is more apparent from the second frequency distribution.

21. (a) & (b) Total number of data points $= 40$.

Relative frequency of 20–29 $= 1/40 = 0.025$ and so on.

HDL Cholesterol	Frequency	Relative Frequency
20–29	1	0.025
30–39	6	0.150
40–49	10	0.250
50–59	14	0.350
60–69	6	0.150
70–79	3	0.075

(c)

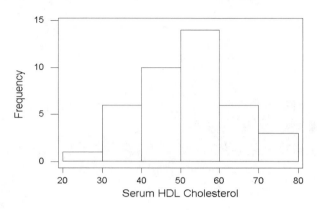

(d)

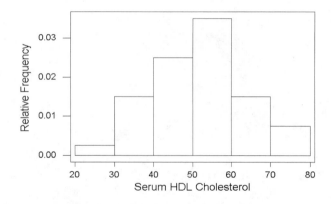

(e) Bell-shaped.

(f)

HDL Cholesterol	Frequency	Relative Frequency
20–24	0	0.000
25–29	1	0.025
30–34	2	0.050
35–39	4	0.100
40–44	2	0.050
45–49	8	0.200
50–54	9	0.225
55–59	5	0.125
60–64	4	0.100
65–69	2	0.050
70–74	3	0.075
Total	40	1.000

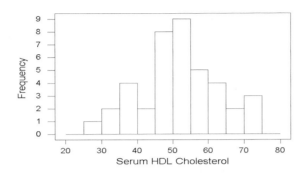

Serum HDL Cholesterol for Age 20-29

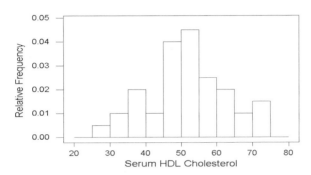

Serum HDL Cholesterol for Age 20-29

The first distribution gives a smoother pattern.

23. (a) & (b) Total number of data points $= 50$.

Relative frequency of 0.76–0.77 $= 1/50 = 0.02$ and so on.

Weight	Frequency	Relative Frequency
0.76–0.77	1	0.02
0.78–0.79	2	0.04
0.80–0.81	0	0.00
0.82–0.83	4	0.08
0.84–0.85	6	0.12
0.86–0.87	11	0.22
0.88–0.89	10	0.20
0.90–0.91	9	0.18
0.92–0.93	5	0.10
0.94–0.95	2	0.04
Total	50	1.00

(c)

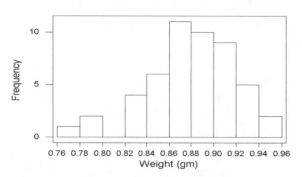

(d)

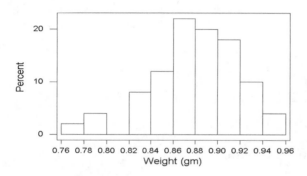

(e) Skewed to the left (or skewed negatively).

(f)

Weight	Frequency	Relative Frequency
0.76–0.79	3	0.06
0.80–0.83	4	0.08
0.84–0.87	17	0.34
0.88–0.91	19	0.38
0.92–0.95	7	0.14
Total	50	1.00

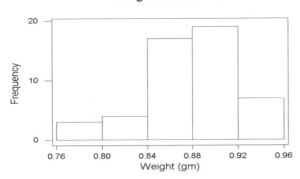

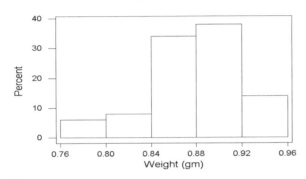

The first distribution shows the pattern clearly without giving up as much detail as the second.

25.

```
4 | 2  3
4 | 6  6  7  8  9  9
5 | 0  0  1  1  1  1  2  2  4  4  4  4  4
5 | 5  5  5  5  6  6  6  7  7  7  7  8
6 | 0  1  1  1  2  4  4
6 | 5  8  9
```

27.

```
0 | 2  8  8
1 | 1  2  5  6  7
2 | 0  3  3  8
3 | 1  1  4  7  8
```

29. The trend was initially downwards but has been fairly flat since 4/00.

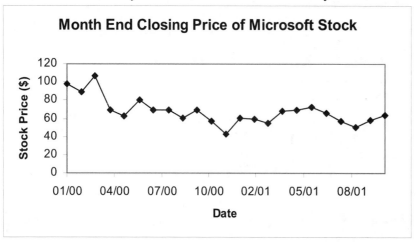

31.

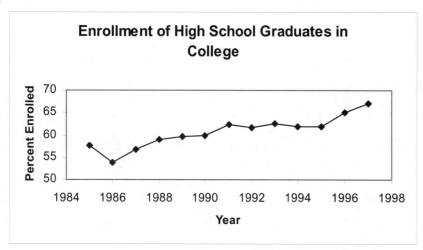

2.3 Graphical Misrepresentations of Data

2.3 Exercises

1. The scaling is incorrect. In particular, the ketchup "bar" is not long enough: since 47% is more than double 22% (for mustard) the ketchup bar should be more than twice the length of the mustard bar.

3. The vertical scale is inconsistent, and has changed from the 0–750 range to the 3000–9000 range, with apparently part of the scale also having been cut out between 750 and 3000, although there is no break in the scale and no break in the graph.

5. **(a)** The vertical scale starts at 1000 and so the relationship between frequencies is distorted.
   (b) Either show a break in the vertical scale or start the vertical scale at 0.

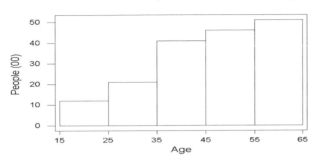

Number of People with Work Disability

7. **(a)** The vertical scale starts at 1500, instead of at 0, and so exaggerates the increase in expenditures from 1985 to 1996.
   (b) That per-person health care expenditures have been rising very rapidly.

9. **(a)** The bars do not have lengths that are in proportion to the percentages that they represent. For example, the housing bar should be slightly more than twice as long as the transportation bar.
   (b) Adjust the lengths of the bars to be proportional.

11. **(a)**

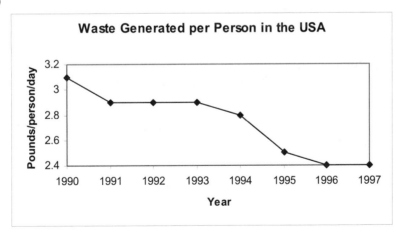

(b)

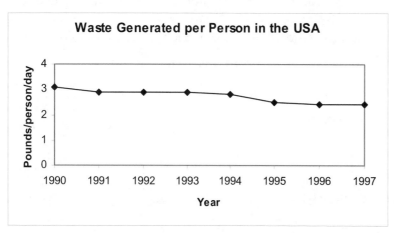

(c)

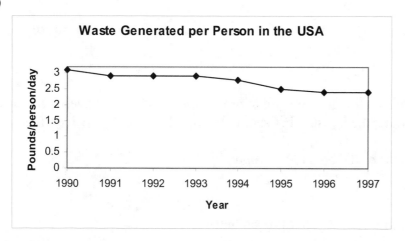

13. **(a)** For the graphic to accurately represent CFC's decreasing to one third of their 1990 level, the area should decrease by a factor of 3 and so its height and width should each decrease by a factor of $\sqrt{3}$, since $\sqrt{3} \cdot \sqrt{3} = 3$.

   (b) An inaccurate representation would be given by a graphic in which both height and width decreased by a factor of 3, thus decreasing its area by a factor of 9, instead of 3.

Chapter 2 Review Exercises

1. **(a)** 22 quadrillion Btu   **(b)** 4 quadrillion Btu
    (c) $38 + 21 + 22 + 8 + 4 + 4 + 1 = 98$ quadrillion Btu

3. **(a)** Total frequency $= 9222 + 1890 + 753 + 952 + 313 + 1080 = 14210$
    Relative frequency of gun deaths $= 9222 / 14210 = 0.649$ and so on.

Cause of Death	Relative Frequency
Gun	0.649
Cutting/stabbing	0.133
Blunt object	0.053
Personal weapons (hands, fists, etc.)	0.067
Strangulation	0.022
Other	0.076

(b) 5.3%

(c)

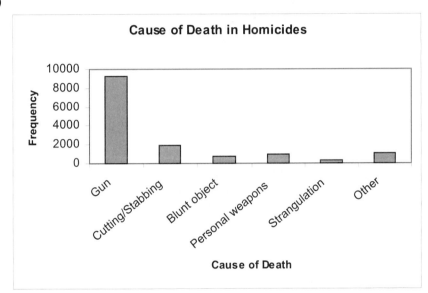

(d)

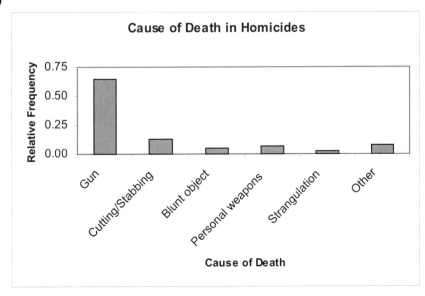

(e)

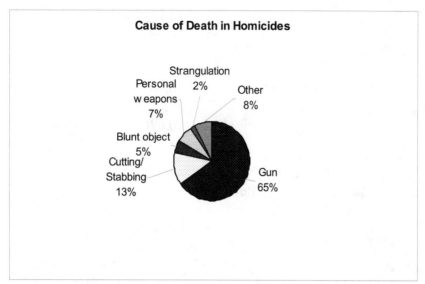

5. **(a)** Relative frequency for age 20-24 $= 8067 / 45587 = 0.1770$ and so on.

Age	Frequency	Relative Frequency
20–24	8067	0.1770
25–29	6195	0.1359
30–34	6274	0.1376
35–39	5130	0.1125
40–44	4631	0.1016
45–49	3636	0.0798
50–54	3021	0.0663
55–59	2332	0.0512
60–64	1606	0.0352
65–69	1341	0.0294
70–74	1273	0.0279
75–79	1179	0.0259
80–84	902	0.0198

(b)

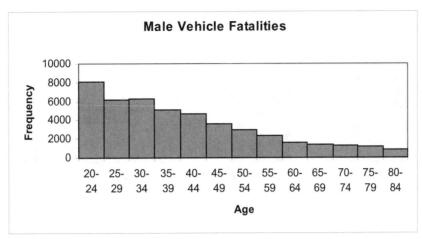

Skewed to the right

(c)

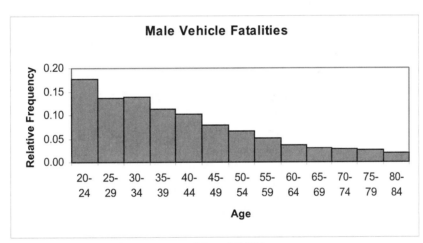

(d) From the relative frequency table: 17.7%

(e) $17.7 + 13.6 = 31.3\%$

7. (a) & (b)

Affiliation	Frequency	Relative Frequency
Democrat	46	0.46
Republican	38	0.38
Independent	16	0.16

(c)

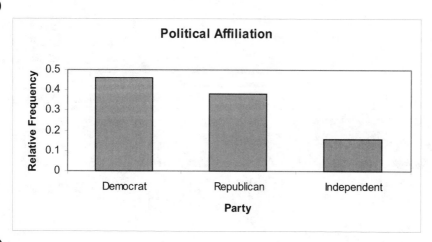

(d)

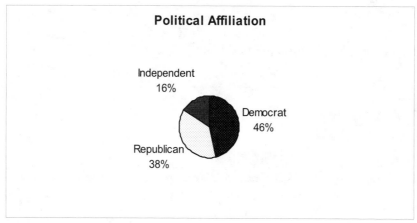

(e) Democrat

9. **(a) & (b)**

Family Size	Frequency	Relative Frequency
0	7	0.1167
1	7	0.1167
2	18	0.3000
3	20	0.3333
4	7	0.1167
5	1	0.0167
	60	

(c) & (d)

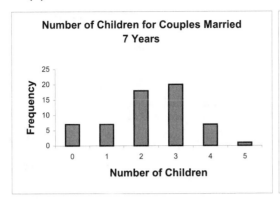

The distribution is more or less symmetric.

(e) From the relative frequency table, the relative frequency of two children is 0.3000 and so the percentage is 30%.

(f) From the relative frequency table, the relative frequency of at least two children (i.e. two or more) is $0.3000 + 0.3333 + 0.1167 + 0.0167 = 0.7667$ or 76.7%.

11. (a) & (b)

Crime Rate	Frequency	Relative Frequency
2000 - 2499	1	0.0196
2500 - 2999	4	0.0784
3000 - 3499	4	0.0784
3500 - 3999	9	0.1765
4000 - 4499	9	0.1765
4500 - 4999	7	0.1373
5000 - 5499	8	0.1569
5500 - 5999	4	0.0784
6000 - 6499	1	0.0196
6500 - 6999	3	0.0588
7000 - 7499	0	0.0000
7500 - 7999	0	0.0000
8000 - 8499	0	0.0000
8500 - 8999	1	0.0196

(c) & (d)

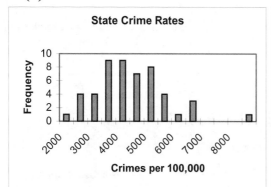
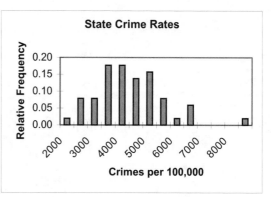

The distribution is more or less symmetric, with an outlier.

(e)

Crime Rate	Frequency	Relative Frequency
2000 - 2999	5	0.0980
3000 - 3999	13	0.2549
4000 - 4999	16	0.3137
5000 - 5999	12	0.2353
6000 - 6999	4	0.0784
7000 - 7999	0	0.0000
8000 - 8999	1	0.0196

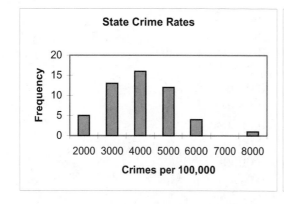
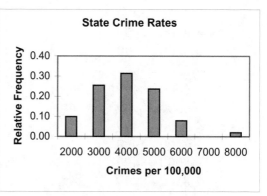

The class width of 1000 seems to provide a better summary of the data because it shows the symmetry more clearly without losing the outlier in the data.

13. (a) & (b)

Towing Capacity	Frequency	Relative Frequency
3000 – 3999	5	0.1613
4000 – 4999	4	0.1290
5000 – 5999	8	0.2581
6000 – 6999	3	0.0968
7000 – 7999	3	0.0968
8000 – 8999	5	0.1613
9000 – 9999	0	0.0000
10000 – 10999	1	0.0323
11000 – 11999	0	0.0000
12000 – 12999	2	0.0645

(c) & (d) The distribution is skewed to the right.

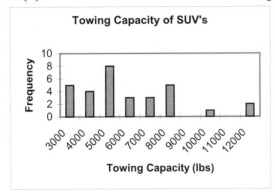

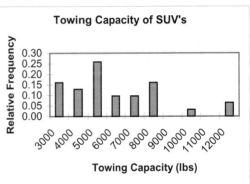

15. The distribution is skewed to the right.

```
 0 | 7  8  8
 1 | 2  4  5  7  8  8
 2 | 1  1  5  7  8
 3 | 0  3  3  4  8
 4 | 0
 5 | 4
 6 |
 7 | 0  1  4
 8 |
 9 |
10 | 2
```

17. (a) & (b) The minimum wage shows a slowly increasing trend.

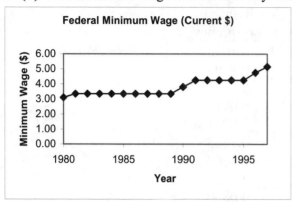

19. It is impossible to interpret this graph because there is no vertical scale.

21. (a) A bar chart that would mislead by exaggerating the difference would be one in which the college graduate bar is both 75% taller and 75% wider.
   (b) A bar chart that is not misleading would have both bars the same width (but the college graduate bar 75% taller).

Chapter 3. Numerically Summarizing Data

3.1 Measures of Central Tendency

3.1 Concepts and Vocabulary

1. A statistic is resistant if it is not influenced by extreme data values. The median is resistant since it is determined only by the middle data values, when the data are put in order. The mean is not resistant because all data values, including extreme values, are used in computing it.

3. Since the distribution of household incomes in the United States is skewed to the right, the mean > the median. Thus the mean household income is $55,263 and the median is $41,349.

5. The mean will be larger as it will be influenced by the extreme data values that are to the right end (or high end) of the distribution.

3.1 Exercises: Basic Skills

1. Mean = (420 + 462 + 409 + 236)/4 = $381.75
   Data in order: 236, 409, 420, 462
   Median = (409 + 420)/2 = $414.50
   No data value occurs more than once so there is no mode.

3. Mean = (3960 + 4080 + … + 3780)/9 = 3668.9 psi
   Median = 5th data value with the data in order = 3830 psi
   No data value occurs more than once so there is no mode.

3.1 Exercises: Applying the Concepts

5.

	Sludge Plot	Spring Disk	No till	Spring Chisele	Great Lakes Bt
Mean	28.3	33.0	28.5	29.3	28.8
Median	27.5	33.5	29	29.5	28.5
Mode	27	34	29	None	27

Spring disk gives the highest yield.

7.

	Monday	Saturday
Mean	10511.3	8476.3
Median	10491.5	8449.5
Mode	None	None

There are more births on a Monday than on a Saturday. Explanations will vary.

9.

	Control Group	Flight Group
Mean	323.2	333.8
Median	320	326
Mode	None	None

The flight group weighs more than the control group. This could be due to a lower level of energy expenditure in the weightless environment of space.

11. (a) Mean = $(76 + 60 + \ldots + 73)/9 = 72.2$ beats per min   **a) & b)** Answers will vary.

13. (a) Mean = 7.875; Median = 8.
   (b) The mean is approximately equal to the median suggesting that the distribution is symmetric, and this is confirmed by the histogram.

15. (a) Mean = 203.934; Median = 206.51.
   (b) The mean is approximately equal to the median suggesting that the distribution is symmetric, and this is confirmed by the histogram.

17. (a) Mean = 51.1; Median = 51.
   (b) The mean is approximately equal to the median suggesting that the distribution is symmetric, and this is confirmed by the histogram.

19. (a) Mean = 0.874; Median = 0.88.
   (b) The mean is approximately equal to the median suggesting that the distribution is symmetric, while the histogram shows that the distribution is slightly skewed to the left.

21. The highest frequency is 15,472, and so the mode region of birth is Latin America.

23. The vote counts are: Bush = 14, Gore = 25, and Nader = 1. The mode is Gore.

25. The frequencies are: Pitcher = 12, Right Field = 6, Center Field = 5, Catcher = 2, 1st Base = 7, 3rd Base = 2, and Shortstop = 2 and so the mode position is Pitcher.

27. Mean = 229.134; Median = 207.88. This significantly changed the mean but only slightly changed the median.

29. (a) The histogram is skewed to the right, suggesting that the mean is greater than the median.
    (b) The histogram is symmetric, suggesting that the mean is approximately equal to the median.
    (c) The histogram is skewed to the left, suggesting that the mean is less than the median.

31. Assuming that NBA salaries are very skewed to the right, the players would rather use the median salary since the median will be lower than the mean. The negotiator for the owners would rather use the (higher) mean salary.

33. Sum $= n \cdot \overline{x} = 6 \cdot 34 = 204$.

35. (a) Median, because the distribution of home prices is likely to be skewed to the right.
    (b) Mode, because the mode is the major with the highest frequency amongst students enrolled in a statistics course.
    (c) Mean or median, because the symmetric distribution of scores suggests that the mean is equal (or approximately equal) to the median.
    (d) Median, because the mean will be inflated by the (few) high test scores.
    (e) Median, because the distribution of incomes is likely to be skewed to the right.

37. Midrange $= (0.76 + 0.94)/2 = 0.85$. The midrange is not resistant because it is computed using the two most extreme data values.

3.2 Measures of Dispersion

3.2 Concepts and Vocabulary

1. No. In comparing two populations, the larger the standard deviation, the more dispersed the distribution, provided that the variable of interest in both populations has the same unit of measurement. Since 5 inches $= 5 \times 2.54 = 12.7$ centimeters, the distribution with a standard deviation of 5 inches is in fact more dispersed.

3. The range, variance, and standard deviation are the three measures of dispersion mentioned in this section. All data values, including extreme values, are used in computing the range, variance, and standard deviation. Since a statistic is resistant only if it is not influenced by extreme data values, none of these measures is resistant.

5. A statistic is biased whenever that statistic consistently overestimates or underestimates a parameter.

3.2 Exercises: Skill Building

1. Range = Largest Data Value − Smallest Data Value = $462 - 236 = \$226.$

Data x_i	Sample Mean $\overline{x}$	Deviations $x_i - \overline{x}$	Squared Deviations $(x_i - \overline{x})^2$
420	381.75	38.25	1463.0625
462	381.75	80.25	6440.0625
409	381.75	27.25	742.5625
236	381.75	-145.75	21,243.0625
		$\sum(x_i - \overline{x})^2 =$	29,888.75

$$s^2 = \frac{\sum(x_i - \overline{x})^2}{n-1} = \frac{29,888.75}{4-1} = 9,962.9$$

$$s = \sqrt{\frac{\sum(x_i - \overline{x})^2}{n-1}} = \sqrt{\frac{29,888.75}{4-1}} = 99.8$$

3. Range = Largest Data Value − Smallest Data Value = $4090 - 2940 = 1150$ psi

Data x_i	Sample Mean $\overline{x}$	Deviations $x_i - \overline{x}$	Squared Deviations $(x_i - \overline{x})^2$
3960	3668.89	291.11	84,745.6790
4080	3668.89	411.11	169,012.3457
3200	3668.89	-468.89	219,856.7901
3100	3668.89	-568.89	323,634.5679
2940	3668.89	-728.89	531,279.0123
3830	3668.89	161.11	25,956.7901
4090	3668.89	421.11	177,334.5679
4040	3668.89	371.11	137,723.4568
3780	3668.89	111.11	12,345.6790
		$\sum(x_i - \overline{x})^2 =$	1,681,888.8889

$$s^2 = \frac{\sum(x_i - \overline{x})^2}{n-1} = \frac{1,681,888.8889}{9-1} = 210,236.1$$

$$s = \sqrt{\frac{\sum(x_i - \overline{x})^2}{n-1}} = \sqrt{\frac{1,681,888.8889}{9-1}} = 458.5 \text{ psi}$$

3.2 Exercises: Applying the Concepts

5. Sludge Plot: Range = 8; $s = 2.8$
    Spring Disk: Range = 5; $s = 1.79$
    No Till: Range = 7; $s = 2.59$
    Spring Chisele: Range = 6; $s = 2.2$
    Great Lakes Bt: Range = 5; $s = 1.9$
    Sludge Plot has the most dispersion based upon the range as well as based upon the standard deviation.

7. Births on Monday: Range = 511; $s = 170.8$
    Births on Saturday: Range = 294; $s = 126.0$
    Yes, there does appear to be more variability in the number of births on Monday versus Saturday. Both the range and standard deviation for the number of births on Monday are larger than those for Saturday. Explanations will vary.

9. Control Group: Range = 40; $s = 15.1$
    Flight Group: Range = 73; $s = 28.5$
    Both the range and standard deviation for the weights of rats in the Flight Group are larger than those for the Control Group. Explanations will vary

11. (a) $\sigma^2 = 58.8$; $\sigma = 7.7$ (b) Answers will vary.   (c) Answers will vary.

13. Range = 11 min; $s^2 = 7.4$ min^2; $s = 2.7$ min

15. Range = 82.32 psi; $s^2 = 335.6$ psi^2; $s = 18.32$ psi

17. Range = 45; $s^2 = 118$; $s = 10.9$

19. Range = 0.18g; $s^2 = 0.002$g^2; $s = 0.04$g

21. (a) Financial Stocks: $\bar{x} = 11.12\%$, M = 9.33%. Energy Stocks: $\bar{x} = 9.71\%$, M = 9.09%. Financial Stocks have higher mean and median rates of return.
    (b) Financial Stocks: $s = 8.06\%$; Energy Stocks: $s = 5.852\%$. Financial Stocks are riskier.
23. (a) Michael: $\bar{x} = 81.1$; Kevin: $\bar{x} = 81.2$
    (b) Michael: M = 81; Kevin: M = 82
    (c) Michael: mode = 83; Kevin: mode = 73
    (d) Michael: range = 13; Kevin: range = 17
    (e) Michael: $s = 3.2$; Kevin: $s = 5.9$
    (f) Michael is the more consistent player because the standard deviation of his scores is less than that of Kevin, indicating that the distribution of his scores is less dispersed than the distribution of Kevin's scores.

25. **(a)** By the Empirical Rule, 99.7% of gas stations have prices within three standard deviations of the mean. That is, 99.7% of the gas prices are greater than or equal to $1.60 − 3($0.07) = $1.39 per gallon, and less than or equal to $1.60 + 3($0.07) = $1.81 per gallon.
(b) Since 1.60 − 1.46 = 0.14 = 2(0.07) and 1.74 − 1.60 = 0.14 = 2(0.07), these limits represent the mean ± two standard deviations and so, by the Empirical Rule, 95% of gas stations have prices between $1.46 and $1.74 per gallon.

27. **(a)** Since the histogram is bell-shaped, it is appropriate to use the Empirical Rule
(b) By the Empirical Rule, 99.7% of patients have serum HDL within three standard deviations of the mean. That is, 99.7% of the patients have serum HDL that is greater than or equal to 51.1 − 3(10.9) = 18.4, and less than or equal to 51.1 + 3(10.9) = 83.8.
(c) According to the Empirical Rule, 95% of patients have serum HDL between 51.1 − 2(10.9) = 29.3 and 51.1 + 2(10.9) = 72.9.
(d) All except two patients have cholesterol between 29.3 and 72.9 and so the actual percentage of patients is 38/40 = 95%, which is identical to the prediction of the Empirical Rule (and consistent with Chebyshev's theorem).

29. Range = 655.53 psi; s = 123.6 psi. This change significantly increased both the range and the standard deviation. The data are more dispersed. These statistics are not resistant because they were influenced by the new extreme data value, 815.97.

31. **(a)** s = 11.6   **(b)** s = 11.6 still   **(c)** No effect.   **(d)** s = 23.3
(e) Multiplying each exam score by 2 doubled the sample standard deviation.

33. **(a)** III, because it is centered between 52 and 57 and has the greatest amount of dispersion of the three histograms with mean = 53.
(b) I, because it is centered near 53 and its dispersion is consistent with s = 1.3 but not with s = 0.12 or s = 9.
(c) IV, because it is centered near 53 and it has the least dispersion of the three histograms with mean = 53.
(d) II, because it has a center near 60.

3.3 Measures of Central Tendency and Dispersion from Grouped Data

3.3 Concepts and Vocabulary

1. When we approximate the mean and standard deviation from grouped data, we assume that all of the data points within each group can be approximated by the midpoint of that group.

3.3 Exercises: Basic Skills

1.

Age	Midpoint x_i	Number (millions)	$x_i f_i$	μ	$x_i - \mu$	$(x_i - \mu)^2 f_i$
25 – 34	29.5	38.5	1135.75	42.51	-13.01	6514.29
35 – 44	39.5	44.7	1765.65	42.51	-3.01	404.39
45 – 54	49.5	35.2	1742.40	42.51	6.99	1720.97
55 – 64	59.5	22.9	1362.55	42.51	16.99	6612.04
		$\sum f_i = $ 141.3	6006.35 $= \sum x_i f_i$		$\sum (x_i - \mu)^2 f_i = $	15251.69

The mean is $\mu = \dfrac{6006.35}{141.3} = 42.51$. The standard deviation is $\sigma = \sqrt{\dfrac{15,251.69}{141.3}} = 10.39$.

3. (a)

High Temperature	Midpoint x_i	Days f_i	$x_i f_i$	μ	$x_i - \mu$	$(x_i - \mu)^2 f_i$
50 – 59	54.5	1	54.5	80.4	-25.9	672.6
60 – 69	64.5	308	19866.0	80.4	-15.9	78208.5
70 – 79	74.5	1519	113165.5	80.4	-5.9	53505.2
80 – 89	84.5	1626	137397.0	80.4	4.1	26868.7
90 – 99	94.5	503	47533.5	80.4	14.1	99505.9
100 – 109	104.5	11	1149.5	80.4	24.1	6370.4
		$\sum f_i = $ 3968	319166.0 $= \sum x_i f_i$		$\sum (x_i - \mu)^2 f_i = $	265131.2

The mean is $\mu = \dfrac{319,166.0}{3968} = 80.4$. The standard deviation is

$$\sigma = \sqrt{\dfrac{265,131.2}{3968}} = 8.17.$$

(b)

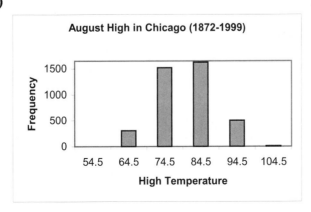

(c) 95% of observations will be between $\mu - 2\sigma = 80.4 - 2(8.2) = 64.0$ and
$\mu + 2\sigma = 80.4 + 2(8.2) = 96.8$.

5.

Tensile Strength	Midpoint x_i	Frequency f_i	$x_i f_i$	μ	$x_i - \mu$	$(x_i - \mu)^2 f_i$
160 – 169	164.5	1	164.5	204.1	-39.6	1568.2
170 – 179	174.5	1	174.5	204.1	-29.6	876.2
180 – 189	184.5	4	738.0	204.1	-19.6	1536.6
190 – 199	194.5	1	194.5	204.1	-9.6	92.2
200 – 209	204.5	9	1840.5	204.1	0.4	1.4
210 219	214.5	6	1287.0	204.1	10.4	649.0
220 – 229	224.5	1	224.5	204.1	20.4	416.2
230 239	234.5	1	234.5	204.1	30.4	924.2
240 – 249	244.5	1	244.5	204.1	40.4	1632.2
		$\sum f_i =$ 25	5102.5 $= \sum x_i f_i$		$\sum (x_i - \mu)^2 f_i =$	7696.0

The mean is $\bar{x} = \dfrac{5102.5}{25} = 204.1$ (compared to 203.9 using the raw data). The standard
deviation is $s = \sqrt{\dfrac{7696.0}{25-1}} = 17.91$ (compared to 18.32 using the raw data).

7.

HDL Cholesterol	Midpoint x_i	Frequency f_i	$x_i f_i$	μ	$x_i - \mu$	$(x_i - \mu)^2 f_i$
20 – 29	24.5	1	24.5	51.3	-26.8	715.6
30 – 39	34.5	6	207.0	51.3	-16.8	1683.4
40 – 49	44.5	10	445.0	51.3	-6.8	455.6
50 – 59	54.5	14	763.0	51.3	3.3	147.9
60 69	64.5	6	387.0	51.3	13.3	1053.4
70 – 79	74.5	3	223.5	51.3	23.3	1621.7
		$\sum f_i =$ 40	2050 $= \sum x_i f_i$		$\sum (x_i - \mu)^2 f_i =$	5677.5

The mean is $\bar{x} = \dfrac{2050.0}{40} = 51.3$ (compared to 51.1 using the raw data). The standard deviation is $s = \sqrt{\dfrac{5677.5}{40-1}} = 12.1$ (compared to 10.9 using the raw data).

9.

Grade	Grade Points	Hours	GP x Hrs
B	3	5	15
A	4	3	12
A	4	4	16
C	2	3	6
Totals		15	49

GPA = 49/15 = 3.267.

11. Cost per pound = weighted average = $\dfrac{4(\$3.50)+3(\$2.75)+2(\$2.25)}{4+3+2}=\$2.97\,/\text{lb}.$

13. (a)

Age	Midpoint x_i	Population f_i	$x_i f_i$	μ	$x_i - \mu$	$(x_i-\mu)^2 f_i$
0 – 9	4.5	19,881	89,464.5	34.6	-30.1	18,066,240.1
10 – 19	14.5	20,174	292,523.0	34.6	-20.1	8,187,004.5
20 – 29	24.5	18,264	447,468.0	34.6	-10.1	1,879,736.4
30 – 39	34.5	21,001	724,534.5	34.6	-0.1	441.3
40 – 49	44.5	20,550	914,475.0	34.6	9.9	1,995,851.4
50 – 59	54.5	14,187	773,191.5	34.6	19.9	5,592,833.7
60 – 69	64.5	9,312	600,624.0	34.6	29.9	8,300,001.1
70 – 79	74.5	6,926	515,987.0	34.6	39.9	11,001,423.6
80 – 89	84.5	2,664	225,108.0	34.6	49.9	6,621,437.4
90 – 99	94.5	384	36,288.0	34.6	59.9	1,375,728.1
		$\sum f_i = $ 133,343	$4{,}619{,}663.5 = \sum x_i f_i$		$\sum(x_i-\mu)^2 f_i = $ 63,020,697.8	

The mean age for males is $\bar{x}=\dfrac{4,619,663.5}{133,343}=34.6$. The standard deviation age for

males is $s=\sqrt{\dfrac{63,020,697.8}{133,343}}=21.7$.

(b)

Age	Midpoint x_i	Population f_i	$x_i f_i$	μ	$x_i - \mu$	$(x_i-\mu)^2 f_i$
0 – 9	4.5	18,994	85,473.0	37.2	-32.7	20,292,701.8
10 – 19	14.5	19,143	277,573.5	37.2	-22.7	9,852,029.2
20 – 29	24.5	18,038	441,931.0	37.2	-12.7	2,902,936.3
30 – 39	34.5	21,305	735,022.5	37.2	-2.7	153,706.5
40 – 49	44.5	21,091	938,549.5	37.2	7.3	1,128,255.8
50 – 59	54.5	15,148	825,566.0	37.2	17.3	4,540,987.8

60	69	64.5	10,669	688,150.5	37.2	27.3	7,959,659.0
70 – 79		74.5	9,191	684,729.5	37.2	37.3	12,796,950.2
80 – 89		84.5	4,788	404,586.0	37.2	47.3	10,718,488.6
90 – 99		94.5	1112	105,084.0	37.2	57.3	3,652,803.3

$$\sum f_i = 139,479 \quad 5,186,665.5 = \sum x_i f_i \quad \sum (x_i - \mu)^2 f_i = 73,998,518.6$$

The mean age for females is $\bar{x} = \dfrac{5,186,665.5}{139,479} = 37.2$. The standard deviation age for

females is $s = \sqrt{\dfrac{73,998,518.6}{139,479}} = 23.0$.

(c) & (d) Females have both a higher mean age and more dispersion in age.

3.4 Measures of Position

3.4 Concepts and Vocabulary

1. The kth percentile of a set of data is the data value that divides the bottom k% of the data from the top $(100-k)$% of the data. For example, if a data value lies at the 60th percentile, then approximately 60% of the data is below it and approximately 40% is above this value.

3. A four-star mutual fund is in the top 40% of its investment class (but not in the top 20%).

5. To qualify for Mensa, you need to have an IQ that places you among the top 2% of people (for IQ).

3.4. Exercises: Basic Skills

1. z-score for the ACT $= \dfrac{x - \mu}{\sigma} = \dfrac{25 - 20.7}{5} = 0.86$

   z-score for the SAT $= \dfrac{x - \mu}{\sigma} = \dfrac{650 - 514}{113} = 1.20$

   The ACT test score is 0.86 standard deviations above the mean, while the SAT test score is 1.20 standard deviations above the mean. Therefore, the SAT test score should be provided to the advisor because it is higher, relative to its mean, than the ACT score.

3. z-score for the 34-week-gestation-period baby $= \dfrac{x - \mu}{\sigma} = \dfrac{3000 - 2600}{680} = 0.59$

   z-score for the 40-week-gestation-period baby $= \dfrac{x - \mu}{\sigma} = \dfrac{3300 - 3500}{480} = -0.42$

The weight of a 34-week-gestation-period baby is 0.59 standard deviations above the mean, while the weight of a 40-week-gestation-period baby is 0.42 standard deviations below the mean. Therefore, the 40-week-gestation-period baby weighs less relative to the mean for its gestation period.

5. z-score for the man $= \dfrac{x-\mu}{\sigma} = \dfrac{75-69.9}{3} = 1.70$

z-score for the woman $= \dfrac{x-\mu}{\sigma} = \dfrac{70-64.6}{2.8} = 1.93$

The height of the man is 1.7 standard deviations above the mean, while the height of the woman is 1.93 standard deviations above the mean. Therefore, the woman is relatively taller than the man.

7. (The data provided in Table 14 are already listed in ascending order.)

(a) $i = \left(\dfrac{k}{100}\right) \cdot n = \left(\dfrac{40}{100}\right) \cdot 130 = 52$. We average the 52nd ($608,535) and 53rd ($610,432) observations and so $P_{40} = \$609,483.50$. This means that approximately 40% of the 130 players earned less than $609,483.50, and approximately 60% of the 130 players earned more than this.

(b) $i = \left(\dfrac{k}{100}\right) \cdot n = \left(\dfrac{95}{100}\right) \cdot 130 = 123.5$, and round 123.5 up to 124. Therefore P_{95} is the 124th observation in the data set and so $P_{95} = \$2,462,846$. This means that approximately 95% of the 130 players earned less than $2,462,846, and approximately 5% of the 130 players earned more than $2,462,846.

(c) $i = \left(\dfrac{k}{100}\right) \cdot n = \left(\dfrac{10}{100}\right) \cdot 130 = 13$. We average the 13th ($406,591) and 14th ($414,123) observations in the data set and so $P_{10} = \$410,357$. This means that approximately 10% of the 130 players earned less than $410,357, and approximately 90% of the 130 players earned more than this.

(d) Of the 130 players, there are 20 players who earned less than $459,812. Therefore,

percentile rank $= \left(\dfrac{\#\text{ of data values less than }\$459,812}{n}\right) \cdot 100 = \left(\dfrac{20}{130}\right) \cdot 100 = 15.38$.

Round 15.38 to 15. Thus $459,812 is at the 15th percentile. This means that approximately 15% of the 130 players earned less than $459,812, and approximately 85% of the 130 players earned more than $459,812.

(e) Of the 130 players, there are 102 players who earned less than $1,563,115. Thus, percentile rank $= \left(\dfrac{\#\text{ of data values less than }\$1,563,115}{n}\right) \cdot 100 = \left(\dfrac{102}{130}\right) \cdot 100 = 78.46$.

Round 78.46 to 78. Thus $1,563,115 is at the 78th percentile. This means that approximately 78% of the 130 players earned less than $1,563,115, and approximately 22% of the 130 players earned more than $1,563,115.

9. **(a)** Computing the sample mean (μ) and standard deviation (σ) for the data yields $\mu =$ 3.994 and $\sigma = 1.779$. The z-score for 0.97 is $z = \dfrac{x - \mu}{\sigma} = \dfrac{0.97 - 3.994}{1.779} = -1.70$. The rainfall in 1971 (0.97 inches) is 1.70 standard deviations below the mean.

   (b) The data are put in order from low to high. There are $n = 20$ data points. The index, i, for the first quartile, Q_1, is $i = \left(\dfrac{25}{100}\right) \cdot n = \left(\dfrac{25}{100}\right) \cdot 20 = 5$. For the second quartile, $i = \left(\dfrac{50}{100}\right) \cdot n = \left(\dfrac{50}{100}\right) \cdot 20 = 10$. For the third quartile, $i = \left(\dfrac{75}{100}\right) \cdot n = \left(\dfrac{75}{100}\right) \cdot 20 = 15$. Since the indices for Q_1, Q_2, and Q_3 (5, 10, and 15, respectively) are all integers, Q_1, Q_2, and Q_3 will be the arithmetic means of the 5th and 6th, 10th and 11th, and 15th and 16th data values, respectively. Therefore, $Q_1 = \dfrac{(2.47 + 2.78)}{2} = 2.625$; $Q_2 = \dfrac{(3.97 + 4.0)}{2} = 3.985$; and $Q_3 = \dfrac{(5.22 + 5.5)}{2} = 5.36$.

   (c) $\text{IQR} = Q_3 - Q_1 = 5.36 - 2.625 = 2.735$

   (d) Lower fence $= Q_1 - 1.5 \cdot (\text{IQR}) = 2.625 - 1.5 \cdot (2.735) = -1.478$.
   Upper fence $= Q_3 + 1.5 \cdot (\text{IQR}) = 5.36 + 1.5 \cdot (2.735) = 9.463$. There are no outliers.

11. **(a)** Computing the sample mean (μ) and standard deviation (σ) for the data yields $\mu =$ 6.245 and $\sigma = 1.6333$. The z-score for 0.2 is $z = \dfrac{x - \mu}{\sigma} = \dfrac{0.2 - 6.245}{1.633} = -3.70$. The red blood cell count of Sampson (0.2 M/μL) is 3.70 standard deviations below the mean.

   (b) The data are put in order from low to high. There are $n = 20$ data points. Just as in Problem 9, Q_1, Q_2, and Q_3 will be the arithmetic means of the 5th and 6th, 10th and 11th, and 15th and 16th data values, respectively. Therefore, $Q_1 = \dfrac{(6 + 6.1)}{2} = 6.05$; $Q_2 = \dfrac{(6.3 + 6.6)}{2} = 6.45$; and $Q_3 = \dfrac{(6.9 + 7)}{2} = 6.95$.

   (c) $\text{IQR} = Q_3 - Q_1 = 6.95 - 6.05 = 0.90$.

   (d) Lower fence $= Q_1 - 1.5 \cdot (\text{IQR}) = 6.05 - 1.5 \cdot (0.9) = 4.7$.
   Upper fence $= Q_3 + 1.5 \cdot (\text{IQR}) = 6.95 + 1.5 \cdot (0.9) = 8.3$. Yes, 0.2 is an outlier because it is less than the lower fence of 4.7.

13. **(a)** Computing the sample mean (μ) and standard deviation (σ) for the data yields $\mu =$ 15.923 and $\sigma = 7.384$. The z-score for 20.46 is $z = \dfrac{x - \mu}{\sigma} = \dfrac{20.46 - 15.923}{7.384} = 0.61$; The concentration of 20.46 is 0.61 standard deviations above the mean.

(b) The data are put in order from low to high. There are $n = 33$ data points. The index, i, for the first quartile, Q_1, is $i = \left(\dfrac{25}{100}\right) \cdot n = \left(\dfrac{25}{100}\right) \cdot 33 = 8.25$, which we round up to 9. For the second quartile, $i = \left(\dfrac{50}{100}\right) \cdot n = \left(\dfrac{50}{100}\right) \cdot 33 = 16.5$, which we round up to 17. For the third quartile, $i = \left(\dfrac{75}{100}\right) \cdot n = \left(\dfrac{75}{100}\right) \cdot 33 = 24.75$, which we round up to 25. Therefore, $Q_1 =$ the 9th data value $= 10.3$, $Q_2 =$ the 17th data value $= 15.42$, and $Q_3 =$ the 25th data value $= 19.8$.

(c) $IQR = Q_3 - Q_1 = 19.8 - 10.3 = 9.5$.

(d) Lower fence $= Q_1 - 1.5 \cdot (IQR) = 10.3 - 1.5 \cdot (9.5) = -3.95$.
Upper fence $= Q_3 + 1.5 \cdot (IQR) = 19.8 + 1.5 \cdot (9.5) = 34.05$. There are no outliers.

15. (a) Both the financial stock data and the energy stock data are put in order from low to high. For financial stocks, $n = 40$. To find the outliers, first we have to determine the quartiles. For financial stocks, the index, i, for the first quartile is $i = \left(\dfrac{25}{100}\right) \cdot n$

$= \left(\dfrac{25}{100}\right) \cdot 40 = 10$. For the third quartile, $i = \left(\dfrac{75}{100}\right) \cdot n = \left(\dfrac{75}{100}\right) \cdot 40 = 30$. Since the indices for Q_1 and Q_3 (10 and 30, respectively) are integers, Q_1 and Q_3 will be the arithmetic means of the 10th and 11th, and 30th and 31st data values, respectively. Therefore, $Q_1 = \dfrac{(5.32 + 5.63)}{2} = 5.475$; and $Q_3 = \dfrac{(14.61 + 16.12)}{2} = 15.365$. Next, we calculate the IQR $= Q_3 - Q_1 = 15.365 - 5.475 = 9.89$, and use the IQR to find the upper and lower fences. Lower fence $= Q_1 - 1.5 \cdot (IQR) = 5.475 - 1.5 \cdot (9.89) = -9.36$. Upper fence $= Q_3 + 1.5 \cdot (IQR) = 15.365 + 1.5 \cdot (9.89) = 30.2$. Therefore, 34.22% is an outlier for the financial stocks because it is greater than the upper fence, 30.2.

For energy stocks, $n = 35$, and so the index, i, for the first quartile is $i = \left(\dfrac{25}{100}\right) \cdot n = \left(\dfrac{25}{100}\right) \cdot 35 = 8.75$, which we round up to 9. For the third quartile, $i = \left(\dfrac{75}{100}\right) \cdot n = \left(\dfrac{75}{100}\right) \cdot 35 = 26.25$, which we round up to 27. Therefore, $Q_1 =$ the 9th data value $= 6.11$, and $Q_3 =$ the 27th data value $= 11.6$. Next, we calculate the $IQR = Q_3 - Q_1 = 11.6 - 6.11 = 5.49$, and use the IQR to find the upper and lower fences. Lower fence $= Q_1 - 1.5 \cdot (IQR) = 6.11 - 1.5 \cdot (5.49) = -2.125$. Upper fence $= Q_3 + 1.5 \cdot (IQR) = 11.6 + 1.5 \cdot (5.49) = 19.835$. Therefore, 21.67%, 23.72%, and

30.39% are outliers for the energy stocks because they are greater than the upper fence, 19.835.

(b)

17. **(a)** The data are put in order from low to high and $n = 50$. To find the outliers, first we have to determine the quartiles. The index, i, for the first quartile is $i = \left(\dfrac{25}{100}\right) \cdot n = \left(\dfrac{25}{100}\right) \cdot 50 = 12.5$, which we round up to $= 13$. For the third quartile, Q_3, is $i = \left(\dfrac{75}{100}\right) \cdot n = \left(\dfrac{75}{100}\right) \cdot 50 = 37.5$, which we round up to $= 38$. Therefore, $Q_1 =$ the 13th data value $= 67$ and $Q_3 =$ the 38th data value $= 479$. Next, we calculate the $\text{IQR} = Q_3 - Q_1 = 479 - 67 = 412$, and use the IQR to find the upper and lower fences: Lower fence $= Q_1 - 1.5 \cdot (\text{IQR}) = 67 - 1.5 \cdot (412) = -551$. Upper fence $= Q_3 + 1.5 \cdot (\text{IQR}) = 479 + 1.5 \cdot (412) = 1097$. Therefore, \$12,777 is an outlier because it is greater than the upper fence, \$1097.

(b) Explanations will vary.

19.

Pulse	z-score	
76	0.49	
60	-1.59	
60	-1.59	
81	1.14	
72	-0.03	
80	1.01	
80	1.01	
68	-0.55	
73	0.10	
μ 72.2	0.0	= mean of the z-scores
σ 7.671	1.00	= standard deviation of the z-scores

3.5 The Five-Number Summary; Boxplots

3.5 Concepts and Vocabulary

1. The median and interquartile range are resistant to extreme values and so would be better measures of central tendency and dispersion when the data have a skewed distribution.

3.5 Exercises: Skill Building

1. The distribution is skewed to the right. From the boxplot we read off the five-number summary to be approximately: 0, 1, 3, 6, 16.

3.5 Exercises: Applying the Concepts

3. Using technology we get the five-number summary:
   42, 51, 55, 58, 69.

   The distribution is fairly symmetric.

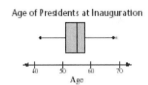

Age of Presidents at Inauguration

5. Using technology we get the five-number summary:
   2, 11.5, 20, 31, 38.

   The distribution appears to be symmetric.

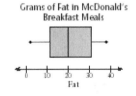

Grams of Fat in McDonald's Breakfast Meals

7. (a) Using technology we get the five-number summary:
   160.44, 188.32, 206.51, 212.75, 242.76
   (b) & (c) The boxplot suggests that the distribution is symmetric or slightly skewed to the left, and this is confirmed by the histogram.

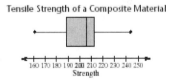

Tensile Strength of a Composite Material

9. (a) Using technology we get the five-number summary:
   28, 45, 51, 57.5, 73
   (b) & (c) The boxplot suggests that the distribution is symmetric, and this is confirmed by the histogram.

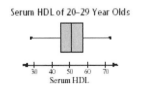

Serum HDL of 20–29 Year Olds

11. (a) Using technology we get the five-number summary:
   0.76, 0.85, 0.88, 0.90, 0.94
   (b) & (c) The boxplot suggests that the distribution is skewed to the left, and this is confirmed by the histogram.

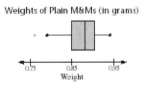

Weights of Plain M&Ms (in grams)

13. Van: 18, 23.5, 41, 47, 81
    SUV: 39, 45, 90.5, 151, 231
    The boxplot suggests that vans are safer.

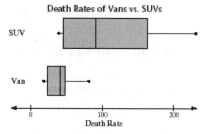

15. Thermocouple 1: 325.97, 326.04, 326.08,
    326.13, 326.20
    Thermocouple 2: 323.55, 323.595, 323.64,
    323.70, 323.76
    Thermocouple 3: 325.95, 326.01, 326.035,
    326.11, 326.20

    From the boxplot, thermocouple 2 appears to be
    broken and both of the other thermocouples ap-
    pear to give equally consistent measurements.

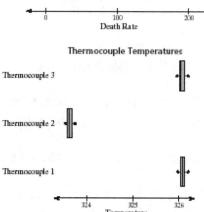

Chapter 3 Review Exercises

1.

Muzzle Velocity	Mean	Deviation	Squared Deviation
793.8	792.51	1.29	1.6641
793.1	792.51	0.59	0.3481
792.4	792.51	-0.11	0.0121
794	792.51	1.49	2.2201
791.4	792.51	-1.11	1.2321
792.4	792.51	-0.11	0.0121
791.7	792.51	-0.81	0.6561
792.3	792.51	-0.21	0.0441
789.6	792.51	-2.91	8.4681
794.4	792.51	1.89	3.5721
Total 7925.1			18.229

(a) Sample mean = 7925.1/10 = 792.51
    There are 10 data points and so the median is the average of the 5th and 6th (when the
    data are put in order) = (792.4 + 792.4)/2 = 792.4
(b) Range = largest – smallest data point = 794.4 – 789.6 = 4.8
    Sample variance = 18.229/(10 – 1) = 2.0254 or 2.03
    Sample standard deviation = $\sqrt{\text{variance}} = \sqrt{2.0254} = 1.42$

3.

Price	Mean	Deviation	Squared Deviation
16,495	13,068.11	3,426.89	11,743,567.46
15,300	13,068.11	2,231.89	4,981,328.01
13,995	13,068.11	926.89	859,123.01
13,995	13,068.11	926.89	859,123.01
12,995	13,068.11	-73.11	5,345.23
11,990	13,068.11	-1,078.11	1,162,323.57
10,995	13,068.11	-2,073.11	4,297,789.68
10,948	13,068.11	-2,120.11	4,494,871.12
10,900	13,068.11	-2,168.11	4,700,705.79
Total 117,613			33,104,176.89

(a) Sample mean = 117,613/9 = $13,068.11

There are 9 data points and so the median is the 5th (when the data are put in order, which they already are) = $12,995

(b) Range = largest – smallest data point = 16,495 – 10,900 = $5,595

Sample standard deviation = $\sqrt{\text{variance}} = \sqrt{\dfrac{33,104,176.89}{9-1}} = \$2,034.21$

(c) Using technology, we recomputed the statistics when 16,495 is replaced by 61,495 and get mean = $18,068.11, median = $12,995, range = $50,595, s = $16,361.25. The median is not affected but the other statistics are increased significantly. Only the median is resistant.

5.

Age	Mean	Deviation	Squared Deviation
44	58.31	-14.31	204.85
56	58.31	-2.31	5.35
51	58.31	-7.31	53.47
46	58.31	-12.31	151.60
59	58.31	0.69	0.47
56	58.31	-2.31	5.35
58	58.31	-0.31	0.10
55	58.31	-3.31	10.97
65	58.31	6.69	44.72
64	58.31	5.69	32.35
68	58.31	9.69	93.85

69	58.31	10.69	114.22
56	58.31	-2.31	5.35
62	58.31	3.69	13.60
62	58.31	3.69	13.60
62	58.31	3.69	13.60
Total 933			763.44

(a) Population mean = 933/16 = 58.3 years
There are 16 data points and so the median is the average of the 8th and 9th (when the data are put in order) = (58 + 59)/2 = 58.5 years
There are two modes, 56 years and 62 years (both with a frequency of 3)

(b) Range = largest – smallest data point = 69 – 44 = 25 years

Population standard deviation = $\sqrt{\text{population variance}}$ = $\sqrt{\dfrac{763.44}{16}}$ = 6.91 years

(c) Answers will vary.

7. (a) Using technology we get mean = 2.2 children and median = 2.5 children
    (b) Using technology we get range = 4 – 0 = 4 children and s = 1.3 children

9. (a) By the Empirical Rule, 99.7% of the light bulbs will have life times between 600 – 3(53) = 441 hours and 600 + 3(53) = 759 hours.
    (b) From (b) we know that these values are 2 standard deviations above and below the mean and so the Empirical Rule tells us that about 95% of light bulbs have life times between these values.
    (c) Since 441 hours is 3 standard deviations below the mean and the distribution is symmetric, only $\frac{1}{2}(100-99.7)=0.15\%$ of light bulbs will last less than 441 hours.

11. (a) & (b)

Age	Midpoint x_i	Number f_i	$x_i f_i$	μ	$x_i - \mu$	$(x_i - \mu)^2 f_i$
20 – 24	22	6,148	135,256	40.3	-18.3	2,058,501.51
25 – 29	27	5,073	136,971	40.3	-13.3	897,121.77
30 – 34	32	4,834	154,688	40.3	-8.3	332,870.83
35 – 39	37	4,414	163,318	40.3	-3.3	48,016.40
40 – 44	42	3,563	149,646	40.3	1.7	10,318.74
45 – 49	47	2,935	137,945	40.3	6.7	131,822.46
50 – 54	52	2,164	112,528	40.3	11.7	296,320.48
55 – 59	57	1,655	94,335	40.3	16.7	461,661.77
60 – 64	62	1,398	86,676	40.3	21.7	658,412.68
65 – 69	67	1,154	77,318	40.3	26.7	822,785.22
70 – 74	72	1,055	75,960	40.3	31.7	1,060,278.52

| 75 – 79 | 77 | 894 | 68,838 | 40.3 | 36.7 | 1,204,236.96 |
| 80 – 84 | 82 | 684 | 56,088 | 40.3 | 41.7 | 1,189,502.73 |

$$\sum f_i = 35,971 \quad 1,449,567 = \sum x_i f_i \quad \sum (x_i - \mu)^2 f_i = 9,171,850.08$$

The mean is $\mu = \dfrac{1,449,567}{35,971} = 40.3$. The standard deviation is

$$\sigma = \sqrt{\dfrac{9,171,850.08}{35,971}} = 16.0.$$

13.

Grade	Grade Points	Hours	GP x Hrs
A	4	5	20
B	3	4	12
A	4	3	12
C	2	3	6
Totals		15	50

GPA = 50/15 = 3.333.

15. (a) Using technology we get mean salaries of $2,973,911 and $4,278,218.4 for the Mets and Yankees respectively.

(b) Since there are 25 data points the median is the 13th salary (in order, and the data are in order) for each team. Thus the respective medians are $2,200,000 and $3,500,000.

(c) In both cases the mean is greater than the median and so both distributions are skewed to the right.

(d) Using technology the respective population standard deviations are $3,005,819.2 and $3,581,882.8. Thus the salaries of the Yankees are more dispersed.

(e) Since there are 25 players on each roster, Q_1 will be the salary of the 7th player from the bottom and Q_3 will be the salary of the 7th player from the top. Thus
Mets: $200,000, $462,500, $2,200,000, $4,375,000, $12,121,428
Yankees: $200,000, $1,250,000, $3,500,000, $6,500,000, $12,357,143

Salaries of Mets vs. Yankees

(f) & (g) Both distributions are clearly skewed to the right.

(h) Outliers are data values beyond the upper and lower fences, and these are found by adding and subtracting 1.5 times the IQR to/from Q_1 and Q_3, respectively, where the IQR is the difference between the first and third quartiles. The calculations are summarized in the table below. From the table we see that Mike Piazza is an outlier for the Mets because his salary of $12,121,428 exceeds the upper fence for the Mets, but there are no outliers for the Yankees.

	Mets	Yankees
Q1	462,500	1,250,000
Q3	4,375,000	6,500,000
IQR = Q3 - Q1	3,912,500	5,250,000
1.5(IQR)	5,868,750	7,875,000
Lower Fence = Q1 - 1.5(IQR)	-5,406,250	-6,625,000
Upper Fence = Q3 + 1.5(IQR)	10,243,750	14,375,000

17. We can compare these individuals based on their z-scores.

Female: $z = \dfrac{230 - 206}{44.7} = 0.54$

Male: $z = \dfrac{230 - 202}{41.0} = 0.68$

Thus the cholesterol of the male is relatively higher.

19. **(a)** 20% of 226 = 45.2 and so P_{20} = the 46th data value = 7.9

   (b) 95% of 226 = 214.7 and so P_{95} = the 215th data value = 120.06

   (c) 99% of 226 = 223.74 and so P_{99} = the 224th data value = 148.66

   (d) The United States ranks 39 out of 226. Thus (39/226) × 100 = 17.3% which we round to 17, and so the U.S. is at the 17th percentile for infant mortality rates.

   (e) Nepal ranks 185. Thus (185/226) × 100 = 81.9% which we round to 82 and so Nepal is at the 82nd percentile.

   (f) Since 0.25 × 226 = 56.5, which we round up to 57, Q_1 = the 57th value = 9.61.
   Since 0.50 × 226 = 113, Q_2 = the average of the 113th and 114th values = 24.7.
   Since 0.75 × 226 = 169.5, which we round up to 170, Q_3 = the 170th value = 64.9.

   (g) IQR = 64.9 − 9.61 = 55.29. Lower fence = 9.61 − 1.5(55.29) = −73.3 Upper fence = 64.9 + 1.5(55.29) = 147.8 and hence Sierra Leone, Afghanistan and Angola are outliers because they have infant mortality rates above the upper fence.

Chapter 4. Describing the Relation Between Two Variables

4.1 Scatter Diagrams; Correlation

4.1 Concepts and Vocabulary

1. Univariate data measures the value of a single variable for each individual in the study. Bivariate data measures values of two variables for each individual.

3. Two variables that are linearly related are positively associated if increases in the predictor variable tend to be associated with increases in the response variable.

5. If $r = 0$ then there is no **linear** relationship between the variables.

7. The linear correlation coefficient can only be calculated from bivariate **quantitative** data, and the gender of a driver is a qualitative variable.

4.1 Exercises: Skill Building

1. Nonlinear   3. Positive, linear

5. (a) III   (b) IV   (c) II   (d) I

7. (a)

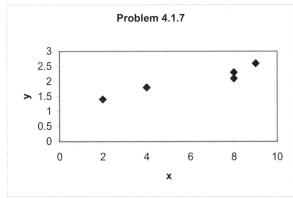

(b)

x_i	y_i	$\dfrac{x_i - \overline{x}}{s_x}$	$\dfrac{y_i - \overline{y}}{s_y}$	$\left(\dfrac{x_i - \overline{x}}{s_x}\right)\left(\dfrac{y_i - \overline{y}}{s_y}\right)$
2	1.4	-1.3847	-1.3867	1.9202
4	1.8	-0.7253	-0.5200	0.3772
8	2.1	0.5934	0.1300	0.0772
8	2.3	0.5934	0.5634	0.3343
9	2.6	0.9231	1.2134	1.1201

Mean	6.2	2.04	Total =	3.8290
S.d.	3.033	0.462	$r =$	0.9572

(c) Positive, linear

9. (a)

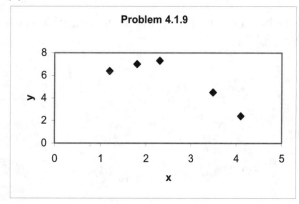

(b)

x_i	y_i	$\dfrac{x_i - \overline{x}}{s_x}$	$\dfrac{y_i - \overline{y}}{s_y}$	$\left(\dfrac{x_i - \overline{x}}{s_x}\right)\left(\dfrac{y_i - \overline{y}}{s_y}\right)$
1.2	6.4	-1.1512	0.4280	-0.4927
1.8	7	-0.6507	0.7199	-0.4684
2.3	7.3	-0.2336	0.8658	-0.2022
3.5	4.5	0.7675	-0.4961	-0.3808
4.1	2.4	1.2680	-1.5175	-1.9242

Mean	2.58	5.52	Total =	-3.4683
S.d.	1.199	2.056	$r =$	-0.8671

(c) Nonlinear

4.1 Exercises: Applying the Concepts

11. (a) Predictor: height. Response: head circumference.
   (b)

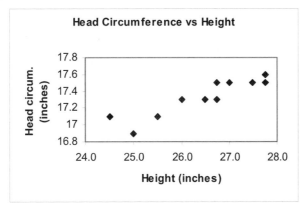

   (c) $r = 0.911$
   (d) Strong positive linear association.

13. (a) Predictor: gestation period. Response: life expectancy
   (b)

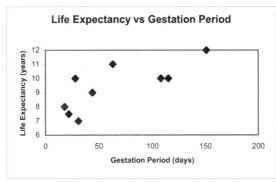

   (c) $r = 0.7257$
   (d) Moderately strong positive linear association
   (e) $r = 0.5923$. The goat conforms strongly to the linear pattern and removing it from the data weakens the association.

15. (a)

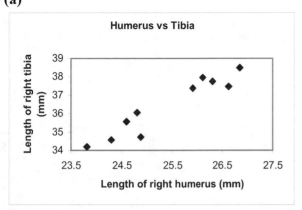

(b) $r = 0.9513$
(c) Strong positive linear association
(d) The correlation coefficient is unchanged.

17. (a)

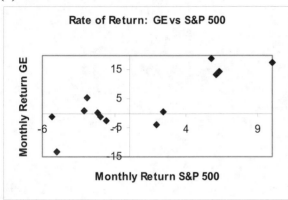

(b) $r = 0.8290$
(c) Positive linear association.

19. (a) No association.

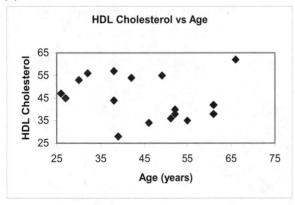

(b) $r = -0.1637$

(c) No association.

21. (a) There appears to be a weak positive linear association.

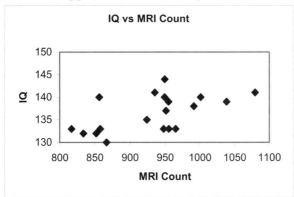

(b) $r = 0.5483$, suggesting a weak positive linear association.

(c)

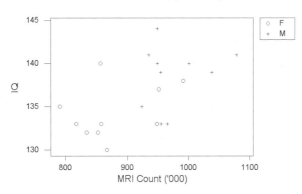

There is no clear relationship when the two genders are separated. The females tend to have lower MRI counts, presumably because females tend to be smaller than males.

(d) Females: $r = 0.3591$
Males: $r = 0.2361$

These values of r indicate no linear relationship. The moral of the story is to consider your data carefully for the possible deceptive effects from mixing distinct populations.

23. (a)

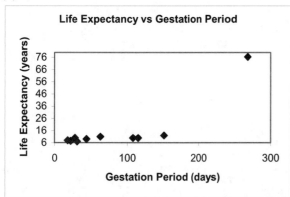

(b) $r = 0.847$

(c) Humans appear to be an outlier in this scatterplot. Because this data point is very far from the others (and so many standard deviations above the mean for both gestation period and life expectancy) it has a strong influence on the value of r, making it larger than before.

25. (a) $r = 0.2280$

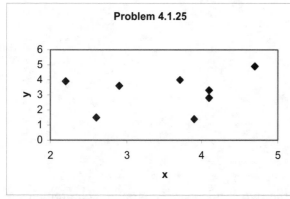

(b) $r = 0.8598$

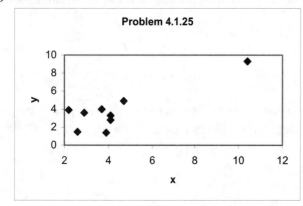

The additional data point increase r from a value that suggests no linear association to one that suggests a strong linear association. However, the second scatterplot shows that the new data point is very far from the rest of the data and so has a big influence on the value of r, even though there is no apparent association between the variables.

27. **(a)** Positive association because the more infants the more diapers will be needed.
   (b) Negative association, because the lower the interest rates the more people can afford to buy a car.
   (c) Negative association, because more exercise can lower cholesterol.
   (d) Negative association, because the higher the price of a Big Mac, the fewer Big Macs and French fries will be sold.
   (e) No association.

29. **(a)** All four give a correlation coefficient of 0.82 and yet the nature of the association between x and y is completely different in each case, as can be seen from the scatterplots.
   (b)

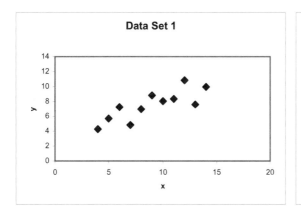

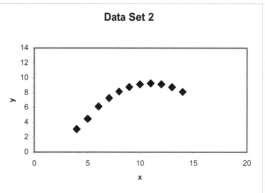

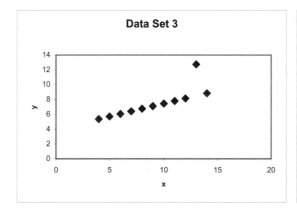

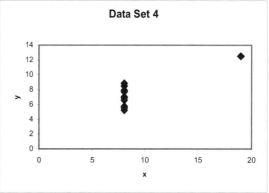

31. The correlation is +1 because any two points lie on a (perfect) straight line and the straight line joining these two points has positive slope.

33. Lurking variables could be expected to have a strong association with both response and predictor variables and show should give values of the correlation coefficient close to +1 or −1 with both of those variables.

4.2 Least-Squares Regression

4.2 Concepts and Vocabulary

1. The least squares regression line is the line that minimizes the sum of the squared residuals, i.e. of the squared vertical distances from the data points to the line.

3. Values of the predictor variable that are much larger than, or much smaller than the observed values of the predictor variable are said to be "outside the scope of the model." It is dangerous to make predictions outside the scope of the model because there is no data to support those predictions.

5. This means that the regression line is no more likely to over-predict than to under-predict.

4.2 Exercises: Skill Building

1. (a) & (c) Negative linear association

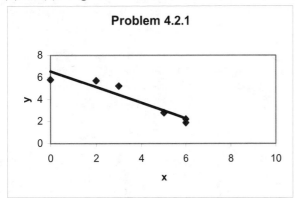

(b) $b_1 = r \cdot \dfrac{s_y}{s_x} = -0.9476938 \cdot \dfrac{1.8239152}{2.42212} = -0.713636$

$b_0 = \bar{y} - b_1 \bar{x} = 3.933 - (-0.713636)(3.667) = 6.5499$

Equation: $\hat{y} = -0.7136x + 6.55$

3. (a) & (c) & (e) Both lines are shown, and almost coincide.

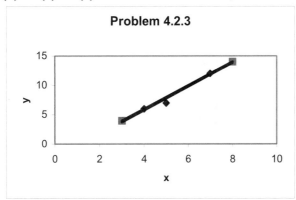

(c) Using the two points (3,4) and (8,14) gives:

$$m = \frac{14-4}{8-3} = 2$$

$$y - 4 = 2(x-3)$$

$$y - 4 = 2x - 6$$

$$y = 2x - 2$$

(d) See above.

(e) Using technology, we get: $\hat{y} = 2.0233x - 2.3256$

(f) See above.

(g) Sum of squared residuals = 1.0:

x	y	$\hat{y} = 2x-2$	$y - \hat{y}$	$(y - \hat{y})^2$
3	4	4	0	0
4	6	6	0	0
5	7	8	-1	1
7	12	12	0	0
8	14	14	0	0
			Total:	1

(h) Sum of squared residuals = 0.79

x	y	$\hat{y}$	$y - \hat{y}$	$(y - \hat{y})^2$
3	4	3.74	0.26	0.07
4	6	5.77	0.23	0.05
5	7	7.79	-0.79	0.63
7	12	11.84	0.16	0.03
8	14	13.86	0.14	0.02
			Total:	0.79

(i) The regression line gives a smaller sum of squared residuals and so is a better fit.

5. **(a) & (c) & (e)** Both lines are shown, and the lower line is (b).

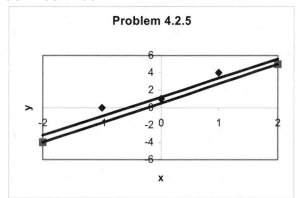

Problem 4.2.5

(b) Using the two points $(-2, -4)$ and $(2,5)$ gives:

$$m = \frac{5--4}{2--2} = 2.25$$

$$y--4 = 2.25(x--2)$$

$$y+4 = 2.25x+4.5$$

$$y = 2.25x+0.5$$

(c) See above.

(d) Using technology, we get: $\hat{y} = 2.2x+1.2$

(e) See above.

(f) Sum of squared residuals = 4.875:

x	y	$\hat{y} = 2.25x+0.5$	$y-\hat{y}$	$(y-\hat{y})^2$
-2	-4	-4	0	0
-1	0	-1.75	1.75	3.0625
0	1	0.5	0.5	0.25
1	4	2.75	1.25	1.5625
2	5	5	0	0
			Total:	4.875

(g) Sum of squared residuals = 2.40:

x	y	$\hat{y}$	$y-\hat{y}$	$(y-\hat{y})^2$
-2	-4	-3.20	-0.80	0.64
-1	0	-1.00	1.00	1.00
0	1	1.20	-0.20	0.04
1	4	3.40	0.60	0.36
2	5	5.60	-0.60	0.36
			Total:	2.40

(h) The regression line gives a smaller sum of squared residuals and so is a better fit.

7. **(a) & (c) & (e)** Both lines are shown, and the two lines almost coincide.

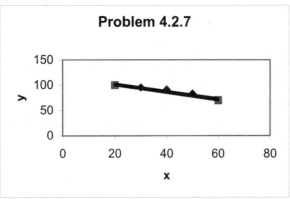

Problem 4.2.7

(b) Using the two points (20, 100) and (60,70) gives:

$$m = \frac{70-100}{60-20} = -0.75$$

$$y - 100 = -0.75(x - 20)$$

$$y - 100 = -0.75x + 15$$

$$y = -0.75x + 115$$

(c) See above.

(d) Using technology, we get: $\hat{y} = -0.72x + 116.6$

(e) See above.

(f) Sum of squared residuals = 72.5:

x	y	$\hat{y} = 2.25x + 0.5$	$y - \hat{y}$	$(y - \hat{y})^2$
20	100	100	0	0
30	95	92.5	2.5	6.25
40	91	85	6	36
50	83	77.5	5.5	30.25
60	70	70	0	0
			Total:	72.5

(g) Sum of squared residuals = 32.4:

x	y	$\hat{y}$	$y - \hat{y}$	$(y - \hat{y})^2$
20	100	102.2	-2.2	4.84
30	95	95	0	0
40	91	87.8	3.2	10.24
50	83	80.6	2.4	5.76
60	70	73.4	-3.4	11.56
			Total:	32.4

(h) The regression line gives a smaller sum of squared residuals and so is a better fit.

4.2 Exercises: Applying the Concepts

9. **(a)** Using technology: Head $=0.1827$ Height $+12.4932$

(b) The slope predicts that each one-inch increase in height is associated with an increase of head circumference of 0.1827 inches. The intercept would make a prediction about a child that is 0 inches tall and so has no sensible interpretation in this context.

(c) Head $=0.1827 \cdot 25 +12.4932 = 17.0607$ or 17.1 inches.

(d) Residual $= y - \hat{y} = 16.9 - 17.1 = -0.2$ inches. This child's head circumference is below average (since the residual is negative).

(e)

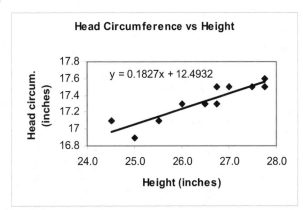

(f) This is just natural variation in the head circumference of children who are 26.75 inches tall.

(g) No, because this is well outside the scope of the model.

11. **(a)** Life expectancy $=0.0261 \cdot$ Gestation $+7.8738$

(b) The slope predicts that each 1-day increase in the gestation period of an animal is associated with an increase in life expectancy of 0.0261 years. The intercept would make a prediction about the life expectancy of an animal with a gestation period of 0 days, and so has no sensible interpretation.

(c) Life expectancy $=0.0261 \cdot 95 + 7.8738 = 10.3533$ years.

(d) Life expectancy $=0.0261 \cdot 18 + 7.8738 = 8.3436$ years.

(e) Life expectancy $=0.0261 \cdot 68 + 7.8738 = 9.6486$ years.

(f) Residual $= y - \hat{y} = 3 - 9.6 = -6.6$ years .

13. **(a)** Tibia $=1.3902 \cdot$ Humerus $+1.1140$

(b) The slope predicts that each 1-mm increase in the length of the right humerus is associated with an increase in the length of the right tibia of 1.3902 mm. The intercept would make a prediction about rats with a right humerus of length 0 mm and so has no sensible interpretation.

(c) Tibia $=1.3902 \cdot 26.11 + 1.1140 = 37.41$ mm.

(d) Residual $= y - \hat{y} = 37.96 - 37.41 = 0.55$ mm above average.

(e)

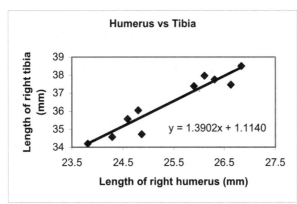

(f) Tibia $= 1.3902 \cdot 25.31 + 1.1140 = 36.30$ mm.

15. (a) Return on GE $= 1.6028 \cdot$ Return on S&P 500 $+ 2.5331$

(b) The slope predicts that each 1% increase in the monthly rate of return on the S&P 500 is associated with a 1.6028% increase in the monthly rate of return on GE stock. The intercept predicts that if the price of the S&P 500 remains unchanged in one month (i.e. if the monthly return is 0) then the return on GE stock would be 2.5331%.

(c) Return on GE $= 1.6028 \cdot 8.9 + 2.5331 = 16.7980$ % or 16.8%.

17. (a) IQ $= 0.0286 \cdot$ MRI Count (000) $+ 109.8940$

(b) The slope is positive which agrees with both the apparent positive linear association shown in the scatter diagram and with the positive correlation coefficient.

(c) Since the correlation coefficient is only 0.548, indicating only a weak association, the best prediction would be the mean IQ, or 136 in both cases.

4.3 The Coefficient of Determination

4.3 Concepts and Vocabulary

1. 75% of total variation in the response variable is explained by the regression.

4.3 Exercises: Skill Building

1. (a) III   **(b)** II   **(c)** IV   **(d)** I

4.3 Exercises: Applying the Concepts

3. 83% of the variation in length of eruption is explained by the regression.

5. **(a)** No, because there does not appear to be a linear pattern to the points on the scatter-plot.
    (b) Only 6.8% of the variation in sugar content is explained by the regression. This confirms the conclusion that sugar content and calories are not linearly related.

7. **(a)** $R^2 = 83.0\%$
    (b) 83% of variation in head circumference is explained by the regression. There is no pattern to the residuals and that, combined with the high value of R^2 suggests that a linear model is appropriate.

9. **(a)** $R^2 = 52.7\%$
    (b) 52.7% of the variation in life expectancy is explained by the regression. The residual plot reveals no obvious deviations from linearity.

11. **(a)** $R^2 = 90.5\%$
    (b) 90.5% of the variation in length of the right tibia is explained by the regression. A linear model appears to be appropriate.

13. **(a)** $R^2 = 68.7\%$
    (b) 68.7% of the variation in the monthly return of GE stock is explained by the regression. A linear model appears to be appropriate.

Chapter 4 Review Exercises

1. **(a)**

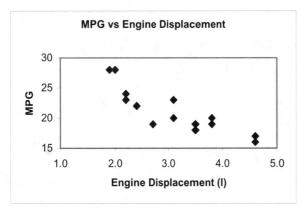

(b) Using technology, $r = -0.871$.

(c) Negative linear association.

3. **(a)**

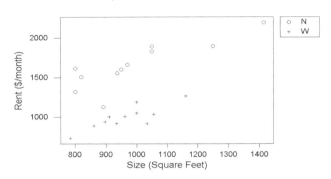

(b) For North Chicago: $r = 0.835$. For West Suburbs: $r = 0.829$

(c) In each case there is a positive linear association between size and rent.

(d) Yes. The points corresponding to apartments in the Western Suburbs lie below those for North Chicago indicating that for the same size apartment, rents are lower in the Western Suburbs.

5. **(a) & (b)**   Using technology: MPG $= -3.5339 \cdot$ Engine Displacement $+ 32.1201$

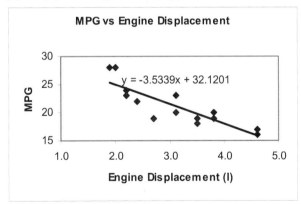

(c) The slope tells us that each 1-liter increase in engine displacement is associated with a decrease in fuel efficiency of 3.5339 mpg. The intercept does not have a sensible interpretation (as it would be making a prediction about an engine with zero displacement).

(d) MPG $= -3.5339 \cdot (3.8) + 32.1201 = 18.69$ or 18.7 mpg.

(e) Since the actual mpg for the Ford Mustang is $y = 20$, the residual is
$y - \hat{y} = 20 - 18.7 = 1.3$ mpg.

(f) Since this residual is positive, the mpg is above average.

7. **(a)** Using technology: Rent $=1.1702 \cdot \text{Size} - 132.57$
    (b)

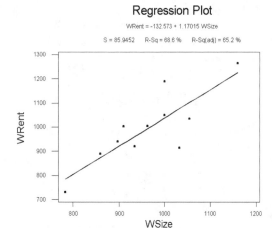

Regression Plot

WRent = -132.573 + 1.17015 WSize

S = 85.9452   R-Sq = 68.6 %   R-Sq(adj) = 65.2 %

(c) The slope tells us that each additional square foot of space in an apartment is associated with an increase of $1.17 in the monthly rent. The intercept, being negative, does not have any sensible interpretation in this case.

(d) Rent $=1.1702 \cdot (934) - 132.57 = \$960.40$ or $960 per month.

(e) Since the observed rent for a 934-square-foot apartment was $y = \$920$ per month, the residual is $y - \hat{y} = 920 - 960 = -\$40$ per month.

(f) The negative residual indicates that the apartment's rent is below average.

9. **(a) & (c) & (e)** Both lines are shown, and almost coincide.

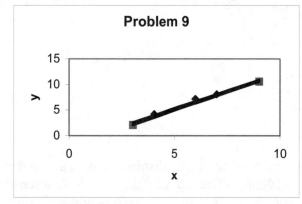

Problem 9

(b) Using the two points (3,2.1) and (9,10.6) gives:

$$m = \frac{10.6 - 2.1}{9 - 3} = 1.417$$

$$y - 2.1 = 1.417(x - 3)$$

$$y - 2.1 = 1.417x - 4.251$$

$$y = 1.417x - 2.151$$

(c) See above.

(d) Using technology, we get: $\hat{y} = 1.3877x - 1.6088$

(e) See above.

(f) Sum of squared residuals = 1.30:

x	y	$\hat{y} = 1.417x - 2.151$	$y - \hat{y}$	$(y - \hat{y})^2$
3	2.1	2.10000	0.00000	0.00000
4	4.2	3.51667	0.68333	0.46694
6	7.2	6.35000	0.85000	0.72250
7	8.1	7.76667	0.33333	0.11111
9	10.6	10.60000	0.00000	0.00000
			Total:	1.30056

(g) Sum of squared residuals = 0.58

x	y	$\hat{y}$	$y - \hat{y}$	$(y - \hat{y})^2$
3	2.1	2.55439	-0.45439	0.20647
4	4.2	3.94211	0.25789	0.06651
6	7.2	6.71754	0.48246	0.23276
7	8.1	8.10526	-0.00526	0.00003
9	10.6	10.88070	-0.28070	0.07879
			Total:	0.58456

(h) The regression line gives a smaller sum of squared residuals and so is a better fit.

11. $R^2 = (-0.871)^2 = 75.9\%$ and so 75.9% of the variation in mpg is explained by the regression.

13. $R^2 = (0.829)^2 = 68.7\%$ and so 68.7% of the variation in rents is explained by the regression.

Chapter 5. Probability

5.1 Probability of Simple Events

5.1 Concepts and Vocabulary

1. The empirical probability of an outcome is the long-term proportion with which that outcome is observed. Classical probabilities can be calculated in situations in which all possible outcomes are equally likely. In that case, the classical probability of an event will be the number of ways that the event can occur as a proportion of the total number of possible outcomes.

3. Subjective probabilities are just the educated guesses of individuals, based on currently available information, and are likely to vary, sometimes considerably, from individual to individual.

5. This means that each simple event has the same probability of occurring as every other simple event.

5.1 Exercises: Basic Skills

1. Probabilities must be between 0 and 1, so the only values which could be probabilities are: 0, 0.01, 0.35 and 1.

3. Since there are 10 equally likely outcomes, and 3 outcomes in the event E, $P(E) = \dfrac{3}{10}$.

5. Since there are 10 equally likely outcomes, and 5 of these outcomes are even numbers, $P(E) = \dfrac{5}{10} = \dfrac{1}{2}$.

5.1 Exercises: Applying the Concepts

7. Since there are 8 equally likely outcomes, only one of which is BBB, the probability is 1/8.

9. The sample space of possible families is {BBBB, BBBG, BBGB, BBGG, BGBB, BGBG, BGGB, BGGG, GBBB, GBBG, GBGB, GBGG, GGBB, GGBG, GGGB, GGGG}. There are 16 equally likely outcomes. Four of these are three-girl families: BGGG, GBGG, GGBG, GGGB. Thus the probability is $\dfrac{4}{16} = \dfrac{1}{4}$.

11. **(a)** Since each of the 100 bulbs is equally likely to be selected, and there are 40 red tulip bulbs, the probability is $\dfrac{40}{100} = 0.4$.

    (b) There are 25 purple tulip bulbs and so the probability is $\dfrac{25}{100} = 0.25$.

13. **(a)** The sample space consists of the 38 equally likely outcomes, {0, 00, 1, 2, ... , 36}.
    (b) Since there are 38 equally likely outcomes, the probability of the ball landing on "8" is $\dfrac{1}{38}$. In many spins of such a roulette wheel, the long-run relative frequency of the ball landing on "8" will be close to $\dfrac{1}{38}$.
    (c) Of the 38 equally likely outcomes, 18 consist of odd numbers (1, 3, 5, ... , 35). Thus the probability of an odd number is $\dfrac{18}{38} = \dfrac{9}{19}$. In many spins of such a roulette wheel, the long-run relative frequency of the ball landing on an odd number will be close to $\dfrac{9}{19}$.

15. **(a)** There are 365 days in the year and we shall assume that a birthday is equally likely to fall on any day of the year. Thus the sample space contains 365 equally likely outcomes, 12 of which are the 1st of a month. The probability of a birthday falling on the first day of a month is $\dfrac{12}{365}$. If many individuals are chosen at random, then close to $\dfrac{12}{365}$ of them will have a birthday on the first of a month.

    (b) Since there are 7 months with 31 days in the month, this probability is $\dfrac{7}{365}$. If many individuals are chosen at random, then close to $\dfrac{7}{365}$ of them will have a birthday on the 31st of a month.

    (c) There are 31 days in December and so this probability is $\dfrac{31}{365}$. If many individuals are chosen at random, then close to $\dfrac{31}{365}$ of them will have a birthday in December.

(d) This probability is $\dfrac{1}{365}$. If many individuals are chosen at random, then close to $\dfrac{1}{365}$ of them will have a birthday on November 8.

(e) No, there is only a 1 in 365 chance that a random guess will be correct.

(f) No, because birthdays are in fact not equally likely on all days of the year. In practice, there tend to be more births at certain times of the year than at others.

17. (a) The total frequency $=125+324+552+1257+2518=4776$. The approximate probability that a student never wears a seat belt when riding in a car driven by someone else is the relative frequency of this response $=\dfrac{125}{4776}=0.026$.

(b) Yes, because the approximate probability of this is only 2.6%.

(c) Approximate probability $=$ relative frequency $=\dfrac{552}{4776}=0.116$. Approximately 11.6% of college students wear a seat belt only sometimes when riding in a car driven by someone else.

19. (a) The approximate probability $=$ the relative frequency $=\dfrac{83}{300}=0.277$. Approximately 27.7% of foreign-born residents of the United States come from Asia.

(b) The approximate probability $=$ the relative frequency $=\dfrac{2}{300}=0.007$.

(c) Yes, very unusual.

21. (a) $\dfrac{28,555}{3,936,935}=0.007$. Of the children born in the United States in 1998, 0.7% weighed 1000–1499 grams at birth.

(b) $\dfrac{335,087}{3,936,935}=0.085$. Of the children born in the United States in 1998, 8.5% weighed 4000–4499 grams at birth.

(c) $\dfrac{6,200}{3,936,935}=0.002$. Yes, this is a very small probability and so it is unusual.

23. Approximate probability $=$ relative frequency $=\dfrac{3,262}{28,538}=0.114$. No, this is not a small enough probability to be unusual.

25. Approximate probability = relative frequency = $\dfrac{7.3}{30} = 0.243.$ Approximately 24.3% of June days are clear in Chicago.

27. (a) {(Secretary of state, secretary of the treasury), (Secretary of state, secretary of war), (Secretary of state, attorney general), (Secretary of state, postmaster general), (Secretary of state, secretary of the navy), (Secretary of the treasury, secretary of war), (Secretary of the treasury, attorney general), (Secretary of the treasury, postmaster general), (Secretary of the treasury, secretary of the navy), (Secretary of war, attorney general), (Secretary of war, postmaster general), (Secretary of war, secretary of the navy), (Attorney general, postmaster general), (Attorney general, secretary of the navy), (Postmaster general, secretary of the navy)}

(b) Since this is one of 15 equally likely choices, the probability is $\dfrac{1}{15}$.

(c) Since 5 of the 15 equally likely choices include the Secretary of State, the probability is $\dfrac{5}{15} = \dfrac{1}{3}$.

29. (a) Probability $= \dfrac{26}{62} = 0.419.$ Mark McGwire hit 41.9% of his home runs to left field that year.

(b) Probability $= \dfrac{0}{62} = 0.$

(c) While McGwire did not hit any home runs to right field in 1998, this does not imply that it is impossible for him to hit a right field homer.

31. Answers will vary.

33. No, because these are not equally likely outcomes.

35. If the die were fair, then each outcome should occur close to $\dfrac{400}{6} \approx 67$ times. Since 1 and 6 occurred with considerably higher frequency, the dice appear to be loaded.

37. Since half of all families are above the median and half below, the probability is just 50% or 0.5.

5.2 The Addition Rule; Complements

5.2. Concepts and Vocabulary

1. If two events have no simple events in common or cannot occur simultaneously, they are said to be mutually exclusive.

3. Two events are complements when they have no outcomes in common (i.e are mutually exclusive) and between them contain all possible outcomes.

5.2. Exercises: Basic Skills

1. $\{5, 6, 7\}$. No, E and F are not mutually exclusive because they have simple events in common.

3. $\{5, 6, 7, 8, 9, 10, 11, 12\}$. $P(F \text{ or } G) = P(F) + P(G) - P(F \text{ and } G) = \dfrac{5}{12} + \dfrac{4}{12} - \dfrac{1}{12} = \dfrac{2}{3}$.

5. $\{\ \}$. Yes, E and G are mutually exclusive because they have no simple events in common.

7. $\{1, 8, 9, 10, 11, 12\}$. $P(\overline{E}) = 1 - P(E) = 1 - \dfrac{6}{12} = \dfrac{1}{2}$.

9. $P(A \text{ or } B) = P(A) + P(B) - P(A \text{ and } B) = 0.25 + 0.45 - 0.15 = 0.55$.

11. $P(A \text{ or } B) = P(A) + P(B) = 0.25 + 0.45 = 0.7$.

13. $P(\overline{A}) = 1 - P(A) = 1 - 0.25 = 0.75$.

15. $P(A \text{ or } B) = P(A) + P(B) - P(A \text{ and } B) \quad \therefore 0.85 = 0.60 + P(B) - 0.05$
$\therefore P(B) = 0.85 - 0.60 + 0.05 = 0.30$.

17. $P(\textit{Titleist or Maxfli}) = \dfrac{9 + 8}{20} = \dfrac{17}{20}$.

19. $P(\overline{\textit{Titleist}}) = 1 - P(\textit{Titleist}) = 1 - \dfrac{9}{20} = \dfrac{11}{20}$

21. The sample space is listed in Section 5.1, Example 5, and contains 8 equally likely outcomes of which 3 contain one boy and 3 contain two boys $\therefore$ probability $= 6/8 = 0.75$.

23. (a) $P(Heart \text{ or } Club) = P(Heart) + P(Club) = \dfrac{13}{52} + \dfrac{13}{52} = \dfrac{1}{2}$.

(b) $P(Heart \text{ or } Club \text{ or } Diamond) = P(Heart) + P(Club) + P(Diamond) =$
$\dfrac{13}{52} + \dfrac{13}{52} + \dfrac{13}{52} = \dfrac{3}{4}$.

(c) $P(Ace \text{ or } Heart) = P(Ace) + P(Heart) - P(Ace \text{ of } Hearts) = \dfrac{4}{52} + \dfrac{13}{52} - \dfrac{1}{52} = \dfrac{16}{52} = \dfrac{4}{13}$.

25. (a) $P(\overline{Nov.\,8}) = 1 - P(Nov.\,8) = 1 - \dfrac{1}{365} = \dfrac{364}{365}$.

(b) $P(\overline{Birthday \text{ on the } 1^{st}}) = 1 - P(Birthday \text{ on the } 1^{st}) = 1 - \dfrac{12}{365} = \dfrac{353}{365}$.

(c) $P(\overline{Birthday \text{ on the } 31^{st}}) = 1 - P(Birthday \text{ on the } 31^{st}) = 1 - \dfrac{7}{365} = \dfrac{358}{365}$.

(d) $P(\overline{Birthday \text{ in } December}) = 1 - P(Birthday \text{ in } December) = 1 - \dfrac{31}{365} = \dfrac{334}{365}$.

27. The total number of students surveyed $= 125 + 324 + \ldots + 2{,}518 = 4776$.

(a) $P(Never \text{ or } Rarely) = P(Never) + P(Rarely) = \dfrac{125}{4776} + \dfrac{324}{4776} = 0.094$.

(b) $P(\overline{Always}) = 1 - P(Always) = 1 - \dfrac{2518}{4776} = 0.473$.

29. (a) $P(Europe \text{ or } Asia) = P(Europe) + P(Asia) = \dfrac{46}{300} + \dfrac{83}{300} = 0.43$.

(b) $P(Europe \text{ or } Asia \text{ or } Latin \text{ } America) = P(Europe) + P(Asia) + P(Latin \text{ } America) =$
$\dfrac{46}{300} + \dfrac{83}{300} + \dfrac{152}{300} = 0.937$.

(c) $P(\overline{Europe}) = 1 - P(Europe) = 1 - \dfrac{46}{300} = 0.847$.

31. (a) $P(<1000) = P(<500) + P(500\text{-}999) = \dfrac{5{,}950 + 22{,}471}{3{,}936{,}935} = 0.007$.

(b) $P(\geq 1000) = 1 - P(<1000) = 1 - 0.007 = 0.993$.

(c) $P(<5000) = 1 - P(\geq 5000) = 1 - \dfrac{6{,}200}{3{,}936{,}935} = 0.998$.

(d) $P(\geq 500) = 1 - P(<500) = 1 - \dfrac{5{,}950}{3{,}936{,}935} = 0.998$.

33. $P(\text{not between 5 p.m. and 6 p.m.}) = 1 - P(\text{between 5 p.m. and 6 p.m.}) = 1 - \dfrac{3,262}{28,538} = 0.886$

35. Total number receiving Medicaid $= 8,550 + 5884 + 4,356 + \ldots + 1,943 = 28,708$ thousand.

   (a) $P(\text{below poverty line}) = \dfrac{8,550 + 4,356 + 1,520 + 958}{28,708} = 0.536$.

   (b) $P(<18 \text{ years}) = \dfrac{8,550 + 5,884}{28,708} = 0.503$.

   (c) $P(\text{below poverty line and} < 18 \text{ years}) = \dfrac{8,550}{28,708} = 0.298$.

   (d) $P(\text{below poverty line or} < 18 \text{ years})$
       $= P(\text{below poverty line}) + P(<18 \text{ years}) - P(\text{below poverty line and} < 18 \text{ years})$
       $= 0.536 + 0.503 - 0.298 = 0.741$.

37. Total number of driver fatalities $= 17,946 + 6387 = 24,333$.

   (a) $P(\text{male}) = \dfrac{17,946}{24,333} = 0.738$.

   (b) $P(\text{20-24}) = \dfrac{2,814 + 699}{24,333} = 0.144$.

   (c) $P(\text{male and 20-24}) = \dfrac{2,814}{24,333} = 0.116$.

   (d) $P(\text{male or 20-24})$
       $= P(\text{male}) + P(\text{20-24}) - P(\text{male and 20-24})$
       $= 0.738 + 0.144 - 0.116 = 0.766$.

5.3 The Multiplication Rule

5.3. Concepts and Vocabulary

1. Multiplication; Addition.

3. *E* and *F* are independent if either:
    (a) $P(E|F) = P(E)$ or $P(F|E) = P(F)$; or
    (b) $P(E \text{ and } F) = P(E) \cdot P(F)$

5. When you sample with replacement, then the outcome of each selection is independent of every other selection. When you sample without replacement, then the outcome of each selection is dependent on the outcomes of previous selections.

5.3. Exercises: Basic Skills

1. **(a)** These events are dependent because it cannot rain unless it is cloudy.
    (b) These events are independent because the occurrence of either has no effect on the occurrence of the other.
    (c) These events are dependent because it is known that smoking regularly reduces life expectancy and hence affects the probability of living at least 80 years.

3. No, because earning a Bachelor's degree does affect the probability of earning more than $75,000 per year.

5. **(a)** $P(F) = \dfrac{13}{52} = \dfrac{1}{4}$

    (b) $P(F \mid E) = \dfrac{P(E \text{ and } F)}{P(E)} = \dfrac{4 \text{ (face cards that are clubs)}}{16 \text{ (face cards)}} = \dfrac{1}{4}$

    (c) Yes, because these two probabilities are the same.

5.3 Exercises: Applying the Concepts

7. First selection   Second Selection   Outcome

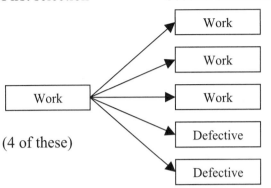

etc.

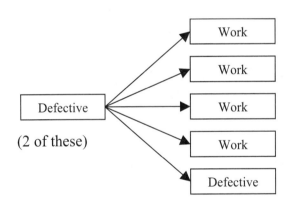

In all, there will be 30 outcomes, of which 4 · 3 = 12 will consist of two working sets. Thus the probability that both televisions work is 12/30 = 0.4. Alternatively, the product rule for dependent events gives:

$P(\text{1st works and 2nd works}) = P(\text{1st works}) \cdot P(\text{2nd works} \mid \text{1st works})$

$$= \frac{4}{6} \cdot \frac{3}{5} = 0.4.$$

9. (a) $\dfrac{4}{52} \cdot \dfrac{3}{51} = \dfrac{1}{221}$ **(b)** $\dfrac{4}{52} \cdot \dfrac{4}{52} = \dfrac{1}{169}$

11. $\dfrac{1}{5} \cdot \dfrac{1}{4} = \dfrac{1}{20}$

13. (a) $\frac{5}{13} \cdot \frac{4}{12} = \frac{5}{39} = 0.128$, which is not a small enough probability to be unusual.

(b) $\frac{8}{13} \cdot \frac{7}{12} = \frac{14}{39}$

(c) Since you either like both or neither or exactly one (and these are mutually exclusive) the probability that you like exactly one is given by $1 - \left(\frac{5}{39} + \frac{14}{39} \right) = \frac{20}{39}$

(d) **(a)** becomes $\frac{5}{13} \cdot \frac{5}{13} = \frac{25}{169}$, **(b)** becomes $\frac{8}{13} \cdot \frac{8}{13} = \frac{64}{169}$ and so **(c)** becomes

$1 - \left(\frac{25}{169} + \frac{64}{169} \right) = \frac{80}{169} = 0.473$

15. (a) $\frac{12}{30} \cdot \frac{11}{29} = 0.152$ **(b)** $\frac{12}{30} \cdot \frac{10}{29} = 0.138$ **(c)** $\frac{10}{30} \cdot \frac{12}{29} = 0.138$

(d) Since one each of red and yellow must be either 1st red, 2nd yellow or vice versa, by the addition rule this probability is 0.276.

17. $P(\text{female and smoker}) = P(\text{female} \mid \text{smoker}) \cdot P(\text{smoker}) = 0.217 \cdot 0.234 = 0.051$

19. (a) $(0.99718)^2 = 0.994$ **(b)** $(0.99718)^5 = 0.986$

(c) Since this is the complement of event **(b)** above, the probability is $1 - 0.986 = 0.014$ which is somewhat unusual.

21. (a) $(0.99)^2 = 0.9801$ **(b)** $(0.99)^6 = 0.9415$

(c) Since this is the complement of event **(b)** above, the probability is $1 - 0.9415 = 0.0585$ which is not unusual.

23. (a) $\frac{365}{365} \cdot \frac{364}{365} \cdot \frac{363}{365} \cdots \frac{356}{365} = 0.883$ **(b)** $1 - 0.883 = 0.117$

25. (a) $\frac{13}{52} \cdot \frac{12}{51} \cdot \frac{11}{50} \cdot \frac{10}{49} \cdot \frac{9}{48} = 0.000495$ **(b)** $4(0.000495) = 0.002$

27. (a) $(0.70)^{10} = 0.028$ **(b)** Not all that unusual.

29. (a) $\frac{50}{10,000} \cdot \frac{49}{9,999} = 0.0000245$ **(b)** $(0.005)^2 = 0.000025$

31. (a) 13   **(b)** $37 + 4 = 41$ cards in the deck or unknown to you; 8 clubs missing.

  (c) $\dfrac{8}{41}$ **(d)** $\dfrac{8}{41} \cdot \dfrac{7}{40} = 0.034$ **(e)** Answers will vary!

5.4 Conditional Probability

5.4 Concepts and Vocabulary

1. E and F are independent if either:
    (a) $P(E|F) = P(E)$ or $P(F|E) = P(F)$; or
    (b) $P(E \text{ and } F) = P(E) \cdot P(F)$

5.4 Exercises: Basic Skills

1. $P(F|E) = \dfrac{P(E \text{ and } F)}{P(E)} = \dfrac{0.6}{0.8} = 0.75$

3. $P(F|E) = \dfrac{N(E \text{ and } F)}{N(E)} = \dfrac{420}{740} = 0.568$

5. Using the Multiplication Rule, if $P(E \text{ and } F) = P(E) \cdot P(F)$, then events E and F are independent. Since $0.24 = (0.6) \cdot (0.4)$, then events E and F are independent.

5.4 Exercises: Applying the Concepts

7. **(a)** $P(\text{below poverty level} \mid \text{less than 18}) = \dfrac{N(\text{below poverty level and less than 18})}{N(\text{less than 18})}$

  $= \dfrac{8,550}{(8,550+5,884)} = 0.592$

  (b) $P(\text{less than 18} \mid \text{below poverty level}) = \dfrac{N(\text{less than 18 and below poverty level})}{N(\text{below poverty level})}$

  $= \dfrac{8,550}{(8,550+4,356+1,520+958)} = \dfrac{8,550}{15,384} 0.556$

9. **(a)** $P(\text{20-24 years old} \mid \text{male}) = \dfrac{N(\text{20-24 years old and male})}{N(\text{male})} = \dfrac{2,814}{17,946} = 0.157$

(b) $P(\text{male} \mid \text{20-24 years old}) = \dfrac{N(\text{male and 20-24 years old})}{N(\text{20-24 years old})} = \dfrac{2{,}814}{(2{,}814+699)} = 0.801$

(c) The victim is more likely to be male because there are more male than female fatalities in the 20–29 age group.

11. $P(\text{rainy day} \mid \text{cloudy day}) = \dfrac{P(\text{rainy day and cloudy day})}{P(\text{cloudy day})} = \dfrac{0.21}{0.37} = 0.568$.

13. $P(\text{White} \mid \text{16-17 year-old dropout}) = \dfrac{P(\text{White and 16-17 year-old dropout})}{P(\text{16-17 year-old dropout})}$

$= \dfrac{0.058}{0.091} = 0.637$.

15. No. From 7(a) we know that $P(\text{below poverty level} \mid \text{less than 18}) = 0.592$. Now, the total number of people receiving Medicaid (the sum of all numbers in the table) is 28,708 (thousand), and the total number below the poverty level is 15,384 (from 7(b)). Thus:

$P(\text{below poverty level}) = \dfrac{15{,}384}{28{,}708} = 0.536 \ne P(\text{below poverty level} \mid \text{less than 18}) = 0.592.$ It follows that the events, "less than 18 years old" and "below poverty level", are not independent.

17. No. From the Multiplication Rule, events A and B are independent if and only if $P(A \text{ and } B) = P(A) \cdot P(B)$. From the table in Problem 9, we find that $P(\text{male and 20-24 years old})$

$= \dfrac{2{,}814}{17{,}946+6{,}387} = \dfrac{2{,}814}{24{,}333} = 0.116$. We also get:

$P(\text{male}) \cdot P(\text{20-24 years old}) = \dfrac{17{,}946}{24{,}333} \cdot \dfrac{3{,}513}{24{,}333} = (0.737...)\cdot(0.144...) \approx 0.106$.

Since these probabilities are not the same, the events "male" and "20-24 years old" are not independent.

19. $P(\text{house in NE} \mid \text{earns \$75K per year}) = \dfrac{P(\text{house in NE and earns \$75K per year})}{P(\text{earns \$75K per year})}$

$= \dfrac{0.042}{0.184} = 0.228$.

5.5 Counting Techniques

5.5. Concepts and Vocabulary

1. In a combination, the order in which objects are selected does not matter, whereas in a permutation it does.

5.5. Exercises: Basic Skills

1. $5 \cdot 4 \cdot 3 \cdot 2 \cdot 1 = 120$

3. $10 \cdot 9 \cdot \ldots \cdot 1 = 3,628,800$

5. 1

7. $_6P_2 = \dfrac{6!}{(6-2)!} = \dfrac{6!}{4!} = 6 \cdot 5 = 30$

9. $_4P_4 = \dfrac{4!}{(4-4)!} = \dfrac{4!}{0!} = \dfrac{24}{1} = 24$

11. $_5P_0 = \dfrac{5!}{(5-0)!} = \dfrac{5!}{5!} = 1$

13. $_8P_3 = \dfrac{8!}{(8-3)!} = \dfrac{8!}{5!} = 8 \cdot 7 \cdot 6 = 336$

15. $_8C_3 = \dfrac{8!}{3!(8-3)!} = \dfrac{8!}{3!5!} = \dfrac{8 \cdot 7 \cdot 6}{3 \cdot 2 \cdot 1} = 56$

17. $_{10}C_2 = \dfrac{10!}{2!(10-2)!} = \dfrac{10!}{2!8!} = \dfrac{10 \cdot 9}{2 \cdot 1} = 45$

19. $_{52}C_1 = \dfrac{52!}{1!(52-1)!} = \dfrac{52!}{1!51!} = \dfrac{52}{1} = 52$

21. $_{48}C_3 = \dfrac{48!}{3!(48-3)!} = \dfrac{48!}{3!45!} = \dfrac{48 \cdot 47 \cdot 46}{3 \cdot 2 \cdot 1} = 17,296$

23. *ab, ac, ad, ae, ba, bc, bd, be, ca, cb, cd, ce, da, db, dc, de, ea, eb, ec, ed*
    Since there are 20 of them, $_5P_2 = 20$.

25. *ab, ac, ad, ae, bc, bd, be, cd, ce, de*
    Since there are 10 of them, $_5C_2 = 10$.

5.5 Exercises: Applying the Concepts

27. $6 \cdot 4 = 24$

29. $12! = 479,001,600$

31. $8! = 40,320$

33. 26 (one letter) $+26^2$ (two letters) $+26^3$ (three letters) $=18,278$

35. (a) $10^4 = 10,000$ **(b)** $\dfrac{1}{10,000} = 0.00001$

37. 26^8

39. (a) $50^3 = 125,000$ **(b)** $\dfrac{1}{125,000} = 0.000008$

41. $40 \cdot 39 \cdot 38 = 59,280$ **43.** $20 \cdot 19 \cdot 18 \cdot 17 = 116,280$

45. $25 \cdot 24 \cdot 23 \cdot 22 = 303,600$

47. $_{50}C_5 = \dfrac{50 \cdot 49 \cdot 48 \cdot 47 \cdot 46}{5 \cdot 4 \cdot 3 \cdot 2 \cdot 1} = 2,118,760$

49. $_6C_2 = \dfrac{6 \cdot 5}{2 \cdot 1} = 15$

51. There are $_{30}C_5 = 142,506$ possible choices (without regard to order) and so the probability of winning is 1/142,506.

53. (a) $\dfrac{_8C_5}{_{18}C_5} = \dfrac{8 \cdot 7 \cdot 6 \cdot 5 \cdot 4}{5 \cdot 4 \cdot 3 \cdot 2 \cdot 1} \cdot \dfrac{5 \cdot 4 \cdot 3 \cdot 2 \cdot 1}{18 \cdot 17 \cdot 16 \cdot 15 \cdot 14} = \dfrac{1}{153}$

(b) $\dfrac{_{10}C_5}{_{18}C_5} = \dfrac{10 \cdot 9 \cdot 8 \cdot 7 \cdot 6}{5 \cdot 4 \cdot 3 \cdot 2 \cdot 1} \cdot \dfrac{5 \cdot 4 \cdot 3 \cdot 2 \cdot 1}{18 \cdot 17 \cdot 16 \cdot 15 \cdot 14} = \dfrac{1}{34}$

(c) $\dfrac{_8C_2 \cdot _{10}C_3}{_{18}C_5} = \dfrac{8 \cdot 7}{2 \cdot 1} \cdot \dfrac{10 \cdot 9 \cdot 8}{3 \cdot 2 \cdot 1} \cdot \dfrac{5 \cdot 4 \cdot 3 \cdot 2 \cdot 1}{18 \cdot 17 \cdot 16 \cdot 15 \cdot 14} = \dfrac{20}{51}$

55. $P(\text{one or more defective}) = 1 - P(\text{none defective})$
$$= 1 - \dfrac{116}{120} \cdot \dfrac{115}{119} \cdot \dfrac{114}{118} \cdot \dfrac{113}{117} = 1 - 0.8717 = 0.1283$$

57. (a) $\dfrac{_5C_2 \cdot _8C_2}{_{13}C_4} = 0.3916$ **(b)** $\dfrac{_5C_3 \cdot _8C_1}{_{13}C_4} = 0.1119$ **(c)** $\dfrac{_5C_4 \cdot _8C_0}{_{13}C_4} = 0.0070$

59. (a) $_{52}C_5 = 2,598,960$

(b) There are $_4C_3 = 4$ ways of choosing 3 two's, and so on for each denomination. Hence there are $13 \cdot 4 = 52$ ways of choosing three of a kind.

(c) There are $_{12}C_2 = 66$ choices of two additional denominations (different from that of the three of a kind) and 4 choices of suit for the first remaining card and then, for each choice of suit for the first remaining card, there are 4 choices of suit for the last card. This gives a total of $66 \cdot 4 \cdot 4 = 1056$ ways of choosing the last two cards.

(d) $\dfrac{52 \cdot 1056}{2,598,960} = 0.0211$

61. $\dfrac{17}{20} \cdot \dfrac{16}{19} \cdot \dfrac{15}{18} \cdot \dfrac{14}{17} = 0.4912$

Chapter 5 Review Exercises

1. (a) Probabilities must be between 0 and 1, so the possible probabilities are: 0, 0.75, 0.41.
   (b) 2/5, 1/3, 6/7.

3. Since there are 5 equally likely simple events in the sample space, $P(F) = 2/5$.

5. Since $P(E) = 1/5$, we have $P(\overline{E}) = 1 - \frac{1}{5} = \frac{4}{5}$.

7. Using the Addition Rule for mutually exclusive events, we get $P(E \text{ or } F) = P(E) + P(F)$ and so $P(E \text{ or } F) = 0.36 + 0.12 = 0.48$.

9. No, because $P(E) \cdot P(F) = 0.8 \cdot 0.5 = 0.4 \neq P(E \text{ and } F)$.

11. $P(E \mid F) = \dfrac{P(E \text{ and } F)}{P(F)} = \dfrac{0.35}{0.7} = 0.5$.

13. (a) $\dfrac{2}{38} = \dfrac{1}{19}$. In many games of roulette, the metal ball lands on green approximately 1/19th of the time.
   (b) $\dfrac{2+18}{38} = \dfrac{10}{19}$. In many games of roulette, the metal ball lands on green or red approximately 10/19th of the time.
   (c) $\dfrac{1+18}{38} = \dfrac{1}{2}$. In many games of roulette, the metal ball lands on 00 or red approximately half the time.
   (d) Since 31 is an odd number and the odd slots are colored red, the probability of this is 0. This event is impossible.

15. (a) $\dfrac{129}{192} = \dfrac{43}{64}$ **(b)** $1 - \dfrac{43}{64} = \dfrac{21}{64}$

(c) $\dfrac{129}{192} \cdot \dfrac{128}{191} = 0.45$ **(d)** $1 - \dfrac{63}{192} \cdot \dfrac{62}{191} = 0.893$

17. The total frequency is $4 + 40 + 436 + \ldots + 8 = 3,980$

(a) $\dfrac{238}{3,980} = 0.0598$ **(b)** $\dfrac{4}{3,980} = 0.001$. Yes, this is unusual.

(c) $\dfrac{238 + 8}{3,980} = 0.0618$ **(d)** $1 - \dfrac{4}{3,980} = 0.999$

19. The data are reproduced with row and column totals:

	Period of Gestation			
Birth Weight (gm)	**Preterm**	**Term**	**Postterm**	**Totals**
Less than 500	2,365	6	0	**2,371**
500–999	7,753	45	4	**7,802**
1,000–1,499	7,868	387	74	**8,329**
1,500–1,999	12,550	2,419	239	**15,208**
2,000–2,499	22,395	21,103	1,440	**44,938**
2,500–2,999	25,941	105,757	8,303	**140,001**
3,000–3,499	18,503	192,488	18,259	**229,250**
3,500–3,999	6,722	105,325	12,045	**124,092**
4,000–4,499	1,137	23,615	2,992	**27,744**
4,500–4,999	187	3,441	507	**4,135**
More than 5,000	38	486	51	**575**
Totals	**105,459**	**455,072**	**43,914**	**604,445**

(a) $\dfrac{43,914}{604,445} = 0.0727$ **(b)** $\dfrac{229,250}{604,445} = 0.3793$

(c) $\dfrac{18,259}{604,445} = 0.0302$

(d) P(3000-3499 gm or Postterm)

$= P$(3000-3499 gm) $+ P$(Postterm) $- P$(3000-3499 gm and Postterm)

$= 0.3793 + 0.0727 - 0.0302 = 0.4218$

(e) 0; yes, this is clearly impossible.

(f) $\dfrac{18,259}{43,914} = 0.4158$

(g) No, because P(3000-3499 gm) $= 0.3793 \neq P$(3000-3499 gm | Postterm) $= 0.4158$.

21. (a) $(0.975)^2 = 0.950625$ **(b)** $(0.975)^5 = 0.8811$ **(c)** $1 - 0.8811 = 0.1189$

23. $\dfrac{9}{10} \cdot \dfrac{8}{9} = 0.8$ **25.** $26 \cdot 26 \cdot 10^4 = 6,760,000$

27. $6! = 720$

29. $_{29}C_5 = 118,755$

31. $\dfrac{1}{_{39}C_5} = \dfrac{1}{575,757}$

33. Answers will vary.

Chapter 6. The Binomial Probability Distribution

6.1 Probability Distributions

6.1 Concepts and Vocabulary

1. A random variable is a numerical measure of the outcome of a probability experiment, so its value is determined by chance.

3. For a discrete probability distribution, each probability must be between zero and one (inclusive) and the sum of the probabilities must equal one.

5. The probability of the batter making a hit on any one at-bat is 0.300, regardless of how many hits the player has or has not made in previous at-bats.

6.1 Exercises: Basic Skills

1. (a) Discrete, because the value of the random variable results from counting. Possible values are $x = 0, 1, \ldots, 20$.
    (b) Continuous. Possible values are $t > 0$.
    (c) Discrete, because the value of the random variable results from counting. Possible values are $x = 0, 1, 2, \ldots$
    (d) Continuous. Possible values are $s \geq 0$.

3. Yes, because $\sum P(X = x) = 1$ and $0 \leq P(X = x) \leq 1$.

5. No, because $P(x = 50) < 0$.

7. No, because $\sum P(X = x) = 0.95 \neq 1$.

9. To satisfy the requirements for a discrete probability distribution, $\sum P(X = x) = 1$; therefore, $P(X = 4) = 0.3$.

6.1 Exercises: Applying the Concepts

11. (a) All probabilities are between 0 and 1, inclusive, and the sum of the probabilities is 1.

(b)

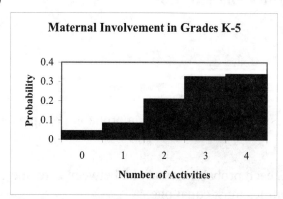

(c) $\mu_X = \sum \left[x \cdot P(X=x) \right] = 0 \cdot (0.044) + 1 \cdot (0.084) + \ldots + 4 \cdot (0.338) = 2.829$ or 2.8.

Interpretation: The average number of activities that the mother of a K-5 student is involved in is approximately 2.8.

(d) $\sigma_X^2 = \sum (x - \mu_X)^2 \cdot P(X=x) = (0 - 2.8)^2 \cdot 0.044 + (1 - 2.8)^2 \cdot 0.084 +$

$(2 - 2.8)^2 \cdot 0.209 + (3 - 2.8)^2 \cdot 0.325 + (4 - 2.8)^2 \cdot 0.338 = 1.249\ldots$ or 1.2.

(e) $\sigma_X = \sqrt{\sigma_X^2} = \sqrt{1.250} = 1.09\ldots \approx 1.1$

(f) $P(X=3) = 0.325$

(g) $P(X=3 \text{ or } 4) = P(X=3) + P(X=4) = 0.325 + 0.338 = 0.663$

13. (a) All probabilities are between 0 and 1 and the sum of the probabilities is 1.

(b)

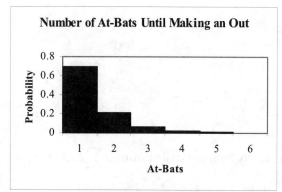

(c) $\mu_X = \sum \left[x \cdot P(X=x) \right] = 1 \cdot (0.7000) + 2 \cdot (0.2100) + \ldots + 6 \cdot (0.0021) = 1.427$ or 1.4.

Interpretation: if a player bats many times, then on average he will make an out every 1.4 at-bats.

(d) $\sigma_X^2 = \sum (x - \mu_X)^2 \cdot P(X=x) = (1 - 1.4)^2 \cdot 0.7000 + (2 - 1.4)^2 \cdot 0.2100 + \ldots$

$\ldots + (6 - 1.4)^2 \cdot 0.0021 = 0.598$ or 0.6.

(e) $\sigma_X = \sqrt{\sigma_X^2} = \sqrt{0.598} = 0.77\ldots \approx 0.8$.

(f) $P(X = 4) = 0.0189$

(g) $P(X = 4 \text{ or more}) = P(X = 4\,) + P(X = 5) + P(X = 6)$
$$= 0.0189 + 0.0060 + 0.0021 = 0.027.$$
This is a small probability and so it would be a little unusual that a batter requires four or more at-bats before making an out.

15. (a) The probabilities are just the relative frequencies.

x	$P(X = x)$	$x \cdot P(X = x)$	$(x - \mu_X)^2 \cdot P(X = x)$
5	0.1930	0.9650	0.8009
6	0.1956	1.1734	0.2103
7	0.2005	1.4036	0.0003
8	0.2032	1.6254	0.1884
9	0.2077	1.8696	0.8004
		7.0371	2.0003

(b)

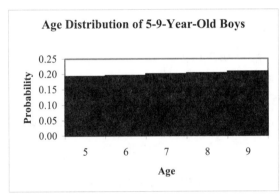

(c) From the table, $\mu_X = 7.0$ years. Interpretation: the average age of 5–9-year-old males in the US in 2000 was 7.0 years.

(d) $\sigma_X = \sqrt{2.0003} = 1.4143$ or 1.4 years.

17. (a) The probabilities are just the relative frequencies.

x	$P(X = x)$	$x \cdot P(X = x)$	$(x - \mu_X)^2 \cdot P(X = x)$
1	0.1321	0.1321	1.5600
2	0.1297	0.2595	0.7705
3	0.1265	0.3795	0.2612
4	0.1233	0.4934	0.0235
5	0.1216	0.6081	0.0386
6	0.1228	0.7371	0.3001
7	0.1238	0.8666	0.8132
8	0.1201	0.9608	1.5247
		4.4369	5.2919

(b)

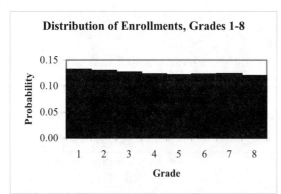

Distribution of Enrollments, Grades 1-8

(c) From the table, $\mu_X = 4.4$. Interpretation: the average of the enrolled grade levels for all students enrolled in grades 1–8 in the US in 1997 was grade 4.4.

(d) $\sigma_X = \sqrt{5.2919} = 2.3004$ or 2.3.

19. (a) $P(X = 4) = 0.124$

    (b) $P(X = 4 \text{ or } 5) = 0.124 + 0.024 = 0.148$

    (c) $P(X = 6 \text{ or more}) = 0.024 + 0.053 + 0.035 = 0.112$

21. $E(X) = \sum x \cdot P(X = x) = \$200 \cdot (0.99952) + (\$200 - 250,000) \cdot (0.00048) = \$80$.

If the company sells many of these policies, then they will make an average of $80 per policy.

23. Expected value = $E(X) = \sum x \cdot P(X = x) = (-\$5) \cdot (37/38) + (\$175) \cdot (1/38) = -\$0.26$.

If you played the game 1,000 times, you would expect to lose about $260.

6.2 The Binomial Probability Distribution

6.2 Concepts and Vocabulary

1. A probability experiment is said to be a binomial probability experiment provided: the experiment is performed a fixed number of times, the trials (repetitions of the experiment) are independent, for each trial there are two mutually exclusive outcomes, success or failure and the probability of success is fixed for each trial.

3. If the binomial probability distribution is bell-shaped, then the Empirical Rule can be used to check for unusual observations, which are observations that are more than two standard deviations above or below the mean.

6.2 Exercises: Basic Skills

1. This is not a binomial experiment because the random variable, age, does not have only two possible values. It is a continuous random variable.

3. This is a binomial experiment. There are $n = 100$ "trials" (each trial corresponding to administering the drug to one of the 100 individuals), the trials are independent, there are two outcomes (favorable or unfavorable response) and the probability of a favorable response is fixed.

5. This is not a binomial experiment because the trials are not independent and the probability of drawing an ace does not remain fixed from one trial (card drawn) to the next.

7. This is not a binomial experiment because the number of trials is not fixed.

9. This is a binomial experiment. There are $n = 10$ independent trials (random selection of a stock), there are two outcomes (stock rises or does not rise in value), the trials are independent and there is a fixed (48%) probability of each stock rising in any one year.

11. Using $P(X = x) = {}_nC_x p^x (1-p)^{n-x}$ with $x = 3$, $n = 10$ and $p = 0.4$:

$$P(X = 3) = {}_{10}C_3 \cdot (0.4)^3 \cdot (1-0.4)^{10-3} = \frac{10!}{3!(10-3)!} \cdot (0.4)^3 \cdot (0.6)^7$$
$$= 120 \cdot (0.064) \cdot (0.0279936) = 0.2150$$

13. Using $P(X = x) = {}_nC_x p^x (1-p)^{n-x}$ with $x = 38$, $n = 40$ and $p = 0.99$:

$$P(X = 38) = {}_{40}C_{38} \cdot (0.99)^{38} \cdot (1-0.99)^{40-38} = \frac{40!}{38!(40-38)!} \cdot (0.99)^{38} \cdot (0.01)^2$$
$$= 780 \cdot (0.6825...) \cdot (0.0001) = 0.0532$$

15. (a) Binomial Probability Distribution:

x	$P(X = x)$	$x \cdot P(X = x)$	$(x-\mu_x)^2 \cdot P(X = x)$
0	0.1176	0.0000	0.3812
1	0.3025	0.3025	0.1936
2	0.3241	0.6483	0.0130
3	0.1852	0.5557	0.2667
4	0.0595	0.2381	0.2881
5	0.0102	0.0510	0.1045
6	0.0007	0.0044	0.0129
		1.8000	1.2600

(b) $\mu_X = 1.8$ (column 3) and $\sigma_X = \sqrt{\sigma_X^2} = \sqrt{1.26} \approx 1.12$ (from column 4)

(c) $\mu_X = n \cdot p = 6 \cdot (0.3) = 1.8$ and $\sigma_X = \sqrt{n \cdot p \cdot (1-p)} = \sqrt{(1.8) \cdot (0.7)} \approx 1.12$

(d)

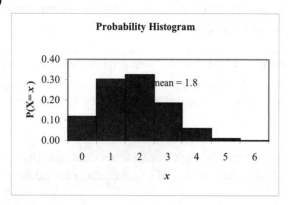

17. (a) Binomial Probability Distribution:

x	$P(X = x)$	$x \cdot P(X = x)$	$(x - \mu_x)^2 \cdot P(X = x)$
0	3.8E-06	0.0000	0.0002
1	0.0001	0.0001	0.0033
2	0.0012	0.0024	0.0271
3	0.0087	0.0261	0.1224
4	0.0389	0.1556	0.2942
5	0.1168	0.5840	0.3578
6	0.2336	1.4016	0.1315
7	0.3003	2.1021	0.0187
8	0.2253	1.8024	0.3519
9	0.0751	0.6759	0.3801
		6.7502	1.6872

(b) $\mu_X = 6.75$ (column 3) and $\sigma_X = \sqrt{\sigma_X^2} = \sqrt{1.6872} \approx 1.30$ (from column 4)

(c) $\mu_X = n \cdot p = 9 \cdot (0.75) = 6.75$ and $\sigma_X = \sqrt{n \cdot p \cdot (1-p)} = \sqrt{(6.75) \cdot (0.25)} \approx 1.3$

(d)

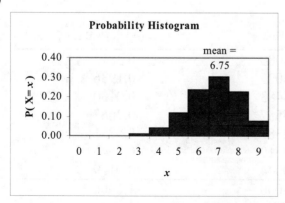

19. (a) Binomial Probability Distribution:

x	$P(X = x)$	$x \cdot P(X = x)$	$(x - \mu_x)^2 \cdot P(X = x)$
0	0.0010	0.0000	0.0250
1	0.0098	0.0098	0.1568
2	0.0439	0.0878	0.3952
3	0.1172	0.3516	0.4690
4	0.2051	0.8204	0.2053
5	0.2461	1.2305	6.1525E-08
6	0.2051	1.2306	0.2049
7	0.1172	0.8204	0.4686
8	0.0439	0.3512	0.3950
9	0.0098	0.0882	0.1568
10	0.0010	0.0100	0.0250
		5.0005	2.5016

(b) $\mu_X = 5.0$ (column 3) and $\sigma_X = \sqrt{\sigma_X^2} = \sqrt{2.5016} \approx 1.58$ (from column 4)

(c) $\mu_X = n \cdot p = 10 \cdot (0.5) = 5$ and $\sigma_X = \sqrt{n \cdot p \cdot (1-p)} = \sqrt{5 \cdot (0.5)} = 1.58$

(d)

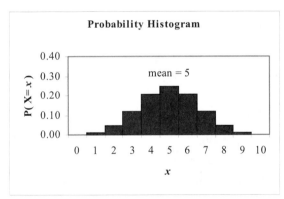

6.2 Exercises: Applying the Concepts

21. Parameters are: $n = 15$ and $p = 0.80$

(a) $P(X = 12) = {}_{15}C_{12} \cdot (0.8)^{12} \cdot (1 - 0.8)^{15-12} = \dfrac{15!}{12!(15-12)!} \cdot (0.8)^{12} \cdot (0.2)^3$

$= 455 \cdot (0.0687...) \cdot (0.008) = 0.2501$

(b) $P(X \geq 12) = P(X = 12) + P(X = 13) + P(X = 14) + P(X = 15)$

$= {}_{15}C_{12} \cdot (0.8)^{12} \cdot (1-0.8)^{15-12} + {}_{15}C_{13} \cdot (0.8)^{13} \cdot (1-0.8)^{15-13} + {}_{15}C_{14} \cdot (0.8)^{14} \cdot (1-0.8)^{15-14}$

$+ {}_{15}C_{15} \cdot (0.8)^{15} \cdot (1-0.8)^{15-15} = 0.25014 + 0.23090 + 0.13194 + 0.03518 = 0.6482$

(c) Use the Complement Rule to find the probability that fewer than 12 flights $(x = 0, 1, ..., 11)$ are on time:

$$P(X < 12) = P(X \le 11) = 1 - P(X \ge 12) = 1 - 0.6482 = 0.3518$$

(d) $P(X = 10 \text{ or } 11 \text{ or } 12) = P(X = 10) + P(X = 11) + P(X = 12)$

$= {}_{15}C_{10} \cdot (0.8)^{10} \cdot (1 - 0.8)^{15-10} + {}_{15}C_{11} \cdot (0.8)^{11} \cdot (1 - 0.8)^{15-11} + {}_{15}C_{12} \cdot (0.8)^{12} \cdot (1 - 0.8)^{15-12}$

$= 0.10318 + 0.18760 + 0.25014 = 0.5409$

23. Parameters are: $n = 12$ and $p = 0.94$

(a) $P(X = 10) = {}_{12}C_{10} \cdot (0.94)^{10} \cdot (1 - 0.94)^{12-10} = \dfrac{12!}{10!(12-10)!} \cdot (0.94)^{10} \cdot (0.06)^2$

$= 66 \cdot (0.5386...) \cdot (0.0036) = 0.1280$

(b) $P(X \ge 10) = P(X = 10) + P(X = 11) + P(X = 12)$

$= {}_{12}C_{10} \cdot (0.94)^{10} \cdot (1 - 0.94)^{12-10} + {}_{12}C_{11} \cdot (0.94)^{11} \cdot (1 - 0.94)^{12-11}$

$+ {}_{12}C_{12} \cdot (0.94)^{12} \cdot (1 - 0.94)^{12-12} = 0.12797 + 0.36453 + 0.47592 = 0.9684$

(c) Use the Complement Rule to find the probability that 9 or fewer of them ($x = 0, 1, ..., 9$) use Microsoft Windows:

$P(X \le 9) = 1 - P(X \ge 10) = 1 - 0.9684 = 0.0316$

(d) $P(X = 9 \text{ or } 10 \text{ or } 11) = P(X = 9) + P(X = 10) + P(X = 11)$

$= {}_{12}C_9 \cdot (0.94)^9 \cdot (1 - 0.94)^{12-9} + {}_{12}C_{10} \cdot (0.94)^{10} \cdot (1 - 0.94)^{12-10}$

$+ {}_{12}C_{11} \cdot (0.94)^{11} \cdot (1 - 0.94)^{12-11} = 0.02723 + 0.12797 + 0.36453 = 0.5197$

25. Parameters are: $n = 30$ and $p = 0.02$

(a) $P(X = 3) = {}_{30}C_3 \cdot (0.02)^3 \cdot (1 - 0.02)^{30-3} = \dfrac{30!}{3!(30-3)!} \cdot (0.02)^3 \cdot (0.98)^{27}$

$= 4060 \cdot (0.000008) \cdot (0.5795...) = 0.0188$

(b) $P(X \le 3) = P(X = 0) + P(X = 1) + P(X = 2) + P(X = 3)$

$= {}_{30}C_0 \cdot (0.02)^0 \cdot (1 - 0.02)^{30-0} + {}_{30}C_1 \cdot (0.02)^1 \cdot (1 - 0.02)^{30-1}$

$+ {}_{30}C_2 \cdot (0.02)^2 \cdot (1 - 0.02)^{30-2} + {}_{30}C_3 \cdot (0.02)^3 \cdot (1 - 0.02)^{30-3}$

$= 0.54548 + 0.33397 + 0.09883 + 0.01882 = 0.9971$

(c) Use the Complement Rule to find the probability that 4 or more patients ($x = 4, 5, 6, ..., 30$) experienced weight gain as a side effect:

$P(X \ge 4) = 1 - P(X \le 3) = 1 - 0.9971 = 0.0029$

(d) $P(X = 1 \text{ or } 2 \text{ or } 3 \text{ or } 4) = P(X = 1) + P(X = 2) + P(X = 3) + P(X = 4)$

$= {}_{30}C_1 \cdot (0.02)^1 \cdot (1 - 0.02)^{30-1} + {}_{30}C_2 \cdot (0.02)^2 \cdot (1 - 0.02)^{30-2} + {}_{30}C_3 \cdot (0.02)^3 \cdot (1 - 0.02)^{30-3}$

$+ {}_{30}C_4 \cdot (0.02)^4 \cdot (1 - 0.02)^{30-4} = 0.33397 + 0.09883 + 0.01882 + 0.00259 = 0.4542$

27. Parameters are: $n = 10$ and $p = 0.45$. The binomial probabilities are tabulated:

x	$P(X = x)$
0	0.00253
1	0.02072
2	0.07630
3	0.16648
4	0.23837
5	0.23403
6	0.15957
7	0.07460
8	0.02289
9	0.00416
10	0.00034

(a) $P(X = 6) = 0.1596$

(b) $P(X \geq 6) = 0.15957 + 0.07460 + 0.02289 + 0.00416 + 0.00034 = 0.2616$

(c) $P(X < 2) = P(X \leq 1) = 0.00253 + 0.02072 = 0.0233$

(d) $P(X = 3 \text{ or } 4 \text{ or } 5) = 0.16648 + 0.23837 + 0.23403 = 0.6389$

29. (a) $\mu_X = np = 100 \cdot (0.80) = 80$. $\sigma_X = \sqrt{np \cdot (1-p)} = \sqrt{(100 \cdot (0.80)) \cdot (1 - 0.80)} = 4$.

(b) In a random sample of 100 flights, on average 80 will be on time.

(c) Since $np(1-p) = 100(0.80)(0.20) = 16 > 10$, we can use the Empirical Rule to check for unusual observations. Then $\mu + 2\sigma = 80 + 2 \cdot 4 = 88$ and so observing 90 on-time flights in a random sample of 100 flights from Chicago to Orlando would be unusual.

31. (a) $\mu_X = np = 200 \cdot (0.94) = 188$. $\sigma_X = \sqrt{np \cdot (1-p)} = \sqrt{(200 \cdot (0.94)) \cdot (1 - 0.94)} = 3.36$.

(b) In a random sample of 200 computer users, on average 188 will use Microsoft Windows as their operating system.

(c) Since $np(1-p) = 200(0.94)(0.06) = 11.28 > 10$, we can use the Empirical Rule to check for unusual observations. Then $\mu + 2\sigma = 188 + 2 \cdot 3.36 = 194.72$ and so observing 195 users of Microsoft Windows in a random sample of 200 computer users would be unusual.

33. (a) $\mu_X = np = 600 \cdot (0.02) = 12$. $\sigma_X = \sqrt{np \cdot (1-p)} = \sqrt{(600 \cdot (0.02)) \cdot (1 - 0.02)} = 3.43$.

(b) In a random sample of 600 users of Depakote, on average 12 will experience weight gain as a side effect.

(c) Since $np(1-p) = 600(0.02)(0.98) = 11.76 > 10$, we can use the Empirical Rule to check for unusual observations. Then $\mu + 2\sigma = 12 + 2 \cdot 3.43 = 18.86$ and so observing 16 patients who experience weight gain in a random sample of 600 patients who take Depakote would not be unusual.

35. (a) $\dfrac{17}{20} = 0.85$.

   (b) Assuming that the percentage who live at home is 59% ($p = 0.59$),

$$P(X \geq 17) = P(X = 17) + P(X = 18) + P(X = 19) + P(X = 20)$$
$$= 0.00999 + 0.00240 + 0.0003... + 0.00003 = 0.0128.$$

   (c) Assuming that 59% of male community college students live at home, as many as 17 out of 20 living at home is an unusual observation. It is likely that more than 59% of community college male students that are 18 to 24 years of age live at home.

37. (a) $\dfrac{8}{15} = 0.53$.

   (b) Assuming that the proportion that prefer a boy is 0.42 ($p = 0.42$),

$$P(X \geq 8) = P(X = 8) + ... + P(X = 15)$$
$$= 0.13757 + 0.07748 + ... = 0.2630.$$

   (c) No. The probability 0.2630 does not indicate that the results of the survey are unusual and so the results of the survey do not contradict the results of the Gallup poll.

39. (a) $\dfrac{6}{20} = 0.30$.

   (b) Assuming that the proportion that graduated in 5 years or less is 0.528 ($p = 0.528$):

$$P(X \leq 6) = P(X = 0) + ... + P(X = 6) = 0.0339 \ \text{(using technology)}.$$

   (c) Yes. The probability indicates an unusual outcome, so we are inclined to believe that the proportion of students graduating from college in 5 years or less is decreasing.

41. (c) $P(X = 29) = 0.3340$ **(e)** $P(X \leq 27) = 1 - P(X \geq 28) = 1 - .9783 = 0.0217$

43. (a) If 25% of residents of the United States 25 years old or older have completed at least four years of college, then we would expect to randomly select $10 \div (0.25) = 40$.

   (b) We would like the probability, $P(X \geq 10)$, to be 0.99 or greater, with $p = 0.25$ and n to be determined. $P(X \geq 10) = 1 - P(X \leq 9) = 1 - (P(X = 0) + ... + P(X = 9))$ and using technology we find that:

$$\text{when } n = 69, \ P(X \geq 10) = 1 - P(X \leq 9) = 1 - 0.0117 = 0.9883; \ \text{and}$$
$$\text{when } n = 70, \ P(X \geq 10) = 1 - P(X \leq 9) = 1 - 0.0099 = 0.9901.$$

   Thus the minimum number we would need in our sample is 70.

Chapter 6. Review Exercises

1. (a) Continuous, because its values could be any real number, $s > 0$.
   (b) Discrete, because it can only take whole number values, $x = 0, 1, ...$.
   (c) Discrete, because it can only take whole number values, $x = 0, 1, ...$.

3. No, because the probabilities do not sum to 1.

5. (a) Probability distribution for the random variable X:

x	$P(X = x)$	$x \cdot P(X = x)$	$(x - \mu_X)^2 \cdot P(X = x)$
4	0.3226	1.2903	0.5237
5	0.2419	1.2097	0.0182
6	0.2742	1.6452	0.1444
7	0.1613	1.1290	0.4804
		5.2742	1.1668

(b)

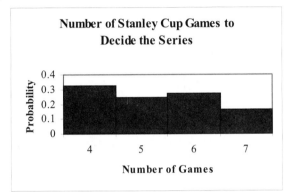

(c) $\mu_X = \sum \left[x \cdot P(X = x) \right] = 5.3$. If many Stanley Cup series are played, then on average it will take 5.3 games to decide the cup.

(d) $\sigma_X = \sqrt{1.1668} = 1.0802$ or 1.1.

7. $E(X) = \sum x \cdot P(X = x) = \$200 \cdot (0.99802) + (-\$99{,}800) \cdot (0.00198) = \$2$. If the company insures many 35-year-old males, then they will make an average profit of \$2 per male.

9. This is a binomial experiment. There are $n = 10$ "trials" (each trial corresponding to a randomly chosen freshman), the trials are independent, there are two outcomes (graduated or did not graduate within six years) and the probability of a graduation within six years is fixed.

11. This is a binomial experiment with X = the number (out of 10 females) with high serum cholesterol, $n = 10$ and $p = 0.08$. The following table gives binomial probabilities (using $P(X = x) = {}_nC_x p^x (1 - p)^{n-x}$).

x	$P(X = x)$
0	0.4344
1	0.3777
2	0.1478
3	0.0343

(a) From the table, $P(X = 0) = 0.4344$. In about 43% of random samples of 10 females 20–34 years old, there will be 0 females with high serum cholesterol.

(b) From the table, $P(X = 2) = 0.1478$. In about 15% of random samples of 10 females 20–34 years old, there will be 2 females with high serum cholesterol.

(c) $P(X \geq 2) = 1 - P(X \leq 1) = 1 - (P(X = 0) + P(X = 1)) = 1 - (0.4344 + 0.3777)$
$$= 0.1879.$$
In about 19% of random samples of 10 females 20–34 years old, there will be at least 2 females with high serum cholesterol.

(d) The probability that 9 will **not** have high cholesterol is the same as the probability that 1 **will** have high cholesterol, which is $P(X = 1) = 0.3777$. In about 38% of random samples of 10 females 20–34 years old, there will be 9 females who do not have high serum cholesterol.

(e) Using the parameters $n = 250$ and $p = 0.08$, $\mu_X = np = 250 \cdot (0.08) = 20$ and
$$\sigma_X = \sqrt{np \cdot (1 - p)} = \sqrt{(250 \cdot (0.08)) \cdot (1 - 0.08)} = 4.3.$$

(f) No. Since $np \cdot (1 - p) = 18.4 > 10$, we can use the Empirical Rule to check for unusual observations. Then $\mu - 2\sigma = 20 - 2 \cdot 4.3 = 11.4$ and so observing 12 females with high serum cholesterol in a random sample of 250 females 20–34 years old would not be unusual.

(g) Yes. The probability of observing 4 or more successes is only
$$P(X \geq 4) = 1 - P(X \leq 3) = 1 - (P(X = 0) + ... + P(X = 3))$$
$$= 1 - (0.4344 + ... + 0.0343) = 0.0058$$

13. This is a binomial experiment with $X =$ the number of households (out of 20) that tune to Monday night football, $n = 20$ and $p = 0.074$. The following table gives binomial probabilities (using $P(X = x) = {}_nC_x p^x (1 - p)^{n-x}$).

x	$P(X = x)$
0	0.2149
1	0.3435
2	0.2607
3	0.1250
6	0.0022

(a) From the table, $P(X = 6) = 0.0022$. In about 0.2% of random samples of 20 households, exactly 6 will have tuned into Monday Night Football.

(b) $P(X < 4) = P(X = 0) + ... + P(X = 3) = 0.2149 + ... + 0.1250 = 0.9441$.

(c) $P(X \geq 2) = 1 - P(X \leq 1) = 1 - (P(X = 0) + P(X = 1))$
$$= 1 - (0.2149 + 0.3435) = 0.4417.$$

(d) The probability that 17 were **not** tuned to the football is the same as the probability that 3 **were** tuned in, which is $P(X = 3) = 0.1250$.

(e) Using the parameters $n = 500$ and $p = 0.074$, $\mu_X = np = 500 \cdot (0.074) = 37$ and
$$\sigma_X = \sqrt{np \cdot (1-p)} = \sqrt{(500 \cdot (0.074)) \cdot (1 - 0.074)} = 5.85.$$

(f) Yes. Since $np \cdot (1-p) = 34.3 > 10$, we can use the Empirical Rule to check for unusual observations. Then $\mu + 2\sigma = 37 + 2 \cdot 5.85 = 48.71$ and so observing 50 households tuned into Monday Night Football in a random sample of 500 households would be unusual.

(g) No. This is binomial with the parameters $n = 30$ and $p = 0.074$. Then, using technology, we find that the probability of observing 1 or fewer successes is
$$P(X \le 1) = P(X = 0) + P(X = 1) = 0.0996 + 0.2388 = 0.3384.$$

15. (a) Binomial Probability Distribution, $n = 5$, $p = 0.2$:

x	$P(X = x)$	$x \cdot P(X = x)$	$(x - \mu_X)^2 \cdot P(X = x)$
0	0.3277	0	0.3277
1	0.4096	0.4096	0.0000
2	0.2048	0.4096	0.2048
3	0.0512	0.1536	0.2048
4	0.0064	0.0256	0.0576
5	0.0003	0.0016	0.0051
		1.0000	0.8000

(b) From the table, $\mu_X = \sum x \cdot P(X = x) = 1$ and
$$\sigma_X = \sqrt{\sum (x - \mu_X)^2 \cdot P(X = x)} = \sqrt{0.8} = 0.8944.$$

(c) $\mu_X = np = 5(0.2) = 1$ and $\sigma_X = \sqrt{np \cdot (1-p)} = \sqrt{5(0.2)(0.8)} = 0.8944$.

(d) The distribution is skewed to the right.

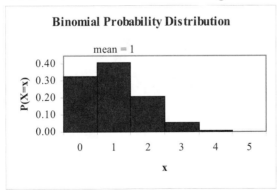

17. If $np \cdot (1-p) \ge 10$, then the Empirical Rule can be used to check for unusual observations.

Chapter 7. The Normal Probability Distribution

7.1 Properties of the Normal Distribution

7.1 Concepts and Vocabulary

1. The graph of a probability density function must lie on or above the horizontal axis and the area under the graph must be 1.

3. An area under the normal curve for a range of values of the random variable, X, can be interpreted as the proportion of the population whose X-values lie within that range, or as the probability of a randomly chosen individual having an X-value within that range.

5. The center of the normal curve is at $x = \mu$ and the curve has inflection points at a distance of σ either side of the center.

7.1 Exercises: Skill Building

1. Probability = area under the uniform density curve = height $\times$ width
    $= \frac{1}{30} \times (10 - 5) = \frac{5}{30} = \frac{1}{6}$.

3. Probability = area under the uniform density curve = height $\times$ width
    $= \frac{1}{30} \times (30 - 20) = \frac{10}{30} = \frac{1}{3}$, since the curve stops at $x = 30$.

5. **(a)**

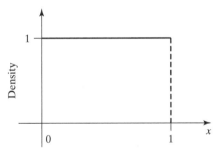

    (b) Probability = area under the uniform density curve = height $\times$ width $=$
    $1 \cdot (0.2 - 0) = 0.2$.

    (c) Probability = area under the uniform density curve = height $\times$ width $=$
    $1 \cdot (0.6 - 0.25) = 0.35$.

    (d) Probability = area under the uniform density curve = height $\times$ width $=$
    $1 \cdot (1 - 0.95) = 0.05$, since the curve stops at 1.

    (e) Answers will vary.

7. The histogram is symmetrical and bell-shaped, indicating a normal distribution.

9. The histogram is skewed to the right and so the distribution is not normal.

11. The center is at 2 and so $\mu = 2$. The distance to the inflection points is ± 3 and so $\sigma = 3$.

13. The center is at 100 and so $\mu = 100$. The distance to the inflection points is ± 15 and so $\sigma = 15$.

7.1 Exercises: Applying the Concepts

15. (a), (b)

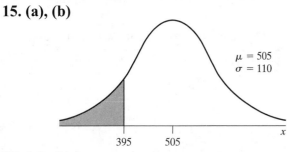

$\mu = 505$
$\sigma = 110$

395   505

(c) The proportion of SAT Verbal scores below 395 is 0.1587. The probability that a randomly selected student scored less than 395 on the SAT Verbal test is 0.1587.

17. (a), (b)

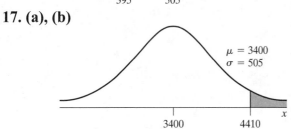

$\mu = 3400$
$\sigma = 505$

3400   4410

(c) The proportion of full-term babies that weigh more than 4410 grams is 0.0228. The probability that a randomly selected full-term baby weighs more than 4410 grams is 0.0228.

19. (a) The proportion of human pregnancies lasting longer than 280 days is 0.1908. The probability that a randomly selected human pregnancy will last longer than 280 days is 0.1908.

(b) The proportion of human pregnancies lasting between 230 and 260 days is 0.3416. The probability that a randomly selected human pregnancy will last between 230 and 260 days is 0.3416.

21. (a) $Z_1 = \dfrac{X_1 - \mu}{\sigma} = \dfrac{8-10}{3} = -\dfrac{2}{3} = -0.67$

(b) $Z_2 = \dfrac{X_2 - \mu}{\sigma} = \dfrac{12-10}{3} = \dfrac{2}{3} = 0.67$

(c) By the properties of normal curves, the area between Z_1 and Z_2 is also 0.495.

23. (a), (b), (c) The normal curve appears to be a good approximation to the histogram.

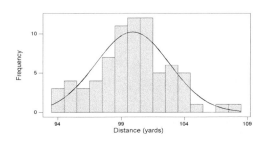

7.2 The Standard Normal Distribution

7.2 Concepts and Vocabulary

1. The standard normal curve is symmetric about its mean, $\mu = 0$, which is also where its highest point occurs. It has inflection points at $+1$ and -1. The area under the curve is 1 and the area each side of $\mu = 0$ is 0.5. The graph approaches, but never touches, the horizontal axis as x gets larger and larger in both the positive and the negative direction. The graph also satisfies the Empirical Rule.

3. False; although the area is 1, for all practical purposes, it is not exactly 1 because the normal curve continues indefinitely to the right.

Note: Answers found using technology may differ from those shown.

7.2 Exercises: Skill Building

1. The standard normal tables give the areas to the left of any Z-value. Thus we just need to look up each Z and read off the corresponding area from the tables. The areas are:
    (a) The area to the left of $Z = -2.45$ is
        0.0071

    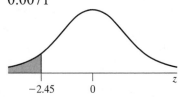

    (b) The area to the left of $Z = -0.43$ is
        0.3336

    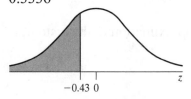

    (c) The area to the left of $Z = 1.35$ is
        0.9115

    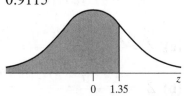

    (d) The area to the left of $Z = 3.49$ is
        0.9998

    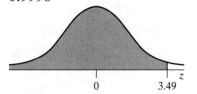

3. The standard normal tables give the areas to the left of any Z-value. Thus we first need to look up each Z and read off the corresponding area from the tables. Then the area to the right is 1 – the area to the left. This gives:

    (a) The area to the right of $Z = -3.01$ is
        $1 - 0.0013 = 0.9987$

    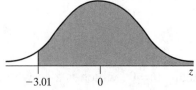

    (b) The area to the right of $Z = -1.59$ is
        $1 - 0.0559 = 0.9441$

    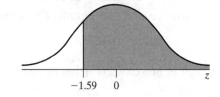

    (c) The area to the right of $Z = 1.78$ is
        $1 - 0.9625 = 0.0375$

    (d) The area to the right of $Z = 3.11$ is
        $1 - 0.9991 = 0.0009$

    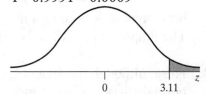

Note: Answers found using technology may differ from those shown.

5. To find the area between two Z-values we first look up the area to the left of each Z-value in the standard normal tables, and then we find the difference between these areas.

(a) The area to the left of $Z = -2.04$ is 0.0207, and the area to the left of $Z = 2.04$ is 0.9793 and so the area between is $0.9793 - 0.0207 = 0.9586$.

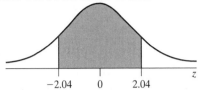

(b) The area to the left of $Z = -0.55$ is 0.2912, and the area to the left of $Z = 0$ is 0.5000 and so the area between is $0.5000 - 0.2912 = 0.2088$.

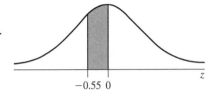

(c) The area to the left of $Z = -1.04$ is 0.1492, and the area to the left of $Z = 2.76$ is 0.9971 and so the area between is $0.9971 - 0.1492 = 0.8479$.

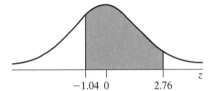

7. (a) The area to the left of $Z = -2$ is 0.0228, and the area to the right of $Z = 2$ is $1 - 0.9772 = 0.0228$ and so the total area is $0.0228 + 0.0228 = 0.0456$.

(b) The area to the left of $Z = -1.56$ is 0.0594, and the area to the right of $Z = 2.56$ is $1 - 0.9948 = 0.0052$ and so the total area is $0.0594 + 0.0052 = 0.0646$.

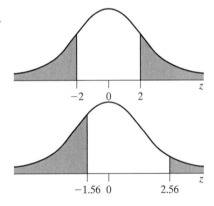

(c) The area to the left of $Z = -0.24$ is 0.4052, and the area to the right of $Z = 1.20$ is $1 - 0.8849 = 0.1151$ and so the total area is $0.4052 + 0.1151 = 0.5203$.

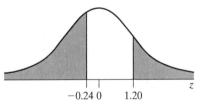

9. (a) The area to the left of $Z = -1.34$ is 0.0901, and the area to the left of $Z = 2.01$ is 0.9778 and so the area between is $0.9778 - 0.0901 = 0.8877$.

(b) The area to the left of $Z = -2.33$ is 0.0099, and the area to the left of $Z = 2.33$ is 0.9901 and so the area between $Z = -2.33$ and $Z = 2.33$ is $0.9901 - 0.0099 = 0.9802$.

Note: Answers found using technology may differ from those shown.

(c) The area to the left of $Z = -2.33$ is 0.0099, and the area to the right of $Z = 2.33$ is $1 - 0.9901 = 0.0099$ and so the total area is $0.0099 + 0.0099 = 0.0198$.

7.2 Exercises: Applying the Concepts

11. The area in the interior of the normal tables that is closest to 0.1000 is 0.1003, corresponding to $Z = -1.28$.

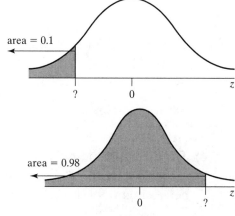

13. The area in the interior of the normal tables that is closest to 0.9800 is 0.9798, corresponding to $Z = 2.05$.

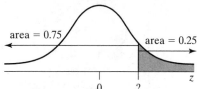

15. The area to the left of the unknown Z-score is $1 - 0.25 = 0.75$. The area in the interior of the normal tables that is closest to 0.7500 is 0.7486, corresponding to $Z = 0.67$.

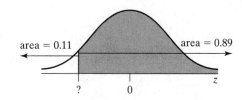

17. The area to the left of the unknown Z-score is $1 - 0.89 = 0.11$. The area in the interior of the normal tables that is closest to 0.1100 is 0.1093, corresponding to $Z = -1.23$.

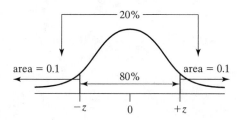

19. The Z-scores for the middle 80% are the Z-scores for the top and bottom 10%. The area in the interior of the normal tables that is closest to 0.1000 is 0.1003, corresponding to $Z = -1.28$. By symmetry, the Z-score for the top 10% is $Z = 1.28$.

Note: Answers found using technology may differ from those shown.

21. The Z-scores for the middle 99% are the Z-scores for the top and bottom 0.5%. The areas in the interior of the normal tables that are closest to 0.0050 are 0.0049 and 0.0051 and so we use the average of their corresponding Z-scores: -2.58 and -2.57, respectively. This gives $Z = -2.575$. By symmetry, the Z-score for the top 0.5% is $Z = 2.575$.

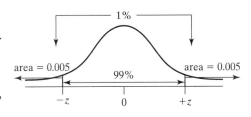

23. The area to the right of the unknown Z-value is 0.05, and so the area to the left is $1 - 0.05 = 0.9500$. From the interior of the normal tables we find that the Z-scores 1.64 and 1.65 have corresponding areas of 0.9495 and 0.9505, respectively, which are equally close to 0.95. Therefore, we take the average of the two Z-scores, giving $Z = 1.645$.

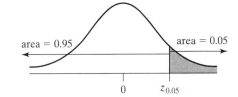

25. The area to the right of the unknown Z-value is 0.01, and so the area to the left is $1 - 0.01 = 0.99$. The area in the interior of the normal tables that is closest to 0.9900 is 0.9901 and so $z_{0.01} = 2.33$.

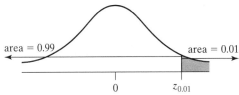

27. The area to the right of the unknown Z-value is 0.20, so the area to the left is $1 - 0.20 = 0.80$. The area in the interior of the normal tables that is closest to 0.8000 is 0.7995 and so $z_{0.20} = 0.84$.

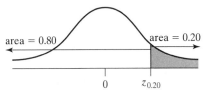

29. From the normal tables, $P(Z < 1.93) = 0.9732$.

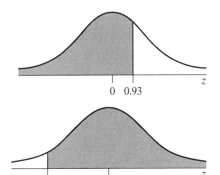

31. From the tables $P(Z < -2.98) = 0.0014$ and so $P(Z > -2.98) = 1 - 0.0014 = 0.9986$.

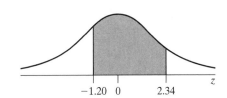

33. From the tables, the area to the left of $Z = -1.20$ is 0.1151, and the area to the left of $Z = 2.34$ is 0.9904. Thus $P(-1.20 \le Z < 2.34) = 0.9904 - 0.1151 = 0.8753$.

Note: Answers found using technology may differ from those shown.

35. From the tables, the area to the left of $Z = 1.84$ is 0.9671, and so $P(Z \geq 1.84) = 1 - 0.9671 = 0.0329$.

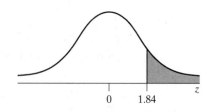

37. From the tables, $P(Z \leq 0.72) = 0.7642$.

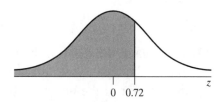

39. From the tables, the area to the left of $Z = -2.56$ is 0.0052. The to the left of $Z = 1.39$ is 0.9177, and so the area to the right of $Z = 1.39$ is $1 - 0.9177 = 0.0823$. Thus
$P(Z < -2.56 \text{ or } Z > 1.39) = 0.0052 + 0.0823 = 0.0875$.

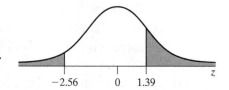

41. From the tables, $P(Z < -1.00) = 0.1587$ and $P(Z < 1.00) = 0.8413$ and so
$P(-1 < Z < 1) = 0.8413 - 0.1587 = 0.6826$ or 68%.

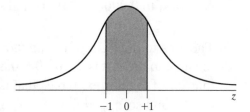

Similarly,
$P(-2 < Z < 2) = 0.9772 - 0.0228 = 0.9544$ or 95%.

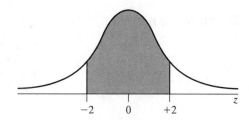

And $P(-3 < Z < 3) = 0.9987 - 0.0013 = 0.9974$ or 99.7%.

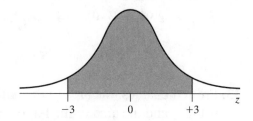

43. By symmetry, the area to the right of $Z = 2.55$ is also 0.0054.

45. By symmetry, the area between $Z = 0.53$ and $Z = 1.24$ is also 0.1906.

Note: Answers found using technology may differ from those shown.

7.3 Applications of the Normal Distribution

7.3 Concepts and Vocabulary

1. Draw a normal curve and shade the relevant area. Convert the values of X to Z-scores using $Z = \dfrac{X - \mu}{\sigma}$. Then use the standard normal tables to find the area corresponding to this range of Z-scores.

Note: The answers to the exercises in this section are based on Table II. Since answers computed using technology do not involve rounding of z-scores, they will often differ from the answers given below in the third and fourth decimal places.

7.3 Exercises: Skill Building

1. $Z = \dfrac{X - \mu}{\sigma} = \dfrac{35 - 50}{7} = -2.14$. From the tables, the area to the left is .0162 and so $P(X > 35) = 1 - 0.0162 = 0.9838$.

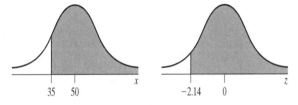

3. $Z = \dfrac{X - \mu}{\sigma} = \dfrac{45 - 50}{7} = -0.71$. From the tables, the area to the left is .2389 and so $P(X \le 45) = 0.2389$.

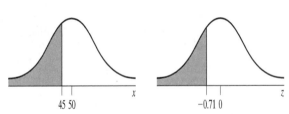

5. $Z_1 = \dfrac{X - \mu}{\sigma} = \dfrac{40 - 50}{7} = -1.43$ and

   $Z_2 = \dfrac{X - \mu}{\sigma} = \dfrac{65 - 50}{7} = 2.14$. From the

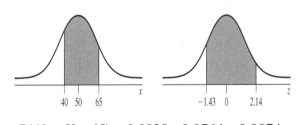

   tables, the area to the left of Z_1 is .0764 and the area to the left of Z_2 is .9838 and so $P(40 < X < 65) = 0.9838 - 0.0764 = 0.9074$.

7. $Z_1 = \dfrac{X - \mu}{\sigma} = \dfrac{55 - 50}{7} = 0.71$ and

   $Z_2 = \dfrac{X - \mu}{\sigma} = \dfrac{70 - 50}{7} = 2.86$. From the

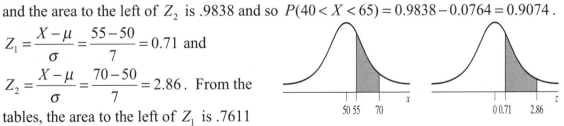

   tables, the area to the left of Z_1 is .7611 and the area to the left of Z_2 is .9979 and so $P(55 < X < 70) = 0.9979 - 0.7611 = 0.2368$.

Note: Answers found using technology may differ from those shown.

9. $Z_1 = \dfrac{X-\mu}{\sigma} = \dfrac{38-50}{7} = -1.71$ and

$Z_2 = \dfrac{X-\mu}{\sigma} = \dfrac{55-50}{7} = 0.71$. From the

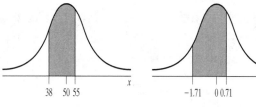

tables, the area to the left of Z_1 is .0436
and the area to the left of Z_2 is .7611 and so $P(38 < X < 55) = 0.7611 - 0.0436 = 0.7175$.

7.3 Exercises: Applying the Concepts

11. (a) $Z = \dfrac{39-53}{13.4} = -1.04$ (area = 0.1492)

and so $P(X < 39) = 0.1492$.

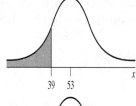

(b) $Z = \dfrac{71-53}{13.4} = 1.34$ (area = 0.9099) and

so $P(X > 71) = 1 - 0.9099 = 0.0901$.

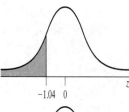

(c) $Z_1 = \dfrac{60-53}{13.4} = 0.52$ (area = 0.6985)

and $Z_2 = \dfrac{75-53}{13.4} = 1.64$ (area =

0.9495). Then
$P(60 < X < 75) = 0.9495 - 0.6985 = 0.2510$.

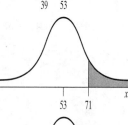
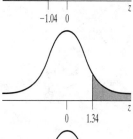

(d) $Z = \dfrac{45-53}{13.4} = -0.60$ (area = 0.2743)

and so $P(X < 45) = 0.2743$.

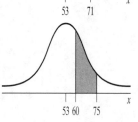
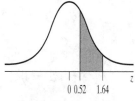

(e) $Z_1 = \dfrac{50-53}{13.4} = -0.22$ (area = 0.4129)

and $Z_2 = \dfrac{60-53}{13.4} = 0.52$ (area =

0.6985). Then
$P(50 < X < 60) = 0.6985 - 0.4129 = 0.2856$.

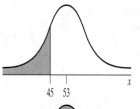
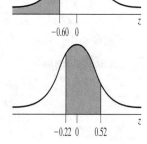
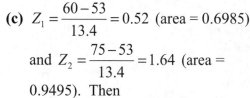
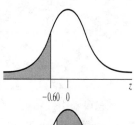

Note: Answers found using technology may differ from those shown.

(f) $Z = \dfrac{30-53}{13.4} = -1.72$ (area = 0.0427)

and so $P(X < 30) = 0.0427$. About 4.27% of females in her age group have HDL cholesterol as low as or lower than hers, which makes her somewhat unusual.

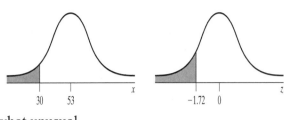

13. (a) $Z = \dfrac{1-0.75}{4.2} = 0.06$ (area = 0.5239)

and so $P(X > 1) = 1 - 0.5239 = 0.4761$.

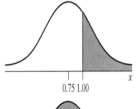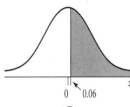

(b) $Z = \dfrac{2-0.75}{4.2} = 0.30$ (area = 0.6179)

and so $P(X < 2) = 0.6179$.

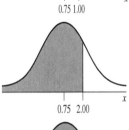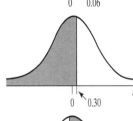

(c) $Z = \dfrac{0-0.75}{4.2} = -0.18$ (area = 0.4286)

and so $P(X > 0) = 1 - 0.4286 = 0.5714$.

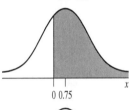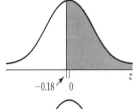

(d) $Z = \dfrac{9.7-0.75}{4.2} = 2.13$ (area = 0.9834)

and so

$P(X > 9.7) = 1 - 0.9834 = 0.0166$

which is a small enough probability to make this an unusual event.

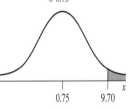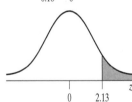

15. (a) $Z = \dfrac{60-64.1}{2.8} = -1.46$ (area = 0.0721)

and so $P(X < 60) = 0.0721$ or 7.21%.

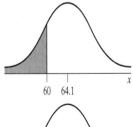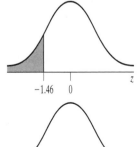

(b) $Z = \dfrac{72-64.1}{2.8} = 2.82$ (area = 0.9976)

and so

$P(X \geq 72) = 1 - 0.9976 = 0.0024$ or 0.24%.

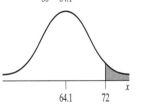

Note: Answers found using technology may differ from those shown.

(c) $Z_1 = \dfrac{60-64.1}{2.8} = -1.46$ (area = 0.0721)

and $Z_2 = \dfrac{70-64.1}{2.8} = 2.11$ (area =

0.9826). Then

$P(60 < X < 70) = 0.9826 - 0.0721 = 0.9105$ or 91.05%.

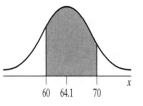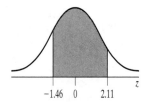

(d) From **(c)**, $P(60 < X < 70) = 0.9105$.

(e) $Z = \dfrac{70-64.1}{2.8} = 2.11$ (area = 0.9826)

and so

$P(X > 70) = 1 - 0.9826 = 0.0174$. This

is unusual.

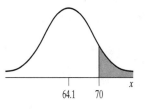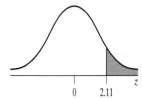

17. (a) $Z = \dfrac{180-161}{18} = 1.06$ (area = 0.8554)

and so

$P(X > 180) = 1 - 0.8554 = 0.1446$ or

14.46%.

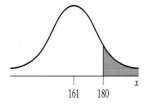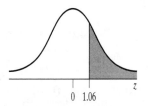

(b) $Z = \dfrac{150-161}{18} = -0.61$ (area = 0.2709)

and so $P(X < 150) = 0.2709$ or

27.09%.

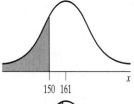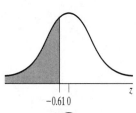

(c) $Z_1 = \dfrac{140-161}{18} = -1.17$ (area = 0.1210)

and $Z_2 = \dfrac{159-161}{18} = -0.11$ (area =

0.4562). Then

$P(140 < X < 159) = 0.4562 - 0.1210 = 0.3352$

or 33.52%.

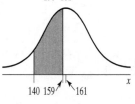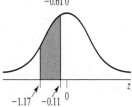

(d) $Z = \dfrac{143-161}{18} = -1.00$ (area = 0.1587)

and so $P(X < 143) = 0.1587$.

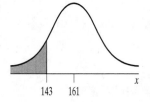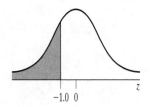

Note: Answers found using technology may differ from those shown.

(e) $Z_1 = \dfrac{155-161}{18} = -0.33$ (area = 0.3707)

and $Z_1 = \dfrac{170-161}{18} = 0.50$ (area =

0.6915). Then

$P(155 < X < 170) = 0.6915 - 0.3707 = 0.3208$.

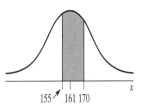 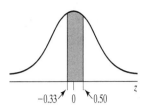

19. (a) $Z = \dfrac{90-80}{8} = 1.25$ (area = 0.8944) and

so $P(X > 90) = 1 - 0.8944 = 0.1056$ or

10.56%.

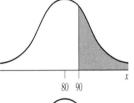 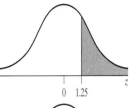

(b) $Z = \dfrac{60-80}{8} = -2.50$ (area = 0.0062)

and so $P(X < 60) = 0.0062$ or 0.62%.

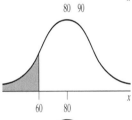 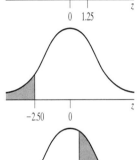

(c) $Z_1 = \dfrac{85-80}{8} = 0.63$ (area = 0.7357)

and $Z_2 = \dfrac{100-80}{8} = 2.50$ (area =

0.9938). Then

$P(85 < X < 100) = 0.9938 - 0.7357 = 0.2581$ or 25.81%.

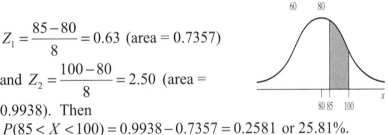 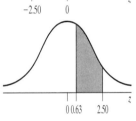

(d) $Z = \dfrac{70-80}{8} = -1.25$ (area = 0.1056)

and so $P(X < 70) = 0.1056$.

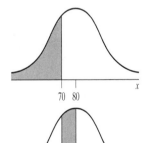

(e) $Z_1 = \dfrac{72-80}{8} = -1.00$ (area = 0.1587)

and $Z_2 = \dfrac{80-80}{8} = 0$ (area = 0.5000).

Then

$P(72 < X < 80) = 0.5000 - 0.1587 = 0.3413$.

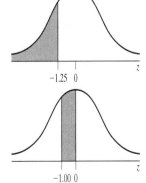

Note: Answers found using technology may differ from those shown.

21. (a) The area in the interior of the normal tables that is closest to 0.2500 is 0.2514, corresponding to a Z-score of -0.67. Then

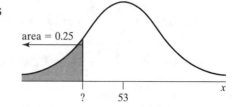

$X = \mu + \sigma Z = 53 + (13.4)(-0.67) = 44.02$ or 44.

Approximately 25% of females 20–29 years old have serum HDL cholesterol at or below 44.

(b) It is identical to our result.

(c) For the middle 80% we need to find the Z-scores that cut off the top and bottom 10% or 0.10. The area in the tables that is closest to 0.1000 is 0.1003 corresponding to $Z = -1.28$. By symmetry, the Z-score for the top 10% is $Z = 1.28$. The corresponding cholesterol levels are

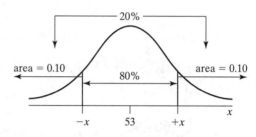

$X = \mu + \sigma Z = 53 + (13.4)(-1.28) = 35.8$ and $X = 53 + (13.4)(1.28) = 70.2$.

23. (a) The area in the interior of the normal tables that is closest to 0.8000 is 0.7995, corresponding to a Z-score of 0.84. Then

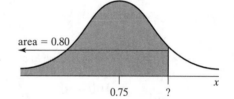

$X = \mu + \sigma Z = 0.75 + (4.2)(0.84) = 4.28\,\%$.

(b) For the middle 95% we need to find the Z-scores that cut off the top and bottom 2.5% or 0.025. The area of 0.0250 corresponds to $Z = -1.96$. By symmetry, the Z-score for the top 2.5% is $Z = 1.96$. The corresponding monthly rates of return are

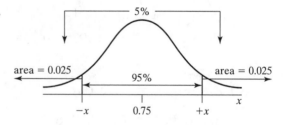

$X = \mu + \sigma Z = 0.75 + (4.2)(-1.96) = -7.48$ % and $X = 0.75 + (4.2)(1.96) = 8.98\,\%$.

25. (a) The area in the interior of the normal tables that is closest to 0.4000 is 0.4013, corresponding to a Z-score of -0.25. Then

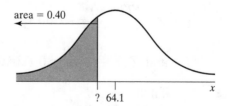

$X = \mu + \sigma Z = 64.1 + (2.8)(-0.25) = 63.4$ inches.

Note: Answers found using technology may differ from those shown.

(b) To find the top 2% we first find the Z-score with 98% of scores below it. The area in the interior of the normal tables that is closest to 0.9800 is 0.9798 corresponding to $Z = 2.05$. Then

$X = \mu + \sigma Z = 64.1 + (2.8)(2.05) = 69.84$ or 69.8 inches.

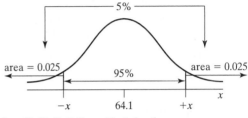

(c) For the middle 95% we need to find the Z-scores that cut off the top and bottom 2.5% or 0.025. The area of 0.0250 corresponds to $Z = -1.96$. By symmetry, the Z-score for the top 2.5% is $Z = 1.96$. The corresponding heights are $X = \mu + \sigma Z =$

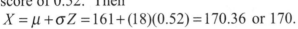

$64.1 + (2.8)(-1.96) = 58.6$ inches and $X = 64.1 + (2.8)(1.96) = 69.6$ inches.

27. (a) The area in the interior of the normal tables that is closest to 0.7000 is 0.6985, corresponding to a Z-score of 0.52. Then

$X = \mu + \sigma Z = 161 + (18)(0.52) = 170.36$ or 170.

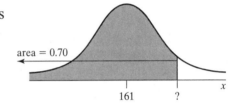

(b) For the middle 60% we need to find the Z-scores that cut off the top and bottom 20% or 0.20. The area in the interior of the tables closest to 0.2000 is 0.2005, corresponding to $Z = -0.84$. By symmetry, the Z-score for the top 20% is $Z = 0.84$. The corresponding blood pressures are $X = \mu + \sigma Z = 161 + (18)(-0.84) = 145.88$ or 146 and $X = 161 + (18)(0.84) = 176.12$ or 176.

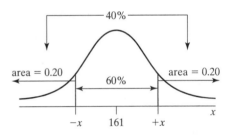

29. (a) The area in the interior of the normal tables that is closest to 0.1000 is 0.1003, corresponding to a Z-score of -1.28. Then

$X = \mu + \sigma Z = 80 + (8)(-1.28) = 69.76$ or 70° F.

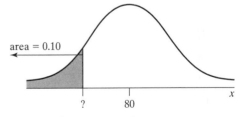

Note: Answers found using technology may differ from those shown.

(b) To find the top 4% we first find the Z-score with 96% of scores below it. The area in the interior of the normal tables that is closest to 0.9600 is 0.9599 corresponding to $Z = 1.75$. Then $X = \mu + \sigma Z = 80 + (8)(1.75) = 94°$ F.

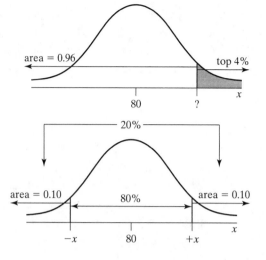

(c) For the middle 80% we need to find the Z-scores that cut off the top and bottom 10% or 0.10. The area in the tables that is closest to 0.1000 is 0.1003 corresponding to $Z = -1.28$. By symmetry, the Z-score for the top 10% is $Z = 1.28$. The corresponding temperatures are

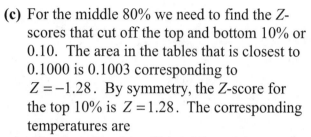

$X = \mu + \sigma Z = 80 + (8)(-1.28) = 69.76$ or $70°$ F and $X = 80 + (8)(1.28) = 90.24$ or $90°$ F.

31. (a), (b) The table summarizes the calculations of Z-scores and of the proportion in each class (the difference between column 6 and column 3. The theoretical proportions are very close to the actual relative frequencies and so SAT scores do appear to be normally distributed.

Lower Limit	Z-score	Area Below	Upper Limit	Z-score	Area Below	Area Between	Actual Relative Frequency
200	-2.78	0.0027	250	-2.34	0.0096	0.0069	0.0073
250	-2.34	0.0096	300	-1.89	0.0294	0.0198	0.0167
300	-1.89	0.0294	350	-1.45	0.0735	0.0441	0.0438
350	-1.45	0.0735	400	-1.01	0.1562	0.0827	0.0797
400	-1.01	0.1562	450	-0.57	0.2843	0.1281	0.1336
450	-0.57	0.2843	500	-0.12	0.4522	0.1679	0.1661
500	-0.12	0.4522	550	0.32	0.6255	0.1733	0.1637
550	0.32	0.6255	600	0.76	0.7764	0.1509	0.1472
600	0.76	0.7764	650	1.20	0.8849	0.1085	0.1095
650	1.20	0.8849	700	1.65	0.9505	0.0656	0.0737
700	1.65	0.9505	750	2.09	0.9817	0.0312	0.0393
750	2.09	0.9817	800	2.53	0.9943	0.0126	0.0195

33. (a), (c) The first table shows the relative frequencies and the computation of the mean and standard deviation using class midpoints as surrogate data values. The mean high temperature (column 6) is $43.5°$ F and the standard deviation is $\sqrt{109.5782} = 10.5°$ F.

Note: Answers found using technology may differ from those shown.

Lower Limit	Upper Limit	Frequency	Relative Frequency	Class Midpoint	Relative Frequency Midpoint	Rel. Freq. Squared deviations
5.0	9.9	1	0.0005	7.45	0.0040	0.6934
10.0	14.9	10	0.0053	12.45	0.0664	5.1439
15.0	19.9	15	0.0080	17.45	0.1396	5.4313
20.0	24.9	40	0.0213	22.45	0.4789	9.4582
25.0	29.9	95	0.0507	27.45	1.3908	13.0616
30.0	34.9	217	0.1157	32.45	3.7555	14.1467
35.0	39.9	325	0.1733	37.45	6.4913	6.3570
40.0	44.9	375	0.2000	42.45	8.4900	0.2230
45.0	49.9	281	0.1499	47.45	7.1112	2.3312
50.0	54.9	233	0.1243	52.45	6.5178	9.9407
55.0	59.9	160	0.0853	57.45	4.9024	16.5918
60.0	64.9	101	0.0539	62.45	3.3640	19.3314
65.0	69.9	21	0.0112	67.45	0.7554	6.4211
70.0	74.9	1	0.0005	72.45	0.0386	0.4468
	Total	1875			43.506	109.5782

(b) Yes, the distribution appears to be normal.

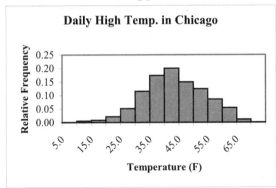

(d), (e) The theoretical proportions agree well with the actual relative frequencies.

Lower Limit Z-score	Area Below	Upper Limit Z-score	Area Below	Area Between	Actual Relative Frequency
-3.67	0.0000	-3.20	0.0007	0.0007	0.0005
-3.19	0.0007	-2.72	0.0033	0.0026	0.0053
-2.71	0.0034	-2.25	0.0122	0.0088	0.0080
-2.24	0.0125	-1.77	0.0384	0.0259	0.0213
-1.76	0.0392	-1.30	0.0968	0.0576	0.0507
-1.29	0.0985	-0.82	0.2061	0.1076	0.1157

Note: Answers found using technology may differ from those shown.

-0.81	0.2090	-0.34	0.3669	0.1579	0.1733
-0.33	0.3707	0.13	0.5517	0.1810	0.2000
0.14	0.5557	0.61	0.7291	0.1734	0.1499
0.62	0.7324	1.09	0.8621	0.1297	0.1243
1.10	0.8643	1.56	0.9406	0.0763	0.0853
1.57	0.9418	2.04	0.9793	0.0375	0.0539
2.05	0.9798	2.51	0.9940	0.0142	0.0112
2.52	0.9941	2.99	0.9986	0.0045	0.0005

7.4 Assessing Normality

7.4 Concepts and Vocabulary

1. Normal random variables are linearly related to their Z-scores (by the formula $X = \mu + \sigma Z$ and so the plot of X-values against their expected Z-values should be linear.

7.4 Exercises: Skill Building

1. The plotted points do not lie within the bounds and so the data are not normal.

3. The pattern of the plotted points is linear and the points all lie within the bounds. The data appear to be normal.

5. The pattern of the plotted points is linear and the points all lie within the bounds. The data appear to be normal.

7.4 Exercises: Applying the Concepts

7. The pattern of the plotted points is linear and the points all lie within the bounds. The data appear to be normal.

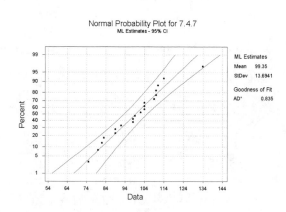

Note: Answers found using technology may differ from those shown.

9. The pattern of the plotted points is linear but the points do not all lie within the bounds, and so the data are not normal.

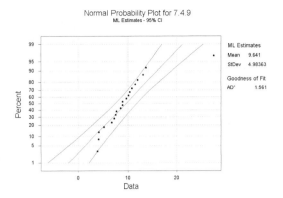

7.5 Sampling Distributions; The Central Limit Theorem

7.5 Concepts and Vocabulary

1. The sampling distribution of a statistic (such as the sample mean) is the probability distribution for all possible values of the statistic computed from samples of fixed size, n.

3. The population from which the sample is drawn must be normally distributed.

5. Four, because $\sigma_{\bar{x}} = \dfrac{\sigma}{\sqrt{4n}} = \dfrac{1}{2} \cdot \dfrac{\sigma}{\sqrt{n}}$.

7. No, because the sample size is large, i.e. $n \geq 30$. The sampling distribution is approximately normal with mean $\mu_{\bar{x}} = \mu = 50$ and $\sigma_{\bar{x}} = \dfrac{\sigma}{\sqrt{n}} = \dfrac{4}{\sqrt{40}} = 0.63$.

Note: The answers to the exercises in this section are based on Table II. Since answers computed using technology do not involve rounding of z-scores, they will often differ from the answers given below in the third and fourth decimal places.

7.5 Exercises: Skill Building

1. $\mu_{\bar{x}} = \mu = 50$ and $\sigma_{\bar{x}} = \dfrac{\sigma}{\sqrt{n}} = \dfrac{6}{\sqrt{40}} = 0.95$.

3. $\mu_{\bar{x}} = \mu = 100$ and $\sigma_{\bar{x}} = \dfrac{\sigma}{\sqrt{n}} = \dfrac{12}{\sqrt{20}} = 2.68$.

5. (a) Since $n \geq 30$, the distribution is approximately normal with $\mu_{\bar{x}} = 50$ and

$\sigma_{\bar{x}} = \dfrac{6}{\sqrt{40}} = 0.949$.

Note: Answers found using technology may differ from those shown.

(b) $P(\bar{x} > 51) = P\left(Z > \dfrac{51-50}{6/\sqrt{40}}\right) = P(Z > 1.05) = 1 - 0.8531 = 0.1469$.

(c) $P(\bar{x} \le 48) = P\left(Z \le \dfrac{48-50}{6/\sqrt{40}}\right) = P(Z \le -2.11) = 0.0174$.

(d) $P(47.5 < \bar{x} < 51.2) = P\left(\dfrac{47.5-50}{6/\sqrt{40}} < Z < \dfrac{51.2-50}{6/\sqrt{40}}\right)$

$\qquad\qquad = P(-2.64 < Z < 1.26) = 0.8962 - 0.0041 = 0.8921$.

7. **(a)** The population must have a normal distribution. If this is so, then $\bar{x}$ is normally distributed with $\mu_{\bar{x}} = 105$ and $\sigma_{\bar{x}} = \dfrac{16}{\sqrt{10}} = 5.060$.

(b) $P(\bar{x} > 103.2) = P\left(Z > \dfrac{103.2-105}{16/\sqrt{10}}\right) = P(Z > -0.36) = 1 - 0.3594 = 0.6406$.

(c) $P(\bar{x} < 99.3) = P\left(Z < \dfrac{99.3-105}{16/\sqrt{10}}\right) = P(Z < -1.13) = 0.1292$.

7.5 Exercises: Applying the Concepts

9. **(a)** $P(X > 60) = P\left(Z > \dfrac{60-53}{13.4}\right) = P(Z > 0.52) = 1 - 0.6985 = 0.3015$.

(b) $P(\bar{X} > 60) = P\left(Z > \dfrac{60-53}{13.4/\sqrt{15}}\right) = P(Z > 2.02) = 1 - 0.9783 = 0.0217$.

(c) $P(\bar{X} > 60) = P\left(Z > \dfrac{60-53}{13.4/\sqrt{20}}\right) = P(Z > 2.34) = 1 - 0.9904 = 0.0096$

(d) As the sample size increases, the probability decreases because the standard deviation gets smaller and so the area in the top tail of the distribution gets smaller as the spread of the distribution decreases.

(e) Since this would be an unusual observation, we might conclude that the sample came from a population with mean cholesterol higher than 53.

11. **(a)** $P(X < 260) = P\left(Z < \dfrac{260-266}{16}\right) = P(Z < -0.38) = 0.3520$.

(b) $P(\bar{X} \le 260) = P\left(Z \le \dfrac{260-266}{16/\sqrt{20}}\right) = P(Z \le -1.68) = 0.0465$.

(c) $P(\bar{X} \le 260) = P\left(Z \le \dfrac{260-266}{16/\sqrt{50}}\right) = P(Z \le -2.65) = 0.0040$.

Note: Answers found using technology may differ from those shown.

(d) Since this would be an unusual observation, we might conclude that the sample came from a population with mean gestation period shorter than 266 days.

13. (a) Because this is a large sample, $n = 50 > 30$.

(b) $\mu_{\bar{x}} = \mu = 3$, assuming that we are sampling from a population that is exactly at the

FDAL, and $\sigma_{\bar{x}} = \dfrac{\sigma}{\sqrt{n}} = \dfrac{\sqrt{3}}{\sqrt{50}} \approx 0.245$.

(c) $P(X \geq 3.6) = P\left(Z \geq \dfrac{3.6 - 3}{\sqrt{3}/\sqrt{50}}\right) = P(Z \geq 2.45) = 1 - 0.9929 = 0.0071$, which indicates

that this is an unusual outcome. It appears that this sample comes from a population with a higher mean than 3 insect fragments per ten-gram portion.

15. $P(X \geq 68.3) = P\left(Z \geq \dfrac{68.3 - 67.6}{4.2/\sqrt{50}}\right) = P(Z \geq 1.18) = 1 - 0.8810 = 0.1190$, which is a large

enough probability to indicate that this is not an unusual observation.

17. (a) $P(X < 32{,}030) = P\left(Z < \dfrac{32{,}030 - 45{,}127}{31{,}570/\sqrt{40}}\right) = P(Z < -2.62) = 0.0044$, which indicates

that this is an unusual observation, suggesting that mean household income in Cook County, IL may be below the national mean.

(b) No. Since the median is lower than the mean, it is likely that household income is skewed to the right.

19. (a) $\mu = (98 + 106 + 104 + 120 + 100 + 114)/6 = 107$.

(b), (c), (d)

Sample		Sample Mean	Sample Means	Frequency	Probability	Mean Prob.
98	106	102	99	1	0.067	6.60
98	104	101	101	1	0.067	6.73
98	120	109	102	2	0.133	13.60
98	100	99	103	1	0.067	6.87
98	114	106	105	1	0.067	7.00
106	104	105	106	1	0.067	7.07
106	120	113	107	1	0.067	7.13
106	100	103	109	2	0.133	14.53
106	114	110	110	2	0.133	14.67
104	120	112	112	1	0.067	7.47
104	100	102	113	1	0.067	7.53
104	114	109	117	1	0.067	7.80

Note: Answers found using technology may differ from those shown.

120	100	110
120	114	117
100	114	107

15	107

(d) The mean of the sample means is 107.

(e) From the table, we sum the probabilities associated with sample means between 102 and 112 to get a probability of 0.733.

(f)

Sample			Sample Mean	Sample Means	Frequency	Probability	Mean Prob.
98	106	104	102.67	100.67	1	0.05	5.03
98	106	120	108.00	101.33	1	0.05	5.07
98	106	100	101.33	102.67	1	0.05	5.13
98	106	114	106.00	103.33	1	0.05	5.17
98	104	120	107.33	104.00	1	0.05	5.20
98	104	100	100.67	105.33	1	0.05	5.27
98	104	114	105.33	106.00	3	0.15	15.90
98	120	100	106.00	106.67	1	0.05	5.33
98	120	114	110.67	107.33	1	0.05	5.37
98	100	114	104.00	108.00	3	0.15	16.20
106	104	120	110.00	108.67	1	0.05	5.43
106	104	100	103.33	110.00	1	0.05	5.50
106	104	114	108.00	110.67	1	0.05	5.53
106	120	100	108.67	111.33	1	0.05	5.57
106	120	114	113.33	112.67	1	0.05	5.63
106	100	114	106.67	113.33	1	0.05	5.67
104	120	100	108.00		20		107
104	120	114	112.67				
104	100	114	106.00				
120	100	114	111.33				

The mean of the sample means is again 107. From the table, we sum the probabilities associated with sample means between 102 and 112 to get a probability of 0.8. As the sample size increases, the spread of the sampling distribution decreases, increasing the probability of being within a fixed distance of the sampling distribution mean.

21. (a), (b), (c), (e), (g) Answers will vary.

(d) $\mu_{\bar{x}} = \mu = 100$ and $\sigma_{\bar{x}} = \dfrac{\sigma}{\sqrt{n}} = \dfrac{16}{\sqrt{20}}$.

(f) $P(\bar{X} > 108) = P\left(Z > \dfrac{108 - 100}{16/\sqrt{20}}\right) = P(Z > 2.24) = 1 - 0.9875 = 0.0125$.

Note: Answers found using technology may differ from those shown.

23. Answers will vary.

7.6 The Normal Approximation to the Binomial Probability Distribution

7.6 Concepts and Vocabulary

1. A probability experiment is said to be a binomial experiment if all the following are true: the experiment is performed n independent times; for each trial there are two mutually exclusive outcomes, success or failure; the probability of success, p, is the same for each trial of the experiment.

3. We must use a correction for continuity when using the normal distribution to approximate binomial probabilities because we are using a continuous density function to approximate the probability of a discrete random variable.

Note: The answers to the exercises in this section are based on Table II. Since answers computed using technology do not involve rounding of z-scores, they will often differ from the answers given below in the third and fourth decimal places.

7.6 Exercises: Skill Building

1. Approximate $P(X \geq 40)$ by computing the area to the right of $X = 39.5$.

3. Approximate $P(X = 8)$ by computing the area between $X = 7.5$ and $X = 8.5$.

5. Approximate $P(18 \leq X \leq 24)$ by computing the area between $X = 17.5$ and $X = 24.5$.

7. Approximate $P(X > 20) = P(X \geq 21)$ by computing the area to the right of $X = 20.5$.

9. Using $P(X = x) = {}_nC_x p^x (1-p)^{n-x}$, with the parameters $n = 60$ and $p = 0.4$, we get $P(X = 20) = 0.0616$. Then $np(1-p) = 60 \cdot 0.4 \cdot (1-0.4) = 14.4 \geq 10$, and so the normal approximation can be used, with $\mu = np = 60(0.4) = 24$ and $\sigma = \sqrt{np(1-p)} = \sqrt{14.4}$.

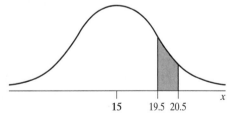

With continuity correction we calculate:

$$P(X = 20) \approx P(19.5 < X < 20.5) = P\left(\frac{19.5 - 24}{\sqrt{14.4}} < Z < \frac{20.5 - 24}{\sqrt{14.4}}\right) = P(-1.19 < Z < -0.92)$$

$$= 0.1788 - 0.1170 = 0.0618.$$

Note: Answers found using technology may differ from those shown.

11. Using $P(X = x) = {}_nC_x p^x (1-p)^{n-x}$, with the parameters $n = 75$ and $p = 0.75$, we get $P(X = 60) = 0.0677$. Then $np(1-p) = 75 \cdot 0.75 \cdot (1-0.75) = 14.06 \geq 10$, and so the normal approximation can be used, with $\mu = np = 75(0.75) = 56.25$ and

$\sigma = \sqrt{np(1-p)} = \sqrt{14.06}$. With continuity correction we calculate:

$$P(X = 60) \approx P(59.5 < X < 60.5) = P\left(\frac{59.5 - 56.25}{\sqrt{14.06}} < Z < \frac{60.5 - 56.25}{\sqrt{14.06}}\right) = P(0.87 < Z < 1.13)$$

$$= 0.8708 - 0.8078 = 0.0630 \,.$$

7.6 Exercises: Applying the Concepts

13. From the parameters $n = 70$ and $p = 0.8$ we get $\mu = np = 70 \cdot 0.8 = 56$ and $\sigma = \sqrt{np \cdot (1-p)} = \sqrt{70 \cdot 0.8 \cdot (1-0.8)} = \sqrt{11.2}$. Note that $np(1-p) = 11.2 > 10$ and so we may use the normal approximation to the binomial.

(a) $P(X = 60) \approx P(59.5 < X < 60.5) = P\left(\dfrac{59.5 - 56}{\sqrt{11.2}} < Z < \dfrac{60.5 - 56}{\sqrt{11.2}}\right)$
$$= P(1.05 < Z < 1.34) = 0.9099 - 0.8531 = 0.0568 \,.$$

(b) $P(X \geq 60) \approx P(X > 59.5) = P\left(Z > \dfrac{59.5 - 56}{\sqrt{11.2}}\right) = P(Z > 1.05) = 1 - 0.8531 = 0.1469 \,.$

(c) $P(X < 50) = P(X \leq 49) \approx P(X < 49.5) = P\left(Z < \dfrac{49.5 - 56}{\sqrt{11.2}}\right) = P(Z < -1.94) = 0.0262 \,.$

(d) $P(50 \leq X \leq 55) \approx P(49.5 < X < 55.5) = P\left(\dfrac{49.5 - 56}{\sqrt{11.2}} < Z < \dfrac{55.5 - 56}{\sqrt{11.2}}\right)$
$$= P(-1.94 < Z < -0.15) = 0.4404 - 0.0262 = 0.4142 \,.$$

15. From the parameters $n = 200$ and $p = 0.94$ we get $\mu = np = 200 \cdot 0.94 = 188$ and $\sigma = \sqrt{np \cdot (1-p)} = \sqrt{200 \cdot 0.94 \cdot (1-0.94)} = \sqrt{11.28}$. Note that $np(1-p) = 11.28 > 10$ and so we may use the normal approximation to the binomial.

(a) $P(X = 180) \approx P(179.5 < X < 180.5) = P\left(\dfrac{179.5 - 188}{\sqrt{11.28}} < Z < \dfrac{180.5 - 188}{\sqrt{11.28}}\right)$
$$= P(-2.53 < Z < -2.23) = 0.0129 - 0.0057 = 0.0072 \,.$$

Note: Answers found using technology may differ from those shown.

(b) $P(X > 180) = P(X \ge 181) \approx P(X > 180.5) = P\left(Z > \dfrac{180.5 - 188}{\sqrt{11.28}}\right)$

$$= P(Z > -2.23) = 1 - 0.0129 = 0.9871.$$

(c) $P(X \le 185) \approx P(X < 185.5) = P\left(Z < \dfrac{185.5 - 188}{\sqrt{11.28}}\right) = P(Z < -0.74) = 0.2296.$

(d) $P(160 \le X \le 180) \approx P(159.5 < X < 180.5) = P\left(\dfrac{159.5 - 188}{\sqrt{11.28}} < Z < \dfrac{180.5 - 188}{\sqrt{11.28}}\right)$

$$= P(-8.49 < Z < -2.23) = 0.0129 - 0.0000 = 0.0129.$$

17. From the parameters $n = 600$ and $p = 0.02$ we get $\mu = np = 600 \cdot 0.02 = 12$ and

$\sigma = \sqrt{np \cdot (1-p)} = \sqrt{600 \cdot 0.02 \cdot (1 - 0.02)} = \sqrt{11.76}$. Note that $np(1-p) = 11.76 > 10$ and so we may use the normal approximation to the binomial.

(a) $P(X = 20) \approx P(19.5 < X < 20.5) = P\left(\dfrac{19.5 - 12}{\sqrt{11.76}} < Z < \dfrac{20.5 - 12}{\sqrt{11.76}}\right)$

$$= P(2.19 < Z < 2.48) = 0.9934 - 0.9857 = 0.0077.$$

(b) $P(X \le 20) \approx P(X < 20.5) = P\left(Z < \dfrac{20.5 - 12}{\sqrt{11.76}}\right) = P(Z < 2.48) = 0.9934$

(c) $P(X \ge 22) \approx P(X > 21.5) = P\left(Z > \dfrac{21.5 - 12}{\sqrt{11.76}}\right)$

$$= P(Z > 2.77) = 1 - 0.9972 = 0.0028.$$

(d) $P(20 \le X \le 30) \approx P(19.5 < X < 30.5) = P\left(\dfrac{19.5 - 12}{\sqrt{11.76}} < Z < \dfrac{30.5 - 12}{\sqrt{11.76}}\right)$

$$= P(2.19 < Z < 5.39) = 1.0000 - 0.9857 = 0.0143.$$

19. From the parameters $n = 100$ and $p = 0.45$ we get $\mu = np = 100 \cdot 0.45 = 45$ and

$\sigma = \sqrt{np \cdot (1-p)} = \sqrt{100 \cdot 0.45 \cdot (1 - 0.45)} = \sqrt{24.75}$. Note that $np(1-p) = 24.75 > 10$ and so we may use the normal approximation to the binomial.

(a) $P(X = 50) \approx P(49.5 < X < 50.5) = P\left(\dfrac{49.5 - 45}{\sqrt{24.75}} < Z < \dfrac{50.5 - 45}{\sqrt{24.75}}\right)$

$$= P(0.90 < Z < 1.11) = 0.8665 - 0.8159 = 0.0506.$$

(b) $P(X \ge 60) \approx P(X > 59.5) = P\left(Z > \dfrac{59.5 - 45}{\sqrt{24.75}}\right)$

$$= P(Z > 2.91) = 1 - 0.9982 = 0.0018.$$

Note: Answers found using technology may differ from those shown.

(c) $P(X \leq 50) \approx P(X < 50.5) = P\left(Z < \dfrac{50.5 - 45}{\sqrt{24.75}}\right) = P(Z < 1.11) = 0.8665$

(d) $P(60 \leq X \leq 90) \approx P(59.5 < X < 90.5) = P\left(\dfrac{59.5 - 45}{\sqrt{24.75}} < Z < \dfrac{90.5 - 45}{\sqrt{24.75}}\right)$

$$= P(2.91 < Z < 9.15) = 1.0000 - 0.9982 = 0.0018 \,.$$

21. $n = 200$, $p = 0.59$ and so $\mu = np = 200 \cdot 0.59 = 118$ and

$\sigma = \sqrt{np \cdot (1 - p)} = \sqrt{200 \cdot 0.59 \cdot (1 - 0.59)} = \sqrt{48.38}$. Note that $np(1 - p) = 48.38 > 10$ and so we may use the normal approximation to the binomial.

(a) $P(X \geq 135) \approx P(X > 134.5) = P\left(Z > \dfrac{134.5 - 118}{\sqrt{48.38}}\right)$

$$= P(Z > 2.37) = 1 - 0.9911 = 0.0089 \,.$$

(b) Since this is an unusual outcome, we may conclude that it is likely that this is a sample from a population with higher than 59% of the male students living at home.

23. $n = 150$, $p = 0.42$ and so $\mu = np = 150 \cdot 0.42 = 63$ and

$\sigma = \sqrt{np \cdot (1 - p)} = \sqrt{150 \cdot 0.42 \cdot (1 - 0.42)} = \sqrt{36.54}$. Note that $np(1 - p) = 36.54 > 10$ and so we may use the normal approximation to the binomial.

(a) $P(X \geq 80) \approx P(X > 79.5) = P\left(Z > \dfrac{79.5 - 63}{\sqrt{36.54}}\right)$

$$= P(Z > 2.73) = 1 - 0.9968 = 0.0032 \,.$$

(b) Since this is a very unusual outcome, it suggests that the preference for boys is higher among the students of this college than among the population sampled by the Gallup poll.

25. $n = 200$, $p = 0.528$ and so $\mu = np = 200 \cdot 0.528 = 105.6$ and

$\sigma = \sqrt{np \cdot (1 - p)} = \sqrt{200 \cdot 0.528 \cdot (1 - 0.528)} = \sqrt{49.8432} \approx 7.060$. Note that $np(1 - p) = 49.8432 > 10$ and so we may use the normal approximation to the binomial.

(a) $P(X \leq 95) \approx P(X < 95.5) = P\left(Z < \dfrac{95.5 - 105.6}{7.060}\right)$

$$= P(Z < -1.43) = 0.0764 \,.$$

(b) This is not an unusual outcome and so does not contradict the results of the ACT study.

Note: Answers found using technology may differ from those shown.

Review Exercises

Note: The answers to the exercises in this section are based on Table II. Since answers computed using technology do not involve rounding of z-scores, they will often differ from the answers given below in the third and fourth decimal places.

1. **(a)** μ is the center (and peak) of the normal distribution and so $\mu = 60$.
    (b) σ is the distance from the center to the points of inflection and so $\sigma = 70 - 60 = 10$.
    (c) The proportion of the population with X-values above 75 is 0.0668. The probability of a randomly selected individual having an X-value above 75 is 0.0668.
    (d) The proportion of the population with X-values between 50 and 75 is 0.7745. The probability of a randomly selected individual having an X-value between 50 and 75 is 0.7745.

3. **(a)** $Z_1 = \dfrac{X_1 - \mu}{\sigma} = \dfrac{18 - 20}{4} = -0.50$.

    (b) $Z_2 = \dfrac{X_2 - \mu}{\sigma} = \dfrac{21 - 20}{4} = 0.25$.

    (c) Also 0.2912.

5. Directly from the tables we get area = 0.1492.

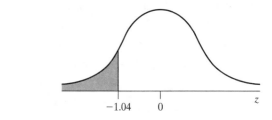

7. From the tables, area between
    $= 0.8485 - 0.3669 = 0.4816$.

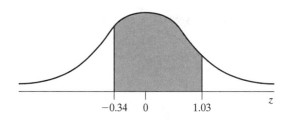

9. $P(Z < 1.19) = 0.8830$.

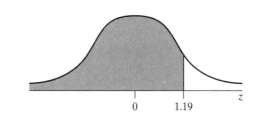

Note: Answers found using technology may differ from those shown.

11. $P(-1.21 \le Z \le 2.28) = 0.9887 - 0.1131 = 0.8756$.

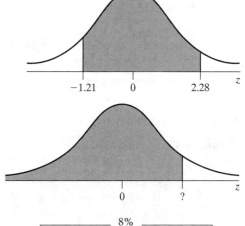

13. We look for 0.8400 in the interior of the tables and find that 0.8389 is closest, corresponding to $Z = 0.99$.

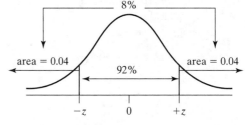

15. The Z-scores for the middle 92% are the Z-scores for the top and bottom 4%. From the interior of the tables, the area closest to 0.0400 is 0.0401, corresponding to $Z = -1.75$. By symmetry the other Z-score is $Z = 1.75$.

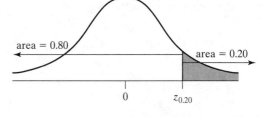

17. $z_{0.20}$ is the Z-score that cuts off an area of 0.20 in the top tail and so has an area of $1 - 0.20 = 0.80$ below it. The area in the interior of the tables that is closest to 0.8000 is 0.7995, corresponding to $Z = 0.84$. Hence $z_{0.20} = 0.84$.

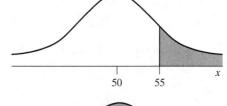

19. $P(X > 55) = P\left(Z > \dfrac{55 - 50}{6}\right)$
$= P(Z > 0.83) = 1 - 0.7967 = 0.2033$.

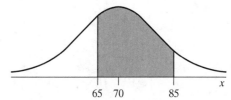

21. $P(65 < X < 85) = P\left(\dfrac{65 - 70}{10} < Z < \dfrac{85 - 70}{10}\right)$
$= P(-0.50 < Z < 1.50) = 0.9332 - 0.3085 = 0.6247$

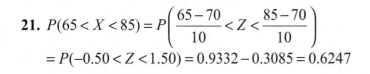

Note: Answers found using technology may differ from those shown.

23. (a) $P(X \geq 75,000) = P\left(Z \geq \dfrac{75,000 - 70,000}{4,400}\right)$

$= P(Z \geq 1.14) = 1 - 0.8729 = 0.1271$ or 12.71%.

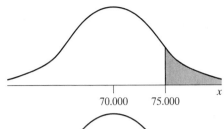

(b) $P(X \leq 60,000) = P\left(Z \leq \dfrac{60,000 - 70,000}{4,400}\right)$

$= P(Z \leq -2.27) = 0.0116$ or 1.16%.

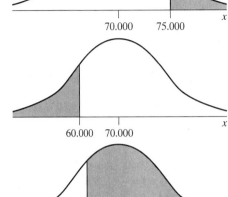

(c) $P(65,000 \leq X \leq 60,000)$

$= P\left(\dfrac{65,000 - 70,000}{4,400} \leq Z \leq \dfrac{80,000 - 70,000}{4,400}\right)$

$= P(-1.14 \leq Z \leq 2.27) = 0.9884 - 0.1271 = 0.8613$

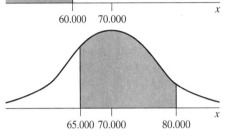

(d) We need the cut-off for the bottom 2%. The area closest to 0.0200 in the interior of the tables is 0.0202, corresponding to $Z = -2.05$. Then $X = \mu + Z\sigma =$ 70,000 − 2.05(4,400) = 60,980 miles.

(e) Normal with $\mu_{\bar{x}} = \mu = 70,000$ and $\sigma_{\bar{x}} = \dfrac{\sigma}{\sqrt{n}} = \dfrac{4,400}{\sqrt{10}} \approx 1391.4$ miles.

(f) $P(\bar{X} \geq 72,500) = P\left(Z \geq \dfrac{72,500 - 70,000}{4,400/\sqrt{10}}\right)$

$= P(Z \geq 1.80) = 1 - 0.9641 = 0.0359$.

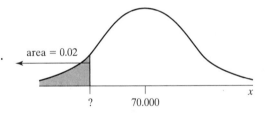

(g) Normal with $\mu_{\bar{x}} = \mu = 70,000$ and $\sigma_{\bar{x}} = \dfrac{\sigma}{\sqrt{n}} = \dfrac{4,400}{\sqrt{25}} = 880$ miles. $\sigma_{\bar{x}}$ is smaller for the larger sample size.

(h) $P(\bar{X} \geq 72,500) = P\left(Z \geq \dfrac{72,500 - 70,000}{4,400/\sqrt{25}}\right) = P(Z \geq 2.84) = 1 - 0.9977 = 0.0023$.

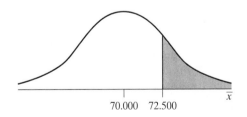

Note: Answers found using technology may differ from those shown.

25. (a) $P(X > 180) = P\left(Z > \dfrac{180 - 171}{39.8}\right)$

$= P(Z > 0.23) = 1 - 0.5910 = 0.4090$.

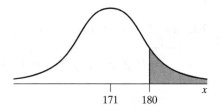

(b) $P(150 < X < 200) = P\left(\dfrac{150 - 171}{39.8} < Z < \dfrac{200 - 171}{39.8}\right)$

$= P(-0.53 < Z < 0.73) = 0.7673 - 0.2981 = 0.4692$.

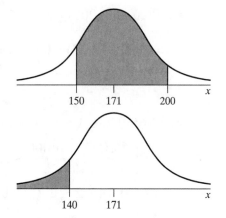

(c) $P(X < 140) = P\left(Z < \dfrac{140 - 171}{39.8}\right)$

$= P(Z < -0.78) = 0.2177$.

(d) The area in the interior of the normal tables that is closest to 0.1000 is 0.1003, corresponding to $Z = -1.28$. Then
$X = \mu + Z\sigma = 171 - 1.28(39.8) = 120.056$ or 120.

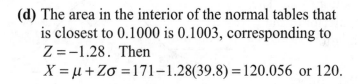

(e) The area in the interior of the normal tables that is closest to 0.2500 is 0.2514, corresponding to $Z = -0.67$. Then
$X = \mu + Z\sigma = 171 - 0.67(39.8) = 144$ which is close to the reported value of 145.

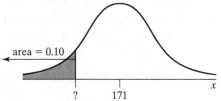

(f) $P(\bar{X} < 167) = P\left(Z < \dfrac{167 - 171}{39.8/\sqrt{8}}\right)$

$= P(Z < -0.28) = 0.3897$.

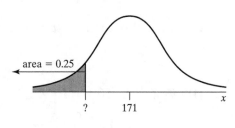

(g) $P(\bar{X} < 167) = P\left(Z < \dfrac{167 - 171}{39.8/\sqrt{20}}\right) = P(Z < -0.45) = 0.3264$.

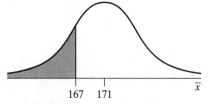

Note: Answers found using technology may differ from those shown.

27. (a) $np(1-p) = 200 \cdot 0.08 \cdot (1-0.08) = 14.72 > 10$. The parameters are
$\mu = np = 200(0.08) = 16$ and
$\sigma = \sqrt{np(1-p)} = \sqrt{200 \cdot 0.08 \cdot (1-0.08)} \approx 3.837$.

(b) $P(X = 15) \approx P(14.5 \le X \le 15.5)$

$$= P\left(\frac{14.5-16}{3.837} \le Z \le \frac{15.5-16}{3.837}\right)$$

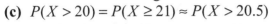

$= P(-.39 \le Z \le -0.13) = 0.4483 - 0.3483 = 0.1000$.

There is about a 10% chance that 15 out of a random sample of 200 20–34-year-old females will have high serum cholesterol.

(c) $P(X > 20) = P(X \ge 21) \approx P(X > 20.5)$

$$= P\left(Z > \frac{20.5-16}{3.837}\right) = P(Z > 1.17)$$

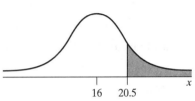

$= 1 - 0.8790 = 0.1210$. There is about a 12% chance that more than 20 out of a random sample of 200 20–34-year-old females will have high serum cholesterol.

(d) $P(X \ge 15) \approx P(X > 14.5) = P\left(Z > \frac{14.5-16}{3.837}\right)$

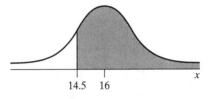

$= P(Z > -0.39) = 1 - 0.3483 = 0.6517$. There is about a 65% chance that at least 15 out of a random sample of 200 20–34-year-old females will have high serum cholesterol.

(e) $P(X < 25) = P(X \le 24) \approx P(X < 24.5)$

$$= P\left(Z < \frac{24.5-16}{3.837}\right) = P(Z < 2.22) = 0.9868.$$ There is about a 99% chance that fewer than 25 out of a random sample of 200 20–34-year-old females will have high serum cholesterol.

(f) $P(15 \le X \le 25) \approx P(14.5 < X < 25.5)$

$$= P\left(\frac{14.5-16}{3.837} < Z < \frac{25.5-16}{3.837}\right)$$

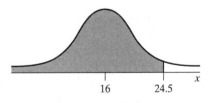

$= P(-0.39 < Z < 2.48) = 0.9934 - 0.3483 = 0.6451.$

There is about a 65% chance that between 15 and 25 out of a random sample of 200 20–34-year-old females will have high serum cholesterol.

29. The plotted points do not all lie within the bounds and so the data are not normal.

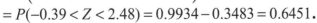

Note: Answers found using technology may differ from those shown.

31. The plotted points do not all lie within the bounds and so the data are not normal.

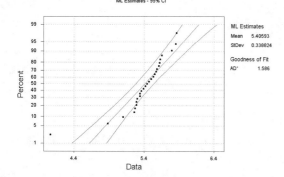

33. (a), (c) The first table shows the relative frequencies and the computation of the mean and standard deviation using class midpoints as surrogate data values. The mean birth weight (column 6) is 2929.1 grams and the standard deviation is $\sqrt{307442.1} = 554.5$ grams.

Lower Limit	Upper Limit	Frequency	Relative Frequency	Class Midpoint	Relative Frequency Midpoint	Rel. Freq. Squared deviations
0	499	3	0.0000	249.5	0.0	131.8
500	999	61	0.0004	749.5	0.3	1773.1
1000	1499	560	0.0034	1249.5	4.3	9666.2
1500	1999	5031	0.0308	1749.5	53.9	42832.9
2000	2499	27902	0.1707	2249.5	384.0	78847.2
2500	2999	59394	0.3634	2749.5	999.2	11720.4
3000	3499	47924	0.2932	3249.5	952.9	30105.7
3500	3999	17873	0.1094	3749.5	410.0	73609.2
4000	4499	3902	0.0239	4249.5	101.5	41627.0
4500	4999	679	0.0042	4749.5	19.7	13768.2
5000	5499	102	0.0006	5249.5	3.3	3360.5
	Total	163431			2929.1	307442.1

Note: Answers found using technology may differ from those shown.

(b) The distribution appears to be normal.

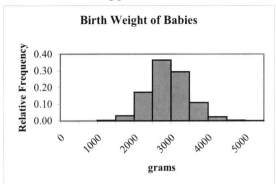

(d), (e) The theoretical proportions agree well with the actual relative frequencies.

Lower Limit Z-score	Area Below	Upper Limit Z-score	Area Below	Area Between	Actual Relative Frequency
-5.28	0.0000	-4.38	0.0000	0.0000	0.0000
-4.38	0.0000	-3.48	0.0003	0.0003	0.0004
-3.48	0.0003	-2.58	0.0049	0.0046	0.0034
-2.58	0.0049	-1.68	0.0465	0.0416	0.0308
-1.68	0.0465	-0.78	0.2177	0.1712	0.1707
-0.77	0.2206	0.13	0.5517	0.3311	0.3634
0.13	0.5517	1.03	0.8485	0.2968	0.2932
1.03	0.8485	1.93	0.9732	0.1247	0.1094
1.93	0.9732	2.83	0.9977	0.0245	0.0239
2.83	0.9977	3.73	1.0000	0.0023	0.0042
3.73	1.0000	4.63	1.0000	0.0000	0.0006

35. (a) Normal (because this is a large sample) with $\mu_{\bar{x}} = \mu = 120$ and

$$\sigma_{\bar{x}} = \frac{\sigma}{\sqrt{n}} = \frac{17}{\sqrt{100}} = 1.7.$$

(b) $P(\bar{X} \geq 125) = P\left(Z \geq \dfrac{125-120}{1.7}\right)$

$= P(Z \geq 2.94) = 1 - 0.9984 = 0.0016.$

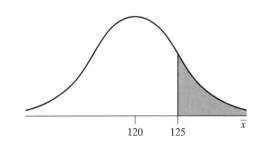

Note: Answers found using technology may differ from those shown.

37. (a)

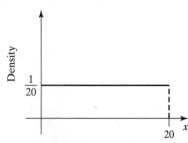

(b) Probability = area under the uniform density curve = height × width = $0.05 \cdot (5-0) = 0.25$.

(c) Probability = area under the uniform density curve = height × width = $0.05 \cdot (18-10) = 0.40$.

39. The sampling distribution of a statistic (such as the sample mean) is the probability distribution for all possible values of the statistic computed from samples of fixed size, n.

Note: Answers found using technology may differ from those shown.

Chapter 8. Confidence Intervals

8.1 Confidence Intervals about a Population Mean, σ Known

8.1 Concepts and Vocabulary

1. An estimator should be unbiased (its expected value should be the value of the parameter), consistent (the larger the sample, the closer the sample statistic should be to the population parameter) and efficient.

3. To increase the level of confidence that the interval contains the population parameter, you must logically widen the interval, i.e. build in a larger margin of error.

5. The sample mean is the midpoint of the interval $= \frac{1}{2}(10+18) = 14$ and the margin of error is the distance from the midpoint to the bounds $= 18-14 = 4$.

8.1 Exercises: Basic Skills

1. Although the plotted points stay inside the bounds of the normal probability plot, the boxplot reveals that there is an outlier and so a z-interval should not be used.

3. The boxplot reveals that there are outliers and so a z-interval should not be used.

5. The plotted points are all within the bounds of the normal probability plot, which also has a generally linear pattern. The boxplot shows that there are no outliers. A z-interval can be used.

7. For a 98% confidence interval we use $\alpha = 1-0.98 = 0.02$ and so $z_{\alpha/2} = z_{0.01}$ which is the z-score with area 0.99 below it. The closest area in the tables to 0.9900 is 0.9901 corresponding to $z_{0.01} = 2.33$.

9. For an 85% confidence interval we use $\alpha = 1-0.85 = 0.15$ and so $z_{\alpha/2} = z_{0.075}$ which is the z-score with area 0.9250 below it. The closest area in the tables to 0.9250 is 0.9251 corresponding to $z_{0.075} = 1.44$.

11. (a) For 95% confidence the critical value is $z_{0.025} = 1.96$. Then:

$$\text{Lower bound} = \bar{x} - z_{0.025} \cdot \frac{\sigma}{\sqrt{n}} = 34.2 - 1.96 \cdot \frac{5.3}{\sqrt{35}} = 34.2 - 1.76 = 32.44$$

Upper bound $= \bar{x} + z_{0.025} \cdot \dfrac{\sigma}{\sqrt{n}} = 34.2 + 1.96 \cdot \dfrac{5.3}{\sqrt{35}} = 34.2 + 1.76 = 35.96$.

(b) Lower bound $= \bar{x} - z_{0.025} \cdot \dfrac{\sigma}{\sqrt{n}} = 34.2 - 1.96 \cdot \dfrac{5.3}{\sqrt{50}} = 34.2 - 1.47 = 32.73$

Upper bound $= \bar{x} + z_{0.025} \cdot \dfrac{\sigma}{\sqrt{n}} = 34.2 + 1.96 \cdot \dfrac{5.3}{\sqrt{50}} = 34.2 + 1.47 = 35.67$.

Increasing the sample size decreases the margin of error.

(c) For 99% confidence the critical value is $z_{0.005} = 2.575$. Then:

Lower bound $= \bar{x} - z_{0.005} \cdot \dfrac{\sigma}{\sqrt{n}} = 34.2 - 2.575 \cdot \dfrac{5.3}{\sqrt{35}} = 34.2 - 2.31 = 31.89$

Upper bound $= \bar{x} + z_{0.005} \cdot \dfrac{\sigma}{\sqrt{n}} = 34.2 + 2.575 \cdot \dfrac{5.3}{\sqrt{35}} = 34.2 + 2.31 = 36.51$.

Increasing the level of confidence increases the margin of error.

(d) For a sample size of $n = 15 < 30$ we can only compute a confidence interval in this way if the population we are sampling from is normal.

13. (a) For 96% confidence the critical value is $z_{0.02} = 2.05$. Then:

Lower bound $= \bar{x} - z_{0.02} \cdot \dfrac{\sigma}{\sqrt{n}} = 108 - 2.05 \cdot \dfrac{13}{\sqrt{25}} = 108 - 5.33 = 102.67$

Upper bound $= \bar{x} + z_{0.02} \cdot \dfrac{\sigma}{\sqrt{n}} = 108 + 2.05 \cdot \dfrac{13}{\sqrt{25}} = 108 + 5.33 = 113.33$.

(b) Lower bound $= \bar{x} - z_{0.02} \cdot \dfrac{\sigma}{\sqrt{n}} = 108 - 2.05 \cdot \dfrac{13}{\sqrt{10}} = 108 - 8.43 = 99.57$

Upper bound $= \bar{x} + z_{0.02} \cdot \dfrac{\sigma}{\sqrt{n}} = 108 + 2.05 \cdot \dfrac{13}{\sqrt{10}} = 108 + 8.43 = 116.43$.

Decreasing the sample size increases the margin of error.

(c) For 88% confidence the critical value is $z_{0.06} = 1.555$. Then:

Lower bound $= \bar{x} - z_{0.06} \cdot \dfrac{\sigma}{\sqrt{n}} = 108 - 1.555 \cdot \dfrac{13}{\sqrt{25}} = 108 - 4.04 = 103.96$

Upper bound $= \bar{x} + z_{0.06} \cdot \dfrac{\sigma}{\sqrt{n}} = 108 + 1.555 \cdot \dfrac{13}{\sqrt{25}} = 108 + 4.04 = 112.04$.

Decreasing the level of confidence decreases the margin of error.

(d) No, because then the sampling distribution of $\bar{x}$ is not normal.

(e) If there are outliers then we should not use this approach to compute a confidence interval. Since the outliers will increase the sample mean, the confidence interval might overstate the population mean.

8.1 Exercises: Applying the Concepts

15. (a) $\bar{x} = (225 + 462 + 729 + 753)/4 = \$542.25$

(b) The plotted points are generally linear and stay within the bounds of the normal probability plot. The boxplot shows that there are no outliers. The conditions for a z-interval are met.

(c) For a 95% confidence interval we use $z_{.025} = 1.96$.

$$\text{Lower bound} = \bar{x} - z_{0.025} \cdot \frac{\sigma}{\sqrt{n}} = 542.25 - 1.96 \cdot \frac{220}{\sqrt{4}} = 542.25 - 215.60 = \$326.65$$

$$\text{Upper bound} = \bar{x} - z_{0.025} \cdot \frac{\sigma}{\sqrt{n}} = 542.25 + 1.96 \cdot \frac{220}{\sqrt{4}} = 542.25 + 215.60 = \$757.85.$$

We are 95% confident that the true mean cost of repairs is between \$326.65 and \$757.85.

(d) For a 90% confidence interval we use $z_{.05} = 1.645$.

$$\text{Lower bound} = \bar{x} - z_{0.05} \cdot \frac{\sigma}{\sqrt{n}} = 542.25 - 1.645 \cdot \frac{220}{\sqrt{4}} = 542.25 - 180.95 = \$361.30$$

$$\text{Upper bound} = \bar{x} - z_{0.05} \cdot \frac{\sigma}{\sqrt{n}} = 542.25 + 1.645 \cdot \frac{220}{\sqrt{4}} = 542.25 + 180.95 = \$723.20.$$

We are 90% confident that the true mean cost of repairs is between \$361.30 and \$723.20.

17. (a) $\bar{x} = (65 + 47 + \ldots + 54)/15 = 50.667$

(b) The plotted points are generally linear and stay within the bounds of the normal probability plot. The boxplot shows that there are no outliers. The conditions for a z-interval are met.

(c) For a 95% confidence interval we use $z_{.025} = 1.96$.

$$\text{Lower bound} = \bar{x} - z_{0.025} \cdot \frac{\sigma}{\sqrt{n}} = 50.667 - 1.96 \cdot \frac{13.4}{\sqrt{15}} = 50.667 - 6.781 = 43.89$$

$$\text{Upper bound} = \bar{x} - z_{0.025} \cdot \frac{\sigma}{\sqrt{n}} = 50.667 + 1.96 \cdot \frac{13.4}{\sqrt{15}} = 50.667 + 6.781 = 57.45.$$

We are 95% confident that the true mean serum HDL cholesterol is between 43.89 and 57.45.

(d) Since 53 falls inside this interval, there is no evidence that his patients have a cholesterol level different from that of the general population.

19. (a) $\bar{x} = (24 + 23 + \ldots + 30)/20 = 22.95$

(b) The plotted points are generally linear and stay within the bounds of the normal probability plot. The boxplot shows that there are no outliers. The conditions for a z-interval are met.

(c) For a 92% confidence interval we use $z_{.04} = 1.75$.

Lower bound $= \bar{x} - z_{.04} \cdot \dfrac{\sigma}{\sqrt{n}} = 22.95 - 1.75 \cdot \dfrac{5}{\sqrt{20}} = 22.95 - 1.96 = 20.99$

Upper bound $= \bar{x} + z_{.04} \cdot \dfrac{\sigma}{\sqrt{n}} = 22.95 + 1.75 \cdot \dfrac{5}{\sqrt{20}} = 22.95 + 1.96 = 24.91$.

We are 92% confident that the true mean ACT Math score for students in High School District 204 is between 20.99 and 24.91.

(d) Since the mean, 20.7, of the general population is not inside this interval, there is evidence that District 204 students have an ACT Math mean score different from that of the general population.

21. (a) $\bar{x} = (279 + 260 + \ldots + 240)/10 = 258.8$

(b) The plotted points are generally linear and stay within the bounds of the normal probability plot. The boxplot shows that there are no outliers. The conditions for a z-interval are met.

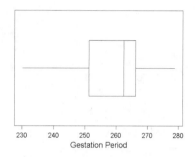

Normal Probability Plot for Gestation
ML Estimates - 95% CI

(c) For a 90% confidence interval we use $z_{.05} = 1.645$.

Lower bound $= \bar{x} - z_{0.05} \cdot \dfrac{\sigma}{\sqrt{n}} = 258.8 - 1.645 \cdot \dfrac{16}{\sqrt{10}} = 258.8 - 8.3 = 250.5$ days.

Upper bound $= \bar{x} + z_{0.05} \cdot \dfrac{\sigma}{\sqrt{n}} = 258.8 + 1.645 \cdot \dfrac{16}{\sqrt{10}} = 258.8 + 8.3 = 267.1$ days.

We are 90% confident that the true gestation period for Dr. Oswiecmiski's patients is between 250.5 and 267.1 days.

(d) Since 266 falls inside this interval, there is no evidence that her patients have a gestation period different from that of the general population.

23. (a) Technology gives $\bar{x} = 11.19$ million shares.

(b) For a 90% confidence interval we use $z_{.05} = 1.645$.

Lower bound $= \bar{x} - z_{0.05} \cdot \dfrac{\sigma}{\sqrt{n}} = 11.19 - 1.645 \cdot \dfrac{4.84}{\sqrt{35}} = 11.19 - 1.35 = 9.84$

Upper bound $= \bar{x} + z_{0.05} \cdot \dfrac{\sigma}{\sqrt{n}} = 11.19 + 1.645 \cdot \dfrac{4.84}{\sqrt{35}} = 11.19 + 1.35 = 12.54$.

We are 90% confident that the true mean number of shares of Philip Morris stock traded per day in 2000 was between 9.84 million and 12.54 million.

(c) For the second sample, technology gives $\bar{x} = 8.63$ million shares.

$$\text{Lower bound} = \bar{x} - z_{0.05} \cdot \frac{\sigma}{\sqrt{n}} = 8.626 - 1.645 \cdot \frac{4.84}{\sqrt{35}} = 8.626 - 1.346 = 7.28$$

$$\text{Upper bound} = \bar{x} + z_{0.05} \cdot \frac{\sigma}{\sqrt{n}} = 8.626 + 1.645 \cdot \frac{4.84}{\sqrt{35}} = 8.626 + 1.346 = 9.97 \ .$$

We are 90% confident that the true mean number of shares of Philip Morris stock traded per day in 2000 was between 7.28 million and 9.97 million.

(d) Sampling variability (i.e. random variation from one sample to another) accounts for the difference.

25. (a) Technology gives $\bar{x} = 49{,}477.7$ miles.

(b) For a 99% confidence interval we use $z_{.005} = 2.575$.

Lower bound

$$= \bar{x} - z_{0.005} \cdot \frac{\sigma}{\sqrt{n}} = 49{,}477.7 - 2.575 \cdot \frac{19{,}700}{\sqrt{33}} = 49{,}477.7 - 8{,}830.5 = 40{,}647$$

Upper bound

$$= \bar{x} + z_{0.005} \cdot \frac{\sigma}{\sqrt{n}} = 49{,}477.7 + 2.575 \cdot \frac{19{,}700}{\sqrt{33}} = 49{,}477.7 + 8{,}830.5 = 58{,}308 \ .$$

We are 99% confident that the true mean number of miles on a four-year-old Saturn SC1 is between 40,647 and 58,308.

(c) For a 95% confidence interval we use $z_{.025} = 1.96$.

Lower bound

$$= \bar{x} - z_{0.025} \cdot \frac{\sigma}{\sqrt{n}} = 49{,}477.7 - 1.96 \cdot \frac{19{,}700}{\sqrt{33}} = 49{,}477.7 - 6{,}721.5 = 42{,}756$$

Upper bound

$$= \bar{x} + z_{0.025} \cdot \frac{\sigma}{\sqrt{n}} = 49{,}477.7 + 1.96 \cdot \frac{19{,}700}{\sqrt{33}} = 49{,}477.7 + 6{,}721.5 = 56{,}199 \ .$$

We are 95% confident that the true mean number of miles on a four-year-old Saturn SC1 is between 42,756 and 56,199.

(d) Decreasing the level of confidence decreases the width of the confidence interval.

(e) No, because the sample was obtained entirely from Saturns in the Chicagoland area.

27. For 99% confidence, we use $z_{.005} = 2.575$. Then the required sample size is

$$n = \left(\frac{z_{\alpha/2} \cdot \sigma}{E} \right)^2 = \left(\frac{2.575 \cdot 13.4}{2} \right)^2 = 297.6 \ \text{which we round up to 298 subjects. For 95\%}$$

confidence we use $z_{.025} = 1.96$ and get $n = \left(\dfrac{1.96 \cdot 13.4}{2}\right)^2 = 172.4$ which we round up to 173 subjects. Decreasing the level of confidence decreases the required sample size.

29. For 95% confidence we use $z_{.025} = 1.96$. Then the required sample size is

$$n = \left(\frac{z_{\alpha/2} \cdot \sigma}{E}\right)^2 = \left(\frac{1.96 \cdot 2.9}{0.5}\right)^2 = 129.2 \text{ which we round up to 130 subjects.}$$

31. (a) For 90% confidence, we use $z_{.05} = 1.645$. Then the required sample size is

$$n = \left(\frac{z_{\alpha/2} \cdot \sigma}{E}\right)^2 = \left(\frac{1.645 \cdot 19,700}{1000}\right)^2 = 1050.2 \text{ which we round up to 1051 cars.}$$

(b) $n = \left(\dfrac{z_{\alpha/2} \cdot \sigma}{E}\right)^2 = \left(\dfrac{1.645 \cdot 19,700}{500}\right)^2 = 4200.7$ which we round up to 4201 cars.

(c) The sample size increases by a factor of 4, approximately. This is because the sample size, n, is inversely proportional to the square of the error, E. To halve the error we must increase the sample size by a factor of $\left(\dfrac{1}{1/2}\right)^2 = 4$.

33. (a), (b) Answers will vary.
   (c) We would expect approximately 95% of the 20 samples, or 19 samples, to generate confidence intervals that include the population mean. Actual results will vary.

35. (a), (b) Answers will vary.
   (c) If these were truly "95% confidence intervals," then we would expect approximately 95% of the 100 samples, or 95 samples, to generate confidence intervals that include the population mean. Actual results will vary.
   (d) Since the sample size is small and we are sampling from a non-normal population, the sampling distribution of the sample mean is not normal, and so our method for computing a 95% confidence interval is not valid—it is not true that close to 95% of our intervals contain the population mean.

37. The sample size must be increased by a factor of 4. This is because the sample size, n, is inversely proportional to the square of the error, E. To decrease the error by a factor of $\frac{1}{2}$ we must increase the sample size by a factor of $\left(\dfrac{1}{1/2}\right)^2 = 4$.

8.2 Confidence Intervals about a Population Mean, σ Unknown

8.2 Concepts and Vocabulary

1. A z-interval should be computed if the population standard deviation is known and either the data are approximately normally distributed with no outliers, or the sample size is large, $n \geq 30$. A t-interval should be computed if the population standard deviation is unknown, but either the data are approximately normally distributed with no outliers, or the sample size is large, $n \geq 30$. If the sample size is small, $n < 30$, and the data do not appear to be normally distributed or there are outliers in the data, then neither a z-interval nor a t-interval should be constructed. In these circumstances we may be able to use non-parametric methods instead.

3. The t-interval procedure is not very sensitive to small departures from the assumption of normality.

5. The t-distribution has all of the same symmetry properties as the standard normal distribution. The one difference is that t-distributions have greater spread than a standard normal distribution. As the degrees of freedom increase, the t-distributions resemble a standard normal distribution more and more closely.

8.2 Exercises: Basic Skills

1. (a) From the row with df = 25 and the column headed 0.10 we read $t = 1.316$.
   (b) From the row with df = 30 and the column headed 0.05 we read $t = 1.697$.
   (c) From the row with df = 18 and the column headed 0.01 we read $t = 2.552$. By symmetry, the t-value with an area to the **left** of 0.01 is $t = -2.552$.
   (d) For a 90% confidence interval we want the t-value with an area in the right tail of 0.05. With df = 20 we read from the tables that $t = 1.725$.

3. (a) For 96% confidence, $\alpha/2 = 0.02$. If $n = 25$, then df = 24. The critical value is $t_{0.02} = 2.172$. Then:

$$\text{Lower bound} = \bar{x} - t_{0.02} \cdot \frac{s}{\sqrt{n}} = 108 - 2.172 \cdot \frac{10}{\sqrt{25}} = 108 - 4.344 = 103.656 \text{ or } 103.7.$$

$$\text{Upper bound} = \bar{x} + t_{0.02} \cdot \frac{s}{\sqrt{n}} = 108 + 2.172 \cdot \frac{10}{\sqrt{25}} = 108 + 4.344 = 112.344 \text{ or } 112.3.$$

   (b) If $n = 10$, then df = 9. The critical value is $t_{0.02} = 2.398$. Then:

$$\text{Lower bound} = \bar{x} - t_{0.02} \cdot \frac{s}{\sqrt{n}} = 108 - 2.398 \cdot \frac{10}{\sqrt{10}} = 108 - 7.583 = 100.417 \text{ or } 100.4.$$

$$\text{Upper bound} = \bar{x} + t_{0.02} \cdot \frac{s}{\sqrt{n}} = 108 + 2.398 \cdot \frac{10}{\sqrt{10}} = 108 + 7.583 = 115.583 \text{ or } 115.6.$$

Decreasing the sample size increases the margin of error.

(c) For 90% confidence, $\alpha/2 = 0.05$. With 24 df, $t_{0.02} = 1.711$. Then:

Lower bound $= \bar{x} - t_{0.02} \cdot \dfrac{s}{\sqrt{n}} = 108 - 1.711 \cdot \dfrac{10}{\sqrt{25}} = 108 - 3.422 = 104.578$ or 104.6.

Upper bound $= \bar{x} + t_{0.02} \cdot \dfrac{s}{\sqrt{n}} = 108 + 1.711 \cdot \dfrac{10}{\sqrt{25}} = 108 + 3.422 = 111.422$ or 111.4.

Decreasing the level of confidence decreases the margin of error.

(d) No, because in all cases the sample was small ($n < 30$) and so the population must be normally distributed.

5. **(a)** For 95% confidence, $\alpha/2 = 0.025$. If $n = 35$, then df = 34. The critical value is $t_{0.025} = 2.032$. Then:

Lower bound $= \bar{x} - t_{0.025} \cdot \dfrac{s}{\sqrt{n}} = 18.4 - 2.032 \cdot \dfrac{4.5}{\sqrt{35}} = 18.4 - 1.546 = 16.854$ or 16.85.

Upper bound $= \bar{x} + t_{0.025} \cdot \dfrac{s}{\sqrt{n}} = 18.4 + 2.032 \cdot \dfrac{4.5}{\sqrt{35}} = 18.4 + 1.546 = 19.946$ or 19.95.

(b) If $n = 50$, then df = 49, but as there is no row in the tables for 49 df we use df = 50 instead. The critical value is $t_{0.025} = 2.009$. Then:

Lower bound $= \bar{x} - t_{0.025} \cdot \dfrac{s}{\sqrt{n}} = 18.4 - 2.009 \cdot \dfrac{4.5}{\sqrt{50}} = 18.4 - 1.279 = 17.121$ or 17.12.

Upper bound $= \bar{x} + t_{0.025} \cdot \dfrac{s}{\sqrt{n}} = 18.4 + 2.009 \cdot \dfrac{4.5}{\sqrt{50}} = 18.4 + 1.279 = 19.679$ or 19.68.

Increasing the sample size decreases the margin of error.

(c) For 99% confidence, $\alpha/2 = 0.005$. With 34 df, $t_{0.005} = 2.728$. Then:

Lower bound $= \bar{x} - t_{0.005} \cdot \dfrac{s}{\sqrt{n}} = 18.4 - 2.728 \cdot \dfrac{4.5}{\sqrt{35}} = 18.4 - 2.075 = 16.325$ or 16.33.

Upper bound $= \bar{x} + t_{0.005} \cdot \dfrac{s}{\sqrt{n}} = 18.4 + 2.728 \cdot \dfrac{4.5}{\sqrt{35}} = 18.4 + 2.075 = 20.475$ or 20.48.

Increasing the level of confidence increases the margin of error.

(d) For a small sample, the population must be normally distributed.

8.2 Exercises: Applying the Concepts

7. For a 99% confidence interval with 1030 df we use 1000 df and so $t_{.005} = 2.581$.

Lower bound $= \bar{x} - t_{0.005} \cdot \dfrac{s}{\sqrt{n}} = 6.9 - 2.581 \cdot \dfrac{2.8}{\sqrt{1031}} = 6.9 - 0.225 = 6.675$ or 6.68.

Upper bound $= \bar{x} + t_{0.005} \cdot \dfrac{s}{\sqrt{n}} = 6.9 + 2.581 \cdot \dfrac{2.8}{\sqrt{1031}} = 6.9 + 0.225 = 7.125$ or 7.13.

We are 99% confident that the true mean number of times an American bathed per week in 1999 was between 6.68 and 7.13.

9. For a 95% confidence interval with 1030 df we use 1000 df and so $t_{.025} = 1.962$.

Lower bound $= \bar{x} - t_{0.025} \cdot \dfrac{s}{\sqrt{n}} = 3.4 - 1.962 \cdot \dfrac{1.8}{\sqrt{1031}} = 3.4 - 0.110 = 3.29$.

Upper bound $= \bar{x} + t_{0.025} \cdot \dfrac{s}{\sqrt{n}} = 3.4 + 1.962 \cdot \dfrac{1.8}{\sqrt{1031}} = 3.4 + 0.110 = 3.51$.

We are 95% confident that the true mean hours per week of television watched by Americans in 1999 was between 3.29 and 3.51.

11. Using technology, $\bar{x} = 15.92$ and $s = 7.38$. There are $n = 33$ data points. For a 99% confidence interval (with 32 df) we use $t_{0.005} = 2.738$.

Lower bound $= \bar{x} - t_{0.005} \cdot \dfrac{s}{\sqrt{n}} = 15.92 - 2.738 \cdot \dfrac{7.38}{\sqrt{33}} = 15.92 - 3.52 = 12.40$.

Upper bound $= \bar{x} + t_{0.005} \cdot \dfrac{s}{\sqrt{n}} = 15.92 + 2.738 \cdot \dfrac{7.38}{\sqrt{33}} = 15.92 + 3.52 = 19.44$.

We are 99% confident that the true mean concentration of dissolved organic carbon in organic soil is between 12.40 and 19.44 mg/l.

13. (a) The plotted points are all within the bounds of the normal probability plot, which also has a generally linear pattern. The boxplot shows that there are no outliers. A *t*-interval can be constructed.

(b) Using technology, $\bar{x} = 3.036$ and $s = 0.0414$. There are $n = 15$ data points. For a 90% confidence interval (with 14 df) we use $t_{0.05} = 1.761$.

Lower bound $= \bar{x} - t_{0.05} \cdot \dfrac{s}{\sqrt{n}} = 3.036 - 1.761 \cdot \dfrac{0.0414}{\sqrt{15}} = 3.036 - 0.0188 = 3.017$.

Upper bound $= \bar{x} + t_{0.05} \cdot \dfrac{s}{\sqrt{n}} = 3.036 + 1.761 \cdot \dfrac{0.0414}{\sqrt{15}} = 3.036 + 0.0188 = 3.055$.

(c) For a more accurate interval we could increase the sample size.

15. (a) The plotted points are all within the bounds of the normal probability plot, which also has a generally linear pattern. The boxplot shows that there are no outliers. A *t*-interval can be constructed.

(b) Using technology, $\bar{x} = 203.93$ and $s = 18.32$. There are $n = 25$ data points. For a 95% confidence interval (with 24 df) we use $t_{0.025} = 2.064$.

Lower bound $= \bar{x} - t_{0.05} \cdot \dfrac{s}{\sqrt{n}} = 203.93 - 2.064 \cdot \dfrac{18.32}{\sqrt{25}} = 203.93 - 7.56 = 196.37$.

Upper bound $= \bar{x} + t_{0.05} \cdot \dfrac{s}{\sqrt{n}} = 203.93 + 2.064 \cdot \dfrac{18.32}{\sqrt{25}} = 203.93 + 7.56 = 211.49$.

17. (a) The plotted points are all within the bounds of the normal probability plots, which also have a generally linear pattern. The boxplot shows that there are no outliers for either airline. t-intervals can be constructed.

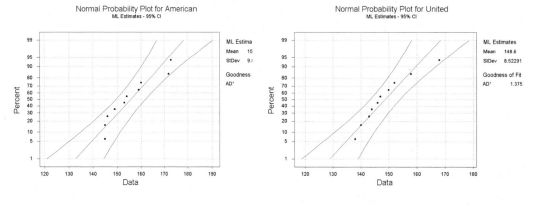

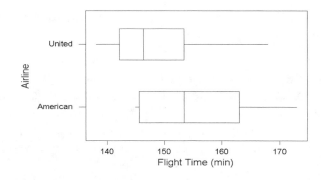

(b) There are $n = 10$ data points for each airline. For a 95% confidence interval (with 9 df) we use $t_{0.025} = 2.262$. For American Airlines, $\bar{x} = 155.6$ and $s = 10.39$ and we get:

Lower bound $= \bar{x} - t_{0.025} \cdot \dfrac{s}{\sqrt{n}} = 155.6 - 2.262 \cdot \dfrac{10.39}{\sqrt{10}} = 155.6 - 7.4 = 148.2$.

Upper bound $= \bar{x} + t_{0.025} \cdot \dfrac{s}{\sqrt{n}} = 155.6 + 2.262 \cdot \dfrac{10.39}{\sqrt{10}} = 155.6 + 7.4 = 163.0$.

For United Airlines, $\bar{x} = 148.6$ and $s = 8.98$ and we get:

Lower bound $= \bar{x} - t_{0.025} \cdot \dfrac{s}{\sqrt{n}} = 148.6 - 2.262 \cdot \dfrac{8.98}{\sqrt{10}} = 148.6 - 6.4 = 142.2$.

Upper bound $= \bar{x} + t_{0.025} \cdot \dfrac{s}{\sqrt{n}} = 148.6 + 2.262 \cdot \dfrac{8.98}{\sqrt{10}} = 148.6 + 6.4 = 155.0$.

(c) Although the sample mean flight time is higher for American than for United, since the confidence intervals overlap, we cannot conclude that there is a difference in the true mean flight times.

19. Since the data comes from a normal distribution and σ is known, we can compute a z-interval, using $z_{.025} = 1.960$. The data give $n = 15$ and $\bar{x} = 69.853$.

Lower bound $= \bar{x} - z_{0.025} \cdot \dfrac{\sigma}{\sqrt{n}} = 69.853 - 1.960 \cdot \dfrac{2.9}{\sqrt{15}} = 69.853 - 1.468 = 68.39$.

Upper bound $= \bar{x} + z_{0.025} \cdot \dfrac{\sigma}{\sqrt{n}} = 69.853 + 1.960 \cdot \dfrac{2.9}{\sqrt{15}} = 69.853 + 1.468 = 71.32$.

21. A normal probability plot shows that the data are not normal and so we cannot compute a confidence interval.

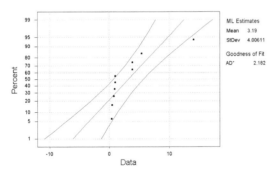

23. A normal probability plot and boxplot show that the data are normal with no outliers.

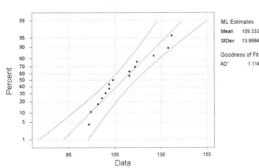
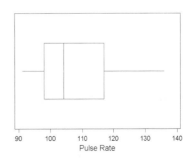

Since σ is unknown we compute a t-interval. The data give $n = 15$, $\bar{x} = 109.333$ and $s = 14.376$. With 14 df we use $t_{.025} = 2.145$.

Lower bound $= \bar{x} - t_{0.025} \cdot \dfrac{s}{\sqrt{n}} = 109.333 - 2.145 \cdot \dfrac{14.376}{\sqrt{15}} = 109.333 - 7.962 = 101.4$.

Upper bound

$$= \bar{x} + t_{0.025} \cdot \frac{s}{\sqrt{n}} = 109.333 + 2.145 \cdot \frac{14.376}{\sqrt{15}} = 109.333 + 7.962 = 117.3.$$

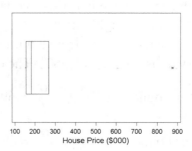

25. (a) The outlier is the house price of $875,000, as verified by the boxplot.

(b) The data give $n = 12$, $\bar{x} = \$253,733$ and $s = \$201,296$. We compute a t-interval. With 11 df for 99% confidence we use $t_{.005} = 3.106$.

Lower bound

$$= \bar{x} - t_{0.005} \cdot \frac{s}{\sqrt{n}} = 253,733 - 3.106 \cdot \frac{201,296}{\sqrt{12}} = 253,733 - 180,487 = \$73,246.$$

Upper bound

$$= \bar{x} + t_{0.005} \cdot \frac{s}{\sqrt{n}} = 253,733 + 3.106 \cdot \frac{201,296}{\sqrt{12}} = 253,733 + 180,487 = \$434,220.$$

(c) With the outlier removed, the data give $n = 11$, $\bar{x} = \$197,254.5$ and $s = \$49,658.4$. We compute a t-interval. With 10 df for 99% confidence we use $t_{.005} = 3.169$.

Lower bound

$$= \bar{x} - t_{0.005} \cdot \frac{s}{\sqrt{n}} = 197,254.5 - 3.169 \cdot \frac{49,658.4}{\sqrt{11}} = 197,254.5 - 47,448.1 = \$149,806.$$

Upper bound

$$= \bar{x} + t_{0.005} \cdot \frac{s}{\sqrt{n}} = 197,254.5 + 3.169 \cdot \frac{49,658.4}{\sqrt{11}} = 197,254.5 + 47,448.1 = \$244,703.$$

(d) The outlier affects both the sample mean and the sample standard deviation, resulting in a confidence interval that is much wider and is centered at a higher value.

27. (a), (b), (c) Answers will vary.
(d) We would expect approximately 95% of the 20 samples, or 19 samples, to generate confidence intervals that include the population mean. Actual results will vary.

29. Answers will vary.

8.3 Confidence Intervals about a Population Proportion

8.3 Concepts and Vocabulary

1. The best point estimate of the population proportion is the sample proportion.

3. By using a prior estimate of p the researcher will get a better estimate of the required sample size, which will be smaller than the "worst-case" sample size given by using no prior estimate of p.

8.3 Exercises: Basic Skills

1. $\hat{p} = \dfrac{x}{n} = \dfrac{30}{150} = 0.20$

   For 90% confidence, $z_{\alpha/2} = z_{.05} = 1.645$

   Lower bound $= \hat{p} - z_{.05} \cdot \sqrt{\dfrac{\hat{p}(1-\hat{p})}{n}} = 0.20 - 1.645 \cdot \sqrt{\dfrac{0.2(1-0.2)}{150}} = 0.20 - 0.054 = 0.146$

   Upper bound $= \hat{p} + z_{.05} \cdot \sqrt{\dfrac{\hat{p}(1-\hat{p})}{n}} = 0.20 + 1.645 \cdot \sqrt{\dfrac{0.2(1-0.2)}{150}} = 0.20 + 0.054 = 0.254$

3. $\hat{p} = \dfrac{x}{n} = \dfrac{120}{500} = 0.240$

   For 99% confidence, $z_{\alpha/2} = z_{.005} = 2.575$

   Lower bound

   $= \hat{p} - z_{.005} \cdot \sqrt{\dfrac{\hat{p}(1-\hat{p})}{n}} = 0.240 - 2.575 \cdot \sqrt{\dfrac{0.24(1-0.24)}{500}} = 0.240 - 0.049 = 0.191$

   Upper bound

   $= \hat{p} + z_{.005} \cdot \sqrt{\dfrac{\hat{p}(1-\hat{p})}{n}} = 0.240 + 2.575 \cdot \sqrt{\dfrac{0.24(1-0.24)}{500}} = 0.240 + 0.049 = 0.289$

5. $\hat{p} = \dfrac{x}{n} = \dfrac{860}{1100} = 0.7818$

   For 94% confidence, $z_{\alpha/2} = z_{.03} = 1.88$

   Lower bound

   $= \hat{p} - z_{.03} \cdot \sqrt{\dfrac{\hat{p}(1-\hat{p})}{n}} = 0.7818 - 1.88 \cdot \sqrt{\dfrac{0.7818(1-0.7818)}{1100}} = 0.7818 - 0.0234 = 0.758$

Upper bound

$$= \hat{p} + z_{.03} \cdot \sqrt{\frac{\hat{p}(1-\hat{p})}{n}} = 0.7818 + 1.88 \cdot \sqrt{\frac{0.7818(1-0.7818)}{1100}} = 0.7818 + 0.0234 = 0.805$$

8.3 Exercises: Applying the Concepts

7. (a) $\hat{p} = \frac{x}{n} = \frac{47}{863} = 0.05446$ or .054.

(b) $n\hat{p}(1-\hat{p}) = 863 \cdot 0.054 \cdot (1-0.054) = 44 \geq 10$.

(c) For 90% confidence, $z_{\alpha/2} = z_{.05} = 1.645$.

Lower bound

$$= \hat{p} - z_{.05} \cdot \sqrt{\frac{\hat{p}(1-\hat{p})}{n}} = 0.0545 - 1.645 \cdot \sqrt{\frac{0.0545(1-0.0545)}{863}} = 0.0545 - 0.0127 = 0.042$$

Upper bound $= \hat{p} + E = 0.0545 + 0.0127 = 0.067$

(d) We are 90% confident that the true population percentage of Lipitor users who will experience headaches as a side effect is between 4.2% and 6.7%.

9. (a) $\hat{p} = \frac{x}{n} = \frac{230}{1000} = 0.23$.

(b) $n\hat{p}(1-\hat{p}) = 1000 \cdot 0.23 \cdot (1-0.23) = 177.1 \geq 10$.

(c) For 98% confidence, $z_{\alpha/2} = z_{.01} = 2.33$.

Lower bound

$$= \hat{p} - z_{.01} \cdot \sqrt{\frac{\hat{p}(1-\hat{p})}{n}} = 0.23 - 2.33 \cdot \sqrt{\frac{0.23(1-0.23)}{1000}} = 0.230 - 0.031 = 0.199$$

Upper bound $= \hat{p} + E = 0.230 + 0.031 = 0.261$

(d) We are 98% confident that the true population percentage of adults who know some-one capable of committing an act of violence in their workplace is between 19.9% and 26.1%.

11. (a) $n\hat{p}(1-\hat{p}) = 10,847 \cdot \left(\frac{5,988}{10,847}\right) \cdot \left(1 - \frac{5,988}{10,847}\right) = 2,682 \geq 10$.

(b) $\hat{p} = \frac{x}{n} = \frac{5,988}{10,847} = 0.5520$.

For 90% confidence, $z_{\alpha/2} = z_{.05} = 1.645$.

Lower bound

$$= \hat{p} - z_{.05} \cdot \sqrt{\frac{\hat{p}(1-\hat{p})}{n}} = 0.552 - 1.645 \cdot \sqrt{\frac{0.552(1-0.552)}{10,847}} = 0.5520 - 0.0079 = 0.544$$

Upper bound $= \hat{p} + E = 0.5520 + 0.0079 = 0.560$

We are 90% confident that the true population percentage of women having a child during 1990–93 who breast-fed their baby is between 54.4% and 56.0%.

(c) For 99% confidence, $z_{\alpha/2} = z_{.005} = 2.575$.

Lower bound

$$= \hat{p} - z_{.005} \cdot \sqrt{\frac{\hat{p}(1-\hat{p})}{n}} = 0.552 - 2.575 \cdot \sqrt{\frac{0.552(1-0.552)}{10,847}} = 0.5520 - 0.0123 = 0.540$$

Upper bound $= \hat{p} + E = 0.5520 + 0.0123 = 0.564$

We are 99% confident that the true population percentage of women having a child during 1990–93 who breast-fed their baby is between 54.0% and 56.4%.

(d) Increasing the level of confidence increases the width of the interval.

13. (a) $\hat{p} = \dfrac{x}{n} = \dfrac{1,950}{10,485} = 0.1860$.

For 95% confidence, $z_{\alpha/2} = z_{.025} = 1.96$.

Lower bound

$$= \hat{p} - z_{.025} \cdot \sqrt{\frac{\hat{p}(1-\hat{p})}{n}} = 0.186 - 1.96 \cdot \sqrt{\frac{0.186(1-0.186)}{10,485}} = 0.186 - 0.007 = 0.179$$

Upper bound $= \hat{p} + E = 0.186 + 0.007 = 0.193$

We are 95% confident that the true population percentage of 30–39-year-old Americans who were obese in 1999 is between 17.9% and 19.3%.

(b) $\hat{p} = \dfrac{x}{n} = \dfrac{1,937}{11,464} = 0.1690$.

For 95% confidence, $z_{\alpha/2} = z_{.025} = 1.96$.

Lower bound

$$= \hat{p} - z_{.025} \cdot \sqrt{\frac{\hat{p}(1-\hat{p})}{n}} = 0.169 - 1.96 \cdot \sqrt{\frac{0.169(1-0.169)}{11,464}} = 0.169 - 0.007 = 0.162$$

Upper bound $= \hat{p} + E = 0.169 + 0.007 = 0.176$

We are 95% confident that the true population percentage of 30-39-year-old Americans who were obese in 1998 is between 16.2% and 17.6%.

(c) Since the confidence intervals do not overlap, it does appear that the percentage of obese 30-39-year-old Americans increased between 1998 and 1999.

15. (a) $n = \hat{p}(1-\hat{p}) \left(\dfrac{z_{\alpha/2}}{E} \right)^2 = 0.185(1-0.185) \left(\dfrac{2.575}{.03} \right)^2 = 1110.8$ which we round up to 1111.

(b) $n = 0.25 \left(\dfrac{z_{\alpha/2}}{E} \right)^2 = 0.25 \left(\dfrac{2.575}{.03} \right)^2 = 1841.8$ which we round up to 1842.

17. (a) $n = \hat{p}(1-\hat{p})\left(\dfrac{z_{\alpha/2}}{E}\right)^2 = 0.80(1-0.80)\left(\dfrac{1.96}{.03}\right)^2 = 682.95$ which we round up to 683.

   (b) $n = 0.25\left(\dfrac{z_{\alpha/2}}{E}\right)^2 = 0.25\left(\dfrac{1.96}{.03}\right)^2 = 1067.1$ which we round up to 1068.

19. (a) $n = \hat{p}(1-\hat{p})\left(\dfrac{z_{\alpha/2}}{E}\right)^2 = 0.07(1-0.07)\left(\dfrac{2.33}{.015}\right)^2 = 1570.8$ which we round up to 1571.

   (Note: using $z_{.01} = 2.326$, from the t-tables gives a sample size of 1565.4 or 1566.)

   (b) $n = 0.25\left(\dfrac{z_{\alpha/2}}{E}\right)^2 = 0.25\left(\dfrac{2.33}{.015}\right)^2 = 6032.1$ which we round up to 6033. (Note: using

   $z_{.01} = 2.326$, from the t-tables gives a sample size of 6011.4 or 6012.)

21. $n = \hat{p}(1-\hat{p})\left(\dfrac{z_{\alpha/2}}{E}\right)^2 = 0.64(1-0.64)\left(\dfrac{1.96}{.03}\right)^2 = 983.4$ which we round up to 984.

23. (a)–(d) Answers will vary.

   (e) $\mu_{\hat{p}} = p = 0.3$ and $\sigma_{\hat{p}} = \sqrt{\dfrac{p(1-p)}{n}} = \sqrt{\dfrac{0.3(1-0.3)}{765}} = 0.0166$. Actual results will vary.

   (f) If we compute 2000 95% confidence intervals then we would expect approximately 95% of them, i.e. 1900 of them to contain p. Actual results will vary.

25. (a) $\hat{p} = \dfrac{x}{n} = \dfrac{410}{500} = 0.82$

   (b) $\sigma_{\hat{p}} = \sqrt{\dfrac{\hat{p}(1-\hat{p})}{n-1}\cdot\left(\dfrac{N-n}{N}\right)} = \sqrt{\dfrac{0.82(1-0.82)}{500-1}\cdot\left(\dfrac{6502-500}{6502}\right)} = 0.0165$

   (c) Lower bound $= 0.82 - 1.96 \cdot 0.017 = 0.82 - 0.033 = 0.787$
   Upper bound $= 0.82 + 0.033 = 0.853$.
   We are 95% confident that the true percentage of all students favoring a student union is between 78.7% and 85.3%.

Review Exercises

1. For a 99% confidence interval we want the t-value with an area in the right tail of 0.005. With df = 17 we read from the tables that $t = 2.898$.

3. (a) For 90% confidence the critical value is $z_{0.05} = 1.645$. Then:

$$\text{Lower bound} = \bar{x} - z_{0.05} \cdot \frac{\sigma}{\sqrt{n}} = 54.8 - 1.645 \cdot \frac{10.5}{\sqrt{20}} = 54.8 - 3.86 = 50.94$$

$$\text{Upper bound} = \bar{x} + z_{0.05} \cdot \frac{\sigma}{\sqrt{n}} = 54.8 + 1.645 \cdot \frac{10.5}{\sqrt{20}} = 54.8 + 3.86 = 58.66 \,.$$

(b) $$\text{Lower bound} = \bar{x} - z_{0.05} \cdot \frac{\sigma}{\sqrt{n}} = 54.8 - 1.645 \cdot \frac{10.5}{\sqrt{30}} = 54.8 - 3.15 = 51.65$$

$$\text{Upper bound} = \bar{x} + z_{0.05} \cdot \frac{\sigma}{\sqrt{n}} = 54.8 + 1.645 \cdot \frac{10.5}{\sqrt{30}} = 54.8 + 3.15 = 57.95 \,.$$

Increasing the sample size decreases the width of the confidence interval.

(c) For 99% confidence the critical value is $z_{0.005} = 2.575$. Then:

$$\text{Lower bound} = \bar{x} - z_{0.05} \cdot \frac{\sigma}{\sqrt{n}} = 54.8 - 2.575 \cdot \frac{10.5}{\sqrt{20}} = 54.8 - 6.05 = 48.75$$

$$\text{Upper bound} = \bar{x} + z_{0.05} \cdot \frac{\sigma}{\sqrt{n}} = 54.8 + 2.575 \cdot \frac{10.5}{\sqrt{20}} = 54.8 + 6.05 = 60.85 \,.$$

Increasing the level of confidence increases the width of the confidence interval.

5. **(a)** Because this is a large sample ($n \geq 30$).

(b) For 90% confidence the critical value is $z_{0.05} = 1.645$. Then:

$$\text{Lower bound} = \bar{x} - z_{0.05} \cdot \frac{\sigma}{\sqrt{n}} = 62,450 - 1.645 \cdot \frac{4400}{\sqrt{35}} = 62,450 - 1,223 = 61,227$$

$$\text{Upper bound} = \bar{x} + z_{0.05} \cdot \frac{\sigma}{\sqrt{n}} = 62,450 + 1.645 \cdot \frac{4400}{\sqrt{35}} = 62,450 + 1,223 = 63,673 \,.$$

We are 95% confident that the true mean mileage for SP4000 tires is between 61,227 and 63,673 miles.

(c) For a 95% confidence interval we use $z_{.025} = 1.96$.

$$\text{Lower bound} = \bar{x} - z_{0.025} \cdot \frac{\sigma}{\sqrt{n}} = 62,450 - 1.96 \cdot \frac{4400}{\sqrt{35}} = 62,450 - 1,458 = 60,992$$

$$\text{Upper bound} = \bar{x} + z_{0.025} \cdot \frac{\sigma}{\sqrt{n}} = 62,450 + 1.96 \cdot \frac{4400}{\sqrt{35}} = 62,450 + 1,458 = 63,908 \,.$$

We are 95% confident that the true mean mileage for SP4000 tires is between 60,992 and 63,908 miles.

(d) For 99% confidence, we use $z_{.005} = 2.575$. Then the required sample size is

$$n = \left(\frac{z_{\alpha/2} \cdot \sigma}{E} \right)^2 = \left(\frac{2.575 \cdot 4400}{3000} \right)^2 = 14.3 \text{ which we round up to 15 tires.}$$

7 . (a) The plotted points are generally linear and stay within the bounds of the normal probability plots. The boxplots show that there are no outliers.

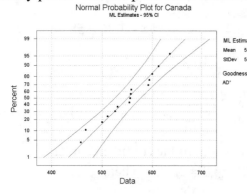

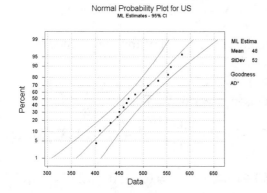

(b) Technology gives us the point estimates:
$\bar{x} = 550.4$ (Canada) and $\bar{x} = 483.5$ (United States).

(c) For a 99% confidence interval for Canada, σ known, we use $z_{.005} = 2.575$.

$$\text{Lower bound} = \bar{x} - z_{0.005} \cdot \frac{\sigma}{\sqrt{n}} = 550.4 - 2.575 \cdot \frac{62.6}{\sqrt{15}} = 550.4 - 41.6 = 508.8.$$

$$\text{Upper bound} = \bar{x} + z_{0.005} \cdot \frac{\sigma}{\sqrt{n}} = 550.4 + 2.575 \cdot \frac{62.6}{\sqrt{15}} = 550.4 + 41.6 = 592.0.$$

(d) For the United States we get (again using $z_{.005} = 2.575$):

$$\text{Lower bound} = \bar{x} - z_{0.005} \cdot \frac{\sigma}{\sqrt{n}} = 483.5 - 2.575 \cdot \frac{71.5}{\sqrt{15}} = 483.5 - 47.5 = 436.0.$$

$$\text{Upper bound} = \bar{x} + z_{0.005} \cdot \frac{\sigma}{\sqrt{n}} = 483.5 + 2.575 \cdot \frac{71.5}{\sqrt{15}} = 483.5 + 47.5 = 531.0.$$

(e) Since the two intervals overlap, we cannot conclude that the Canadian average is higher than the American.

9. (a) Since the sample size is large ($n \geq 30$), $\bar{x}$ has a distribution that is approximately normal. If the population mean number of children (of all married couples who have been married seven years) is μ and the population standard deviation is σ, then the sampling distribution of $\bar{x}$ has mean μ and standard deviation $\dfrac{\sigma}{\sqrt{60}}$.

(b) Since σ is unknown, but $n \geq 30$, we compute a t-interval. Df = 59, but we use df = 60 (the closest to 59 df in our tables). Then the critical value for a 95% confidence interval (the t-value with an area in the right tail of 0.025) is $t = 2.000$. Then:

$$\text{Lower bound} = \bar{x} - t_{0.025} \cdot \frac{s}{\sqrt{n}} = 2.27 - 2.000 \cdot \frac{1.22}{\sqrt{60}} = 2.27 - 0.315 = 1.96.$$

$$\text{Upper bound} = \bar{x} + t_{0.025} \cdot \frac{s}{\sqrt{n}} = 2.27 + 2.000 \cdot \frac{1.22}{\sqrt{60}} = 2.27 + 0.315 = 2.59.$$

We are 95% confident that the true mean number of children for couples who have been married seven years is between 1.96 and 2.59.

(c) The critical value for a 99% confidence interval and 60 df is $t = 2.632$. Then:

$$\text{Lower bound} = \bar{x} - t_{0.005} \cdot \frac{s}{\sqrt{n}} = 2.27 - 2.632 \cdot \frac{1.22}{\sqrt{60}} = 2.27 - 0.41 = 1.86.$$

$$\text{Upper bound} = \bar{x} + t_{0.005} \cdot \frac{s}{\sqrt{n}} = 2.27 + 2.632 \cdot \frac{1.22}{\sqrt{60}} = 2.27 + 0.41 = 2.68.$$

We are 99% confident that the true mean number of children for couples who have been married seven years is between 1.86 and 2.68.

11. (a) Using technology we get $\bar{x} = 3.243$ and $s = 0.487$.

(b) The plotted points are generally linear and stay within the bounds of the normal probability plot. The boxplot shows that there are no outliers.

(c) Since σ is unknown, but the data are normal, we compute a t-interval. Df = 11 and so the critical value for a 95% confidence interval is $t = 2.201$. Then:

$$\text{Lower bound} = \bar{x} - t_{0.025} \cdot \frac{s}{\sqrt{n}} = 3.243 - 2.201 \cdot \frac{0.487}{\sqrt{12}} = 3.243 - 0.309 = 2.934.$$

$$\text{Upper bound} = \bar{x} + t_{0.025} \cdot \frac{s}{\sqrt{n}} = 3.243 + 2.201 \cdot \frac{0.487}{\sqrt{12}} = 3.243 + 0.309 = 3.552.$$

We are 95% confident that the true population mean blood plasma volume is between 2.934 and 3.552 liters.

(d) The critical value for a 99% confidence interval and 11 df is $t = 3.106$. Then:

$$\text{Lower bound} = \bar{x} - t_{0.005} \cdot \frac{s}{\sqrt{n}} = 3.243 - 3.106 \cdot \frac{0.487}{\sqrt{12}} = 3.243 - 0.437 = 2.806.$$

$$\text{Upper bound} = \bar{x} + t_{0.005} \cdot \frac{s}{\sqrt{n}} = 3.243 + 3.106 \cdot \frac{0.487}{\sqrt{12}} = 3.243 + 0.437 = 3.680.$$

We are 99% confident that the true population mean blood plasma volume is between 2.806 and 3.680 liters.

13. (c) For a 99% confidence interval for Canada, σ unknown, and 14 df, we use $t_{.005} = 2.977$. We have $\bar{x} = 550.4$ and $s = 52.2$.

Lower bound $= \bar{x} - t_{0.005} \cdot \dfrac{\sigma}{\sqrt{n}} = 550.4 - 2.977 \cdot \dfrac{52.2}{\sqrt{15}} = 550.4 - 40.1 = 510.3$.

Upper bound $= \bar{x} + t_{0.005} \cdot \dfrac{\sigma}{\sqrt{n}} = 550.4 + 2.977 \cdot \dfrac{52.2}{\sqrt{15}} = 550.4 + 40.1 = 590.5$.

(d) For the United States we have $\bar{x} = 483.5$ and $s = 54.8$. Using $t_{.005} = 2.977$:

Lower bound $= \bar{x} - t_{0.005} \cdot \dfrac{\sigma}{\sqrt{n}} = 483.5 - 2.977 \cdot \dfrac{54.8}{\sqrt{15}} = 483.5 - 42.1 = 441.4$.

Upper bound $= \bar{x} + t_{0.005} \cdot \dfrac{\sigma}{\sqrt{n}} = 483.5 + 2.977 \cdot \dfrac{54.8}{\sqrt{15}} = 483.5 + 42.1 = 525.6$.

(e) Since the two intervals overlap, we cannot conclude that the Canadian average is higher than the American.

15. (a) $\hat{p} = \dfrac{x}{n} = \dfrac{58}{678} = 0.0855$.

(b) For 95% confidence, $z_{\alpha/2} = z_{.025} = 1.96$.

Lower bound

$= \hat{p} - z_{.025} \cdot \sqrt{\dfrac{\hat{p}(1-\hat{p})}{n}} = 0.086 - 1.96 \cdot \sqrt{\dfrac{0.086(1-0.086)}{678}} = 0.086 - 0.021 = 0.065$

Upper bound $= \hat{p} + E = 0.086 + 0.021 = 0.107$

We are 95% confident that the true population percentage of adult males aged 20–34 years who have hypertension is between 6.5% and 10.7%.

(c) $n = \hat{p}(1-\hat{p})\left(\dfrac{z_{\alpha/2}}{E}\right)^2 = 0.086(1-0.086)\left(\dfrac{1.96}{.03}\right)^2 = 335.5$ which we round up to 336.

(d) $n = 0.25\left(\dfrac{z_{\alpha/2}}{E}\right)^2 = 0.25\left(\dfrac{1.96}{.03}\right)^2 = 1067.1$ which we round up to 1068.

17. Also 0.0681, because the t-distribution is symmetric.

19. The t-distribution varies according to the sample size, n, but all t-distributions are centered at 0 and symmetric about 0. The area in the tails of a t-distribution is greater than the area in the tails of a standard normal distribution, but as the sample size increases, the t-distribution approaches a standard normal density curve. For all t-distributions, as t approaches either $+\infty$ or $-\infty$, the density curve approaches, but never equals, zero.

Chapter 9. Hypothesis Testing

9.1 The Language of Hypothesis Testing

9.1 Concepts and Vocabulary

1. A Type I error is the error of rejecting H_0 when in fact H_0 is true. A Type II error is the error of **not** rejecting H_0 when in fact H_1 is true.

3. As α decreases, so β increases. As we decrease α = the probability of incorrectly rejecting H_0, we are effectively making it less likely that we will reject H_0 (since we require stronger evidence against H_0 as α decreases). This means that it is also more likely that we will fail to reject H_0 when H_1 is really true, and so β increases.

5. In a hypothesis test we make a judgement about the validity of a hypothesis based on the available data. If the data contradicts H_0 then we reject H_0. However, if the available data do not contradict H_0, this does not guarantee that H_0 is true.

9.1 Exercises: Basic Skills

1. Parameter $= \mu$. Right-tailed since $H_1 : \mu > 5$

3. Parameter $= \sigma$. Two-tailed since $H_1 : \sigma \neq 4.2$

5. Parameter $= \mu$. Left-tailed since $H_1 : \mu > 120$

7. **(a)** $H_0 : \mu = \$89\,/\text{acre}$, $H_1 : \mu < \$89\,/\text{acre}$
   (b) Type I error: concluding that the mean farm rent in Indiana **has** decreased from $89/acre when in fact it **has not**.
   (c) Type II error: concluding that the mean farm rent in Indiana **has not** decreased from $89/acre when in fact it **has**.

9. **(a)** $H_0 : p = 0.163$, $H_1 : \mu < 0.163$
   (b) Type I error: concluding that the percentage of Americans without health insurance **has** decreased since 1998 when in fact it **has not**.
   (c) Type II error: concluding that the percentage of Americans without health insurance **has not** decreased since 1998 when in fact it **has**.

168 Chapter 9 Hypothesis Testing

11. (a) $H_0 : \mu = \$1338$, $H_1 : \mu \neq \$1338$

    (b) Type I error: concluding that the mean expenditure for residential energy is no longer $1338 when in fact it is still $1338.

    (c) Type II error: concluding that the mean expenditure for residential energy is still $1338 when in fact it is no longer $1338.

13. (a) $H_0 : \sigma = 4.2$, $H_1 : \sigma > 4.2$

    (b) Type I error: concluding that the standard deviation of the monthly return on stocks is higher than 4.2% when in fact it is not.

    (c) Type II error: concluding that the standard deviation of the monthly return on stocks is not higher than 4.2% when in fact it is.

9.1 Exercises: Applying the Concepts

15. There **is** enough evidence to support the claim that the mean farm rent in Indiana has decreased from $89/acre.

17. There **is not** enough evidence to support the claim that the percentage of Americans without health insurance has decreased from 16.3%.

19. There **is not** enough evidence to support the claim that the mean expenditure for residential energy is different from $1338.

21. There **is** enough evidence to support the claim that the standard deviation of monthly return on stocks is higher than 4.2%.

23. There **is not** enough evidence to support the claim that the mean farm rent in Indiana has decreased from $89/acre.

25. There **is** enough evidence to support the claim that the percentage of Americans without health insurance has decreased from 16.3%.

27. (a) $H_0 : \mu = 48.3$, $H_1 : \mu > 48.3$

    (b) There is enough evidence to support the claim that the mean per capita potato consumption is now higher than 48.3 pounds.

    (c) Since H_0 is in fact true, a Type I error has been made. The probability of this $= \alpha = 0.05$.

    (d) To decrease β, we increase α.

29. (a) $H_0 : p = 0.38$, $H_1 : p < 0.38$

(b) There is not enough evidence to support the claim that the proportion of traffic fatalities in which the driver had a BAC of 0.08% or higher is now less than 0.38.

(c) Since H_1 is in fact true, a Type II error has been made.

31. Let $\mu =$ the mean change in gas mileage for cars using the Platinum Gasaver. Then the hypotheses would be $H_0 : \mu = 0$, $H_1 : \mu > 0$.

33. Type I error: concluding that the level of acidity in rain **has** increased when in fact it **has not**. Type II error: concluding that the level of acidity in rain **has not** increased when in fact it **has**. Opinions will vary. If you conclude that a Type I error is more serious than a Type II error, then use a small α, such as $\alpha = 0.01$.

9.2 Testing a Hypothesis about μ, σ Known

9.2 Concepts and Vocabulary

1. The sample must have been obtained using simple random sampling and either the population from which the sample is selected is normally distributed, or the sample size is large ($n \geq 30$).

3. For $\alpha = 0.05$ in a two-tailed test, the critical values are $\pm z_{\alpha/2} = \pm z_{0.025} = \pm 1.96$.

5. The *P*-value is the probability of obtaining sample data at least as extreme as that observed, assuming that the null hypothesis is true. A small *P*-value indicates that the observed data are very unlikely to result from chance variation in samples, and so is evidence that the null hypothesis is not true. More specifically, we will reject the null hypothesis if $P < \alpha$.

7. This indicates that 2% of random samples will give a sample mean as far above or below μ_0 as our observed sample mean, assuming that $\mu = \mu_0$. Since this is an unlikely occurrence, we would probably conclude that our sample data provide strong enough evidence to reject H_0, although this depends on the level of significance that we are using.

9.2 Exercises: Basic Skills

1. (a) $Z = \dfrac{\bar{x} - \mu_0}{\sigma / \sqrt{n}} = \dfrac{47.1 - 50}{12 / \sqrt{24}} = -1.18$

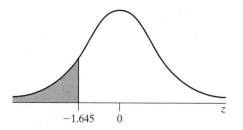

(b) This is a left-tailed test and so the critical value is $-z_{0.05} = -1.645$

(c) The critical region is shaded.

(d) Since the test statistic is not in the critical region, we do not reject the null hypothesis.

3. (a) $Z = \dfrac{\bar{x} - \mu_0}{\sigma / \sqrt{n}} = \dfrac{104.8 - 100}{7 / \sqrt{23}} = 3.29$

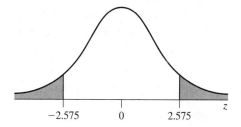

(b) This is a two-tailed test and so the critical values are $\pm z_{0.005} = \pm 2.575$

(c) The critical region is shaded.

(d) Since the test statistic is in the critical region, we reject the null hypothesis.

5. (a) The test statistic is

$$Z = \frac{\bar{x} - \mu_0}{\sigma / \sqrt{n}} = \frac{18.3 - 20}{3 / \sqrt{18}} = -2.40 \,.$$

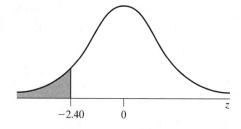

This is a left-tailed test and so the P-value is $P = P(Z < -2.40) = 0.0082$.

About 0.82% of samples will have a sample mean this low, if the population mean is 20.

(b) Since $P = 0.0082 < 0.0500 = \alpha$, we reject the null hypothesis.

7. (a) No, because this sample is large ($n \geq 30$).

(b) The test statistic is

$$Z = \frac{\bar{x} - \mu_0}{\sigma / \sqrt{n}} = \frac{101.2 - 105}{12 / \sqrt{35}} = -1.87. \text{ This is a}$$

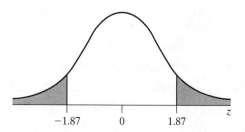

two-tailed test and so the P-value is $P = 2 \cdot P(Z < -1.87) = 2 \cdot 0.0307 = 0.0614$.

About 6.14% of samples will result in a sample mean this extreme, if the population mean is 105.

(c) Since $P = 0.0614 > 0.0200 = \alpha$, we do not reject the null hypothesis.

9.2 Exercises: Applying the Concepts

9. The hypotheses are $H_0 : \mu = 26.4$, $H_1 : \mu > 26.4$.

The test statistic is $Z = \dfrac{\bar{x} - \mu_0}{\sigma / \sqrt{n}} = \dfrac{27.1 - 26.4}{6.4 / \sqrt{40}} = 0.69$.

This is a right-tailed test and so the critical value is $z_{0.05} = 1.645$. Since the test statistic is not in the critical region, we do not reject the null hypothesis. There is not enough evidence to support the claim that the mean age of a woman before she has her first child is greater than 26.4 years.

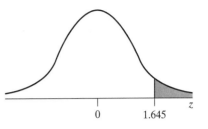

11. **(a)** SAT scores must be normally distributed because this is a small sample ($n < 30$).

(b) The hypotheses are $H_0 : \mu = 516$, $H_1 : \mu < 516$.

The test statistic is $Z = \dfrac{\bar{x} - \mu_0}{\sigma / \sqrt{n}} = \dfrac{458 - 516}{119 / \sqrt{20}} = -2.18$.

This is a left-tailed test and so the critical value is $-z_{0.10} = -1.28$. Since the test statistic is in the critical region, we reject the null hypothesis. There is enough evidence to support the claim that the mean SAT verbal score of students whose first language is not English is lower than 516.

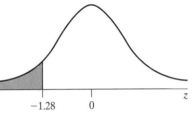

13. **(a)** The plotted points are all within the bounds of the normal probability plot, which also has a generally linear pattern. The boxplot shows that there are no outliers. The conditions for a hypothesis test are satisfied.

(b) The hypotheses are $H_0 : \mu = 5.03$, $H_1 : \mu < 5.03$.

Using technology, $\bar{x} = 4.81$. The test statistic is

$Z = \dfrac{\bar{x} - \mu_0}{\sigma / \sqrt{n}} = \dfrac{4.81 - 5.03}{0.2 / \sqrt{19}} = -4.79$.

This is a left-tailed test and so the critical value is $z_{0.01} = -2.33$. Since the test statistic is in the critical region, we reject the null hypothesis.

There is enough evidence to support the claim that the acidity of the rain has increased (its pH is less than 5.03).

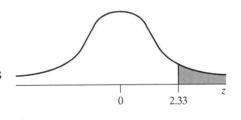

15. **(a)** The plotted points are all within the bounds of the normal probability plot, which also has a generally linear pattern. The boxplot shows that there are no outliers. The conditions for a hypothesis test are satisfied.

(b) The hypotheses are $H_0 : \mu = 64$, $H_1 : \mu \neq 64$. Using technology, $\bar{x} = 63.96$ oz.

The test statistic is $Z = \dfrac{\bar{x} - \mu_0}{\sigma/\sqrt{n}} = \dfrac{63.96 - 64}{0.06/\sqrt{22}} = -3.13$. This is a two-tailed test and so

the critical values are $\pm z_{0.05} = \pm 1.645$. Since the test statistic is in the critical region, we reject the null hypothesis. There is enough evidence to support the claim that the mean amount of juice in each bottle differs from 64 oz.

(c) Yes, the machine needs to be recalibrated.

17. (a) The plotted points are all within the bounds of the normal probability plot, which also has a generally linear pattern. The boxplot shows that there are no outliers. The conditions for a hypothesis test are satisfied.

(b) The hypotheses are $H_0: \mu = 8.33$, $H_1: \mu < 8.33$. Using technology, $\bar{x} = 7.556$. The

test statistic is $Z = \dfrac{\bar{x} - \mu_0}{\sigma/\sqrt{n}} = \dfrac{7.556 - 8.33}{3.8/\sqrt{18}} = -0.86$. This is a left-tailed test and so the

critical value is $-z_{0.1} = -1.28$. Since the test statistic is not in the critical region, we do not reject the null hypothesis. There is not enough evidence to support the claim that cars are younger today than they were in 1995.

19. The hypotheses are $H_0: \mu = 694$, $H_1: \mu > 694$. The

test statistic is $Z = \dfrac{\bar{x} - \mu_0}{\sigma/\sqrt{n}} = \dfrac{731 - 694}{212/\sqrt{40}} = 1.10$. This is a

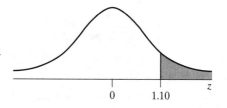

right-tailed test and so the P-value is
$P = P(Z > 1.10) = 1 - 0.8643 = 0.1357$.

Since $P = 0.1357 > 0.0500 = \alpha$, we do not reject the null hypothesis. There is not enough evidence to support the claim that the average farm size in Kansas is now greater than 694 acres.

21. The hypotheses are $H_0: \mu = 40.24$, $H_1: \mu > 40.24$.

The test statistic is $Z = \dfrac{\bar{x} - \mu_0}{\sigma/\sqrt{n}} = \dfrac{45.15 - 40.24}{21.20/\sqrt{49}} = 1.62$.

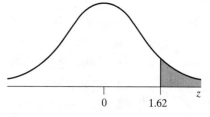

This is a right-tailed test and so the P-value is
$P = P(Z > 1.62) = 1 - 0.9474 = 0.0526$.

Since $P = 0.0526 < 0.1000 = \alpha$, we reject the null hypothesis. There is enough evidence to support the claim that the average monthly cellular phone bill has increased from its 1999 level of $40.24.

23. The hypotheses are $H_0 : \mu = 31.8$, $H_1 : \mu \neq 31.8$.

The test statistic is $Z = \dfrac{\overline{x} - \mu_0}{\sigma / \sqrt{n}} = \dfrac{39.2 - 31.8}{14.8 / \sqrt{35}} = 2.96$.

This is a two-tailed test and so the P-value is
$P = 2 \cdot P(Z < -2.96) = 2 \cdot 0.0015 = 0.0030$.

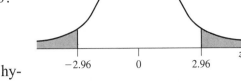

Since $P = 0.0030 < 0.0500 = \alpha$, we reject the null hypothesis. There is enough evidence to support the claim that average daily volume of Dell Computer stock in 2001 differs from its 2000 mean of 31.8 million shares.

25. For 95% confidence the critical value is $z_{0.025} = 1.96$. Then:

$$\text{Lower bound} = \overline{x} - z_{0.025} \cdot \frac{\sigma}{\sqrt{n}} = 63.96 - 1.96 \cdot \frac{0.06}{\sqrt{22}} = 63.96 - 0.03 = 63.93$$

$$\text{Upper bound} = \overline{x} + z_{0.025} \cdot \frac{\sigma}{\sqrt{n}} = 63.96 + 1.96 \cdot \frac{0.06}{\sqrt{22}} = 63.96 + 0.03 = 63.99.$$

Since $\mu_0 = 64$ is not in this interval, we conclude that the true mean amount in the bottles differs from 64 oz (i.e we are rejecting the null hypothesis).

27. For 90% confidence the critical value is $z_{0.05} = 1.645$. Then:

$$\text{Lower bound} = \overline{x} - z_{0.025} \cdot \frac{\sigma}{\sqrt{n}} = 39.2 - 1.645 \cdot \frac{14.8}{\sqrt{35}} = 39.2 - 4.1 = 35.1$$

$$\text{Upper bound} = \overline{x} + z_{0.025} \cdot \frac{\sigma}{\sqrt{n}} = 39.2 + 1.645 \cdot \frac{14.8}{\sqrt{35}} = 39.2 + 4.1 = 43.3.$$

Since $\mu_0 = 31.8$ is not in this interval, we conclude that the true mean daily volume of Dell stock in 2001 differs from 31.8 million shares (i.e we are rejecting the null hypothesis).

29. (a) $H_0 : \mu = 514$, $H_1 : \mu > 514$

(b) The test statistic is $Z = \dfrac{\overline{x} - \mu_0}{\sigma / \sqrt{n}} = \dfrac{518 - 514}{113 / \sqrt{1800}} = 1.50$.

This is a right-tailed test and so the P-value is
$P = P(Z > 1.50) = 1 - 0.9332 = 0.0668$. Since
$P = 0.0668 < 0.1000 = \alpha$, we reject the null hypothesis. There is enough evidence to support the claim that the mean score of students taking this review is greater than 514.

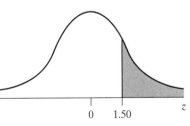

(c) In some states this would be regarded as a highly significant increase, although in most states it is not likely to be thought of as an increase that has any practical significance.

(d) The test statistic is now

$$Z = \frac{\bar{x}-\mu_0}{\sigma/\sqrt{n}} = \frac{518-514}{113/\sqrt{400}} = 0.71.$$ This is a right-

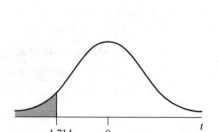

tailed test and so the P-value is

$P = P(Z>0.71) = 1-0.7611 = 0.2389$. Since

$P = 0.2389 > 0.1000 = \alpha$, we do not reject the null hypothesis. In this case, there is not enough evidence to support the claim that the mean score of students taking this review is greater than 514.

31. (a) Results will vary.

(b) Since the samples all come from a population that has mean equal to 8, approximately 5% of them (or 2 out of the 40 samples) should give a sample mean that is in the critical region at a 5% level of significance.

(c) Results will vary.

(d) The true mean is in fact 8, and so the null hypothesis is correct. Therefore to reject it would be to commit a Type I error.

9.3 Testing a Hypothesis about μ, σ Unknown

9.3 Concepts and Vocabulary

1. The sample must have been obtained using simple random sampling and either the population from which the sample is selected is normally distributed, or the sample size is large ($n \geq 30$).

3. For $\alpha = 0.05$ in a two-tailed test with 12 df, the critical values are
$\pm t_{\alpha/2} = \pm t_{0.025} = \pm 2.179$.

9.3 Exercises: Basic Skills

1. **(a)** $t = \frac{\bar{x}-\mu_0}{s/\sqrt{n}} = \frac{47.1-50}{10.3/\sqrt{24}} = -1.379$

(b) This is a left-tailed test with $24-1 = 23$ df and so the critical value is $-t_{0.05} = -1.714$.

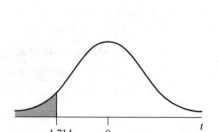

(c) The critical region is shaded.

(d) Since the test statistic is not in the critical region, we do not reject the null hypothesis.

3. **(a)** $t = \dfrac{\bar{x} - \mu_0}{s/\sqrt{n}} = \dfrac{104.8 - 100}{9.2/\sqrt{23}} = 2.502$

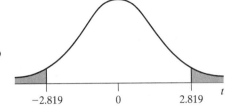

(b) This is a two-tailed test with $23 - 1 = 22$ df and so the critical values are $\pm t_{0.005} = \pm 2.819$

(c) The critical region is shaded.

(d) Since the test statistic is not in the critical region, we do not reject the null hypothesis.

5. **(a)** The test statistic is $t = \dfrac{\bar{x} - \mu_0}{s/\sqrt{n}} = \dfrac{18.3 - 20}{4.3/\sqrt{18}} = -1.677$.

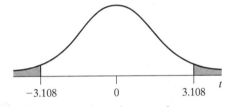

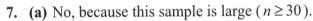

(b) The P-value region is shaded.

(c) This is a left-tailed test with $18 - 1 = 17$ df. We ignore the negative sign on the test statistic and scan across the 17 df row of the tables. Since $t = 1.677$ is between 1.333 and 1.740, we conclude that $0.05 < P < 0.10$ (reading from the top of the tables). Between 5% and 10% of samples will have a sample mean this low, if the population mean is 20.

(d) Since $P > 0.05 = \alpha$, we do not reject the null hypothesis.

7. **(a)** No, because this sample is large ($n \geq 30$).

(b) The test statistic is
$$t = \frac{\bar{x} - \mu_0}{s/\sqrt{n}} = \frac{101.9 - 105}{5.9/\sqrt{35}} = -3.108.$$

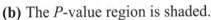

(c) The P-value region is shaded.

(d) This is a two-tailed test with $35 - 1 = 34$ df. We ignore the negative sign on the test statistic and scan across the 34 df row of the tables. Since $t = 3.108$ is between 3.002 and 3.348, we conclude that $0.001 < \frac{1}{2}P < 0.0025$ (reading from the top of the tables).

Note that for a two-tailed test we must double the values that we read from the top of the tables (since they give only the area in **one** tail). Thus $0.002 < P < 0.005$. Between 0.2% and 0.5% of samples will have a sample mean this far from 105, if the population mean is 105.

(e) Since $P < 0.005 < 0.010 = \alpha$, we reject the null hypothesis.

9.3 Exercises: Applying the Concepts

9. **(a)** The hypotheses are $H_0 : \mu = 9.02$, $H_1 : \mu < 9.02$.

The test statistic is $t = \dfrac{\bar{x} - \mu_0}{s/\sqrt{n}} = \dfrac{8.10 - 9.02}{0.7/\sqrt{12}} = -4.553$.

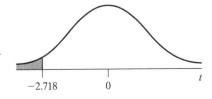

This is a left-tailed test with 11 df and so the critical value is $-t_{0.01} = -2.718$. Since the test statistic is in the critical region (shaded), we reject the null hypothesis. There is not enough evi-

dence to support the claim that the mean hippocampal volume of alcoholic adoles-
cents is less than 9.02 cm^3.

(b) From the 11 df row we find that $t = 4.553 > 4.437$, the last entry, and so $P < .0005$.
Fewer than 0.05% of samples will have a sample mean hippocampal volume this low
if the population mean is 9.02 cm^3.

11. (a) The hypotheses are $H_0 : \mu = 20$, $H_1 : \mu < 20$. The test statistic is

$$t = \frac{\bar{x} - \mu_0}{s / \sqrt{n}} = \frac{19.1 - 20}{9.1 / \sqrt{457}} = -2.114.$$ This is a left-tailed test with 456 df. We use 100

df and so the critical value is $-t_{0.01} = -2.364$. Since the test statistic is not in the critical region, we do not reject the null hypothesis. There is not enough evidence to support the claim that the mean daily consumption of fiber for 20–39-year-old males is
less than 20 grams.

(b) From the 100 df row, since $t = 2.114$ is between 2.081 and 2.364 we conclude that
$.01 < P < .02$. Between 1% and 2% of random samples will have a sample mean consumption this low, if the population mean daily consumption is 20 grams.

13. (a) The hypotheses are $H_0 : \mu = 98.6$, $H_1 : \mu < 98.6$. The test statistic is

$$t = \frac{\bar{x} - \mu_0}{s / \sqrt{n}} = \frac{98.2 - 98.6}{0.7 / \sqrt{700}} = -15.119.$$ This is a left-tailed test with 699 df. We use

1000 df and so the critical value is $-t_{0.01} = -2.330$. Since the test statistic is in the
critical region, we reject the null hypothesis. There is enough evidence to support the
claim that the mean temperature of humans is less than 98.6° F.

(b) From the 1000 df row, since $t = 15.119 > 3.300$ we conclude that $P < .0005$. Less
than 0.05% of random samples will have a sample mean temperature this low, if the
population mean temperature is 98.6° F.

15. (a) The hypotheses are $H_0 : \mu = 36.2$, $H_1 : \mu \neq 36.2$.
The test statistic is

$$t = \frac{\bar{x} - \mu_0}{s / \sqrt{n}} = \frac{38.9 - 36.2}{9.6 / \sqrt{32}} = 1.591.$$ This is a two-

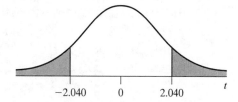

tailed test with 31 df and so the critical values are
$\pm t_{0.025} = \pm 2.040$. Since the test statistic is not in the critical region (shaded), we do
not reject the null hypothesis. There is not enough evidence to support the claim that
the mean age of death-row inmates is different from 36.2 years.

(b) From the 31 df row, since $t = 1.591$ is between 1.309 and 1.696 we conclude that
$0.05 < \frac{1}{2} P < 0.10$ and so $0.10 < P < 0.20$. Between 10% and 20% of random samples
will have a sample mean age this far from 36.2 years if the population mean age is
36.2 years.

17. (a) The hypotheses are $H_0 : \mu = 200$, $H_1 : \mu > 200$.

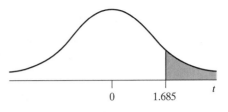

The test statistic is

$t = \dfrac{\bar{x} - \mu_0}{s / \sqrt{n}} = \dfrac{211 - 200}{39.2 / \sqrt{40}} = 1.775$. This is a right-

tailed test with 39 df and so the critical value is

$t_{0.05} = 1.685$. Since the test statistic is in the critical region (shaded), we reject the null hypothesis. There is enough evidence to support the claim that the mean total cholesterol for 40–49-yer-old males is higher than 200.

(b) From the 39 df row, since $t = 1.775$ is between 1.685 and 2.023 we conclude that $0.025 < P < 0.05$. Between 2.5% and 5% of random samples will have a sample mean cholesterol this high if the population mean cholesterol is 200.

19. (a) The plotted points are all within the bounds of the normal probability plot, which also has a generally linear pattern. The boxplot shows that there are no outliers. The conditions for a hypothesis test are satisfied.

(b) The hypotheses are $H_0 : \mu = 1.68$, $H_1 : \mu \neq 1.68$.

Using technology, $\bar{x} = 1.681$ and $s = 0.0045$.

The test statistic is

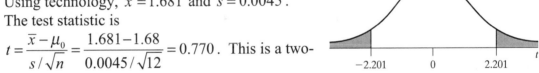

$t = \dfrac{\bar{x} - \mu_0}{s / \sqrt{n}} = \dfrac{1.681 - 1.68}{0.0045 / \sqrt{12}} = 0.770$. This is a two-

tailed test with 11 df and so the critical values are $\pm t_{0.025} = \pm 2.201$. Since the test statistic is not in the critical region (shaded), we do not reject the null hypothesis. There is not enough evidence to support the claim that the mean diameter of Maxfli XS golf balls is different from 1.68 inches.

(c) From the 11 df row, since $t = 0.770$ is between 0.697 and 0.876 we conclude that $0.20 < \frac{1}{2}P < 0.25$ and so $0.40 < P < 0.50$. Between 40% and 50% of random samples will have a sample mean diameter this far from 1.68 inches if the population mean diameter is 1.68 inches.

21. (a) The plotted points are all within the bounds of the normal probability plot, which also has a generally linear pattern. The boxplot shows that there are no outliers. The conditions for a hypothesis test are satisfied.

(b) The hypotheses are $H_0 : \mu = 7.0$, $H_1 : \mu \neq 7.0$.

Using technology, $\bar{x} = 7.01$ and $s = 0.0316$. The

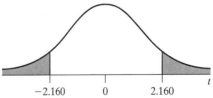

test statistic is $t = \dfrac{\bar{x} - \mu_0}{s / \sqrt{n}} = \dfrac{7.01 - 7.0}{0.0316 / \sqrt{14}} = 1.184$.

This is a two-tailed test with 13 df and so the critical values are $\pm t_{0.025} = \pm 2.160$. Since the test statistic is not in the critical region (shaded), we do not reject the null hypothesis. There is not enough evidence to support the claim that the pH meter is incorrectly calibrated.

(c) From the 13 df row, since $t = 1.184$ is between 1.771 and 2.160 we conclude that $0.025 < \frac{1}{2}P < 0.05$ and so $0.05 < P < 0.10$. Between 5% and 10% of random samples will have a sample mean pH for a neutral solution this far from 7.0.

23. (a) The plotted points are all within the bounds of the normal probability plot, which also has a generally linear pattern. The boxplot shows that there are no outliers. The conditions for a hypothesis test are satisfied.

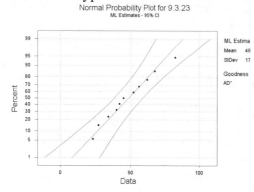

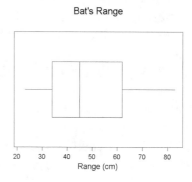

(b) The hypotheses are $H_0 : \mu = 35$, $H_1 : \mu > 35$.

Using technology, $\bar{x} = 48.36$ and $s = 18.08$. The test statistic is $t = \dfrac{\bar{x} - \mu_0}{s / \sqrt{n}} = \dfrac{48.36 - 35}{18.08 / \sqrt{11}} = 2.451$.

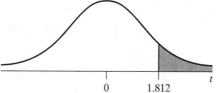

This is a right-tailed test with 10 df and so the critical value is $t_{0.05} = 1.812$. Since the test statistic is in the critical region (shaded), we reject the null hypothesis. There is enough evidence to support the claim that the mean detection distance of bats is greater than 35 cm.

(c) From the 10 df row, since $t = 2.451$ is between 2.359 and 2.764 we conclude that $0.01 < P < 0.02$. Between 1% and 2% of random samples will have a sample mean detection distance this far above 35 cm if the population mean detection distance is 35 cm.

25. The hypotheses would have been $H_0 : \mu = 0$, $H_1 : \mu > 0$, where μ = the mean change in the urinary flow rate. The *P*-value indicates that fewer than 1% of random samples of subjects would have had a sample mean increase in urinary flow rate as high as 0.8 mL/sec if the drug had no effect.

27. (a) The hypotheses are $H_0 : \mu = 98.2$, $H_1 : \mu > 98.2$.

(b) The *P*-value is 0.23, which is high, and so the nursing student will not reject the null hypothesis. There is not enough evidence to support the claim that the mean temperature of her patients is above 98.2° F.

29. (a) Results will vary.
    (b) We would expect 5% of the 40 samples, i.e. approximately 2 of them to result in a Type I error.
    (c) Results will vary.
    (d) Since our samples were drawn from a population that does have a mean of 50, if we reject the null hypothesis then we are making a mistake and hence committing a Type I error.

9.4 Testing a Hypothesis about a Population Proportion

9.4 Concepts and Vocabulary

1. The sample must have been obtained using simple random sampling and $np_0(1-p_0) \geq 10$ with $n \leq 0.05N$.

9.4 Exercises: Basic Skills

1. (a) Note that $np_0(1-p_0) = 200 \cdot 0.3(1-0.3) = 12.6 \geq 10$ and so the requirements of the hypothesis test are satisfied. Next we calculate $\hat{p} = \dfrac{75}{200} = 0.375$. Then

$$Z = \frac{\hat{p} - p_0}{\sqrt{p_0(1-p_0)/n}} = \frac{0.375 - 0.3}{\sqrt{0.3(1-0.3)/200}} = 2.31.$$ This is a right-tailed test and so the critical value is $z_{0.05} = 1.645$. The test statistic is in the critical region and so we reject the null hypothesis.

    (b) From the normal tables we get that the P-value is $P = 1 - 0.9896 = 0.0104 < 0.05$ and so we reject the null hypothesis.

3. (a) Note that $np_0(1-p_0) = 150 \cdot 0.55(1-0.55) = 37.125 \geq 10$ and so the requirements of the hypothesis test are satisfied. Next we calculate $\hat{p} = \dfrac{78}{150} = 0.52$. Then

$$Z = \frac{\hat{p} - p_0}{\sqrt{p_0(1-p_0)/n}} = \frac{0.52 - 0.55}{\sqrt{0.55(1-0.55)/150}} = -0.74.$$ This is a left-tailed test and so the critical value is $-z_{0.1} = -1.28$. The test statistic is not in the critical region and so we do not reject the null hypothesis.

    (b) From the normal tables we get that the P-value is $P = 0.2296 > 0.1$ and so we do not reject the null hypothesis.

5. (a) Note that $np_0(1-p_0) = 500 \cdot 0.9(1-0.9) = 45 \geq 10$ and so the requirements of the hypothesis test are satisfied. Next we calculate $\hat{p} = \dfrac{440}{500} = 0.88$. Then

$$Z = \frac{\hat{p} - p_0}{\sqrt{p_0(1-p_0)/n}} = \frac{0.88 - 0.9}{\sqrt{0.9(1-0.9)/500}} = -1.49.$$ This is a two-tailed test and so the critical values are $\pm z_{0.025} = \pm 1.96$. The test statistic is not in the critical region and so we do not reject the null hypothesis.

(b) From the normal tables we get that the P-value is $P = 2(0.0681) = 0.1362 > 0.05$ and so we do not reject the null hypothesis.

9.4 Exercises: Applying the Concepts

7. The hypotheses are $H_0 : p = 0.47$, $H_1 : p < 0.47$.

Note that $np_0(1-p_0) = 1012 \cdot 0.47(1-0.47) = 252.1 \geq 10$ and so the requirements of the hypothesis test are satisfied. From the survey, $\hat{p} = \dfrac{395}{1012} = 0.390$.

(a) The test statistic is $Z = \dfrac{\hat{p} - p_0}{\sqrt{p_0(1-p_0)/n}} = \dfrac{0.39 - 0.47}{\sqrt{0.47(1-0.47)/1012}} = -5.10$. This is a left-tailed test and so the critical value is $-z_{0.05} = -1.645$. The test statistic is in the critical region and so we reject the null hypothesis. There is strong evidence that gun ownership has declined from its 1990 level.

(b) From the normal tables, since the test statistic is off the tables, we get that the P-value is $P < 0.0002 < 0.05$ and so we reject the null hypothesis.

9. The hypotheses are $H_0 : p = 0.019$, $H_1 : p > 0.019$. Note that $np_0(1-p_0) = 863 \cdot 0.019(1-0.019) = 16.1 \geq 10$ and so the requirements of the hypothesis test are satisfied. From the survey, $\hat{p} = \dfrac{19}{863} = 0.022$.

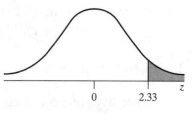

(a) The test statistic is $Z = \dfrac{\hat{p} - p_0}{\sqrt{p_0(1-p_0)/n}} = \dfrac{0.022 - 0.019}{\sqrt{0.019(1-0.019)/863}} = 0.65$. This is a right-tailed test and so the critical value is $z_{0.01} = 2.33$. The test statistic is not in the critical region (shaded) and so we do not reject the null hypothesis. There is not enough evidence to support the claim that more than 1.9% of Lipitor users experience flulike symptoms as a side effect.

(b) From the normal tables we get that the P-value is $P = 1 - 0.7422 = 0.2578 > 0.01$ and so we do not reject the null hypothesis.

11. The hypotheses are $H_0 : p = 0.071$, $H_1 : p > 0.071$.

Note that $np_0(1 - p_0) = 240 \cdot 0.071(1 - 0.071) = 15.8 \geq 10$ and so the requirements of the hypothesis test are satisfied. From the survey, $\hat{p} = \dfrac{22}{240} = 0.092$.

(a) The test statistic is $Z = \dfrac{\hat{p} - p_0}{\sqrt{p_0(1 - p_0)/n}} = \dfrac{0.092 - 0.071}{\sqrt{0.071(1 - 0.071)/240}} = 1.27$. This is a right-tailed test and so the critical value is $z_{0.01} = 2.33$. The test statistic is not in the critical region and so we do not reject the null hypothesis. There is not enough evidence to support the claim that more than 7.1% of mothers aged 35–39 years give birth to low-birth-weight babies.

(b) From the normal tables we get that the P-value is $P = 1 - 0.8980 = 0.1020 > 0.01$ and so we do not reject the null hypothesis.

13. The hypotheses are $H_0 : p = 0.33$, $H_1 : p > 0.33$.

Note that $np_0(1 - p_0) = 1015 \cdot 0.33(1 - 0.33) = 224.4 \geq 10$ and so the requirements of the hypothesis test are satisfied. From the survey, $\hat{p} = \dfrac{416}{1015} = 0.410$.

(a) The test statistic is $Z = \dfrac{\hat{p} - p_0}{\sqrt{p_0(1 - p_0)/n}} = \dfrac{0.410 - 0.33}{\sqrt{0.33(1 - 0.33)/1015}} = 5.42$. This is a right-tailed test and so the critical value is $z_{0.05} = 1.645$. The test statistic is in the critical region and so we reject the null hypothesis. There is enough evidence to support the claim that the percentage of Americans who believe that one parent should stay home is now greater than 33%.

(b) From the normal tables, since the test statistic is off the tables, we get that the P-value is $P < 1 - 0.9998 = 0.0002 < 0.05$ and so we reject the null hypothesis.

15. The hypotheses are $H_0 : p = 0.438$, $H_1 : p > 0.438$.

Note that $np_0(1 - p_0) = 80 \cdot 0.438(1 - 0.438) = 19.7 \geq 10$ and so the requirements of the hypothesis test are satisfied. From the survey, $\hat{p} = \dfrac{39}{80} = 0.4875$.

(a) The test statistic is $Z = \dfrac{\hat{p} - p_0}{\sqrt{p_0(1 - p_0)/n}} = \dfrac{0.4875 - 0.438}{\sqrt{0.438(1 - 0.438)/80}} = 0.89$. This is a right-tailed test and so the critical value is $z_{0.05} = 1.645$. The test statistic is not in the critical region and so we do not reject the null hypothesis. There is not enough evidence to support the claim that Shaq's free-throwing has improved.

(b) From the normal tables we get that the P-value is $P = 1 - 0.8133 = 0.1867 > 0.05$ and so we do not reject the null hypothesis.

17. The hypotheses are $H_0 : p = 0.58$, $H_1 : p \neq 0.58$.

Note that $np_0(1-p_0) = 1004 \cdot 0.58(1-0.58) = 244.6 \geq 10$ and so the requirements of the

hypothesis test are satisfied. From the survey, $\hat{p} = \dfrac{592}{1004} = 0.5896$.

(a) The test statistic is

$$Z = \frac{\hat{p} - p_0}{\sqrt{p_0(1-p_0)/n}} = \frac{0.5896 - 0.58}{\sqrt{0.58(1-0.58)/1004}} = 0.62.$$

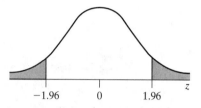

This is a two-tailed test and so the critical values are $\pm z_{0.025} = \pm 1.96$. The test statistic is not in the critical region and so we reject the null hypothesis. There is not enough evidence to support the claim that the percentage of Americans having a great deal of concern about the environment has changed since 1990.

(b) From the normal tables, using $Z = -0.62$, we get that the P-value is $P = 2(0.2676) = 0.5352 > 0.05$ and so we reject the null hypothesis.

19. The hypotheses are $H_0 : p = 0.85$, $H_1 : p > 0.85$.

Note that $np_0(1-p_0) = 340 \cdot 0.85(1-0.85) = 43.35 \geq 10$ and so the requirements of the

hypothesis test are satisfied. From the survey, $\hat{p} = \dfrac{302}{340} = 0.888$.

(a) The test statistic is $Z = \dfrac{\hat{p} - p_0}{\sqrt{p_0(1-p_0)/n}} = \dfrac{0.888 - 0.85}{\sqrt{.85(1-.85)/340}} = 1.96$. This is a right-

tailed test and so the critical value is $z_{0.10} = 1.28$. The test statistic is in the critical region and so we reject the null hypothesis. There is enough evidence to support the claim that the percentage of teachers using the internet in their teaching has increased.

(b) From the normal tables we get that the P-value is $P = 1 - 0.9750 = 0.0250 < 0.10$ and so we reject the null hypothesis.

21. The hypotheses are $H_0 : p = 0.37$, $H_1 : p < 0.37$.

Note that $np_0(1-p_0) = 150 \cdot 0.37(1-0.37) = 35.0 \geq 10$ and so the requirements of the hy-

pothesis test are satisfied. From the survey, $\hat{p} = \dfrac{54}{150} = 0.36$.

(a) The test statistic is $Z = \dfrac{\hat{p} - p_0}{\sqrt{p_0(1-p_0)/n}} = \dfrac{0.36 - 0.37}{\sqrt{0.37(1-0.37)/150}} = -0.25$. This is a left-

tailed test and so the critical value is $-z_{0.05} = -1.645$. The test statistic is not in the critical region and so we do not reject the null hypothesis. There is not enough evidence to support the claim that fewer than 37% of pet owners speak to their pets on the answering machine or telephone.

(b) From the normal tables we get that the P-value is $P = 0.4013 > 0.05$ and so we do not reject the null hypothesis.

23. The hypotheses are $H_0 : p = 0.04$, $H_1 : p < 0.04$.

Note that $np_0(1 - p_0) = 120 \cdot 0.04(1 - 0.04) = 4.6 < 10$ and so we must use small sample techniques. Since this is a left-tailed test we need to calculate the probability of 3 or fewer successes in 120 binomial trials with $p = 0.04$. Using technology we get:

$P = P(X \leq 3) = P(X = 0) + \ldots + P(X = 3) = 0.0075 + \ldots + 0.1515 = 0.2887 > 0.05$ and so we do not reject the null hypothesis. There is not enough evidence to support the claim that fewer than 4% of pregnant mothers smoke more than 21 cigarettes per day.

25. The hypotheses are $H_0 : p = 0.096$, $H_1 : p > 0.096$.

Note that $np_0(1 - p_0) = 80 \cdot 0.096(1 - 0.096) = 6.9 < 10$ and so we must use small sample techniques. Since this is a right-tailed test we need to calculate the probability of 13 or more successes in 80 binomial trials with $p = 0.096$. Using technology we get:

$P = P(X \geq 13) = 1 - P(X < 12) = 1 - (P(X = 0) + \ldots + P(X = 12)) = 1 - 0.9590 = 0.041 < 0.1$ and so we reject the null hypothesis. There is enough evidence to support the claim that more than 9.6% of Californians have to travel more than 60 minutes to work.

Review Exercises

1. **(a)** The hypotheses are $H_0 : \mu = 1100$, $H_1 : \mu > 1100$.

   (b) A Type I error would have been made if it were concluded that the mean charitable contribution in 2002 was more than $1100 per household when in fact it was not (i.e. reject H_0 when H_0 is true).

   (c) A Type II error would have been made if it were concluded that there was not enough evidence to justify that the mean charitable contribution in 2002 was more than $1100 per household when in fact it was (i.e. do not reject H_0 when in fact H_0 is false).

   (d) There is not enough evidence to justify that the mean charitable contribution in 2002 was more than $1100 per household.

   (e) There is enough evidence to justify that the mean charitable contribution in 2002 was more than $1100 per household.

3. Probability $= \alpha = 0.05$.

5. **(a)** $Z = \dfrac{\bar{x} - \mu_0}{\sigma / \sqrt{n}} = \dfrac{28.6 - 30}{4.5 / \sqrt{12}} = -1.08$.

   (b) This is a left-tailed test and so the critical value is
   $-z_{0.05} = -1.645$.

   (c)

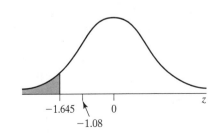

(d) Since the test statistic is not in the critical (shaded) region, we do not reject the null hypothesis.

(e) $P = P(Z < -1.08) = 0.1401$.

7. **(a)** Since σ is unknown, the test statistic is a t-statistic.
$$t = \frac{\bar{x} - \mu_0}{s/\sqrt{n}} = \frac{7.3 - 8}{1.8/\sqrt{15}} = -1.506.$$

(b) This is a two-tailed test with 14 df and so the critical values are $\pm t_{0.01} = \pm 2.624$.

(c)

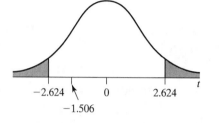

(d) Since the test statistic is not in the critical (shaded) region, we do not reject the null hypothesis.

(e) In the 14 df row, $t = 1.506$ is between 1.345 and 1.761 and so $0.05 < \frac{1}{2}P < 0.10$. Thus $0.10 < P < 0.20$.

9. **(a)** Note that $np_0(1-p_0) = 250 \cdot 0.6(1-0.6) = 60 \geq 10$ and so the requirements of the hypothesis test are satisfied. Next we calculate $\hat{p} = \frac{165}{250} = 0.66$. Then

$$Z = \frac{\hat{p} - p_0}{\sqrt{p_0(1-p_0)/n}} = \frac{0.66 - 0.6}{\sqrt{0.6(1-0.6)/250}} = 1.94.$$ This is a right-tailed test and so the critical value is $z_{0.05} = 1.645$. The test statistic is in the critical region and so we reject the null hypothesis.

(b) From the normal tables we get that the P-value is $P = 1 - 0.9738 = 0.0262 < 0.05$ and so we reject the null hypothesis.

11. The hypotheses are $H_0 : \mu = 78.62$, $H_1 : \mu \neq 78.62$. The test statistic is $t = \frac{\bar{x} - \mu_0}{s/\sqrt{n}} = \frac{80.04 - 78.62}{10.83/\sqrt{50}} = 0.927$. This is a two-tailed test with 49 df, which we approximate by 50 df, and so the critical values are $\pm t_{0.025} = \pm 2.009$.

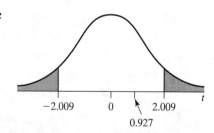

Since the test statistic is not in the critical region, we do not reject the null hypothesis. There is not enough evidence to support the claim that the average price of a motel room is now different from $78.62 per night.

13. The hypotheses are $H_0 : \mu = 474$, $H_1 : \mu > 474$. The test statistic is $Z = \frac{\bar{x} - \mu_0}{\sigma/\sqrt{n}} = \frac{539 - 474}{103/\sqrt{50}} = 4.46$. This is a right-tailed test and so the critical value is $z_{0.01} = 2.33$. Since the test statistic is in the critical region, we reject

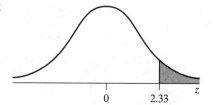

the null hypothesis. There is enough evidence to support the claim that students who use a calculator frequently score higher on the SAT Math test than students who use a calculator infrequently.

15. (a) The hypotheses are $H_0 : \mu = 300$, $H_1 : \mu > 300$. The test statistic is

$t = \dfrac{\bar{x} - \mu_0}{s / \sqrt{n}} = \dfrac{326 - 300}{342 / \sqrt{404}} = 1.528$. This is a right-tailed test with 403 df, which we approximate by 100 df, and so the critical value is $t_{0.05} = 1.660$. Since the test statistic is not in the critical region, we do not reject the null hypothesis. There is not enough evidence to support the claim that 20–39-year-old males consume too much cholesterol.

(b) If the nutritionist were to reject the null hypothesis, and the null hypothesis were true, then this would be a Type I error. In this test the nutritionist did not reject the null hypothesis. If in fact the alternative hypothesis is true, then a Type II error has been made.

(c) The probability of making a Type I error is 0.05.

17. (a) The plotted points are all within the bounds of the normal probability plot, which also has a generally linear pattern. The boxplot shows that there are no outliers. The conditions for a hypothesis test are satisfied.

(b) The hypotheses are $H_0 : \mu = 4.61$, $H_1 : \mu < 4.61$.

Using technology, $\bar{x} = 4.4808$. The test statistic is

$Z = \dfrac{\bar{x} - \mu_0}{\sigma / \sqrt{n}} = \dfrac{4.4808 - 4.61}{0.26 / \sqrt{25}} = -2.48$.

This is a left-tailed test and so the critical value is

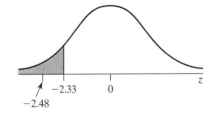

$z_{0.01} = -2.33$. Since the test statistic is in the critical region, we reject the null hypothesis. There is enough evidence to support the claim that the acidity of the rain has increased (its pH is less than 4.61).

(c) This is a left-tailed test and so $P = P(Z < -2.48) = 0.0066$. About 0.66% of samples will have a sample mean pH this low, if the population mean pH is 4.61.

19. The hypotheses are $H_0 : p = 0.56$, $H_1 : p > 0.56$.

Note that $np_0(1 - p_0) = 300 \cdot 0.56(1 - 0.56) = 73.92 \geq 10$ and so the requirements of the

hypothesis test are satisfied. From the survey, $\hat{p} = \dfrac{170}{300} = 0.5667$.

The test statistic is

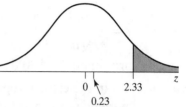

$Z = \dfrac{\hat{p} - p_0}{\sqrt{p_0(1 - p_0)/n}} = \dfrac{0.5667 - 0.56}{\sqrt{0.56(1 - 0.56)/300}} = 0.23$. This

is a right-tailed test and so the critical value is

$z_{0.01} = 2.33$. The test statistic is not in the critical region

and so we do not reject the null hypothesis. There is not enough evidence to support the claim that the percentage of cases of tuberculosis that are among foreign-born residents has increased.

21. The hypotheses are $H_0 : p = 0.49$, $H_1 : p > 0.49$.

Note that $np_0(1 - p_0) = 40 \cdot 0.49(1 - 0.49) = 9.996 < 10$ and so we must use small sample techniques. Since this is a right-tailed test we need to calculate the probability of 22 or more successes in 40 binomial trials with $p = 0.49$. Using technology we get:

$P = P(X \geq 22) = P(X = 23) + \ldots + P(X = 40) = 0.2740 > 0.05$ and so we do not reject the null hypothesis. There is not enough evidence to support the claim that the percentage of Americans who believe that being a teacher is a prestigious occupation is now higher than 49%.

23. Answers will vary.

Chapter 10. Inference on Two Samples

10.1 Inference about Two Means: Dependent Samples

10.1   Concepts and Vocabulary

1. A sampling method is independent when the individuals selected for one sample do not dictate which individuals are to be in the second sample. It is dependent when they do.

3. The sample data must be matched-pairs data from samples obtained one by simple random sampling (and the other by matching pairs) and the differences must either be normally distributed or the sample size must be large ($n \geq 30$).

10.1   Exercises: Skill Building

1. Dependent, since the members of the two samples are married to each other.

3. Independent because the 80 students are randomly allocated to one of two groups.

5. Independent because the two sets of twins are chosen at random.

7. **(a)**

Observation	1	2	3	4	5	6	7
X_1	7.6	7.6	7.4	5.7	8.3	6.6	5.6
X_2	8.1	6.6	10.7	9.4	7.8	9.0	8.5
$X_1 - X_2$	−0.5	1.0	−3.3	−3.7	0.5	−2.4	−2.9

(b) Using technology, $\overline{d} = -1.614$ and $s_d = 1.915$.

(c) The hypotheses are $H_0 : \mu_d = 0$, $H_1 : \mu_d < 0$. Since this is a left-tailed test with 6 df, the critical value is $-t_{0.05} = -1.943$. Then $t = \dfrac{\overline{d}}{s_d / \sqrt{n}} = \dfrac{-1.614}{1.915/\sqrt{7}} = -2.230$, which is in the critical region and so we reject H_0.

(d) $\overline{d} \pm t_{0.025} \cdot \dfrac{s_d}{\sqrt{n}} = -1.614 \pm 2.447 \cdot \dfrac{1.915}{\sqrt{7}} = -1.614 \pm 1.771 = (-3.39, 0.16)$. Note that this confidence interval would match a one-tailed test of significance at the 0.025 level.

10.1   Exercises: Applying the Concepts

9. **(a)** The data consist of pairs of measurements each of the same round.

    (b) Using technology, $\bar{d} = 0.117$ and $s_d = 0.475$, where we measure differences as
    A – B. The hypotheses are $H_0 : \mu_d = 0$, $H_1 : \mu_d \neq 0$. Since this is a two-tailed test
    with 11 df, the critical values are $\pm t_{0.005} = \pm 3.106$. The test statistic is

    $$t = \frac{\bar{d}}{s_d / \sqrt{n}} = \frac{0.117}{0.475 / \sqrt{12}} = 0.853,$$ which is not in the critical region and so we do not

    reject H_0. There is not enough evidence to show that there is a difference in the
    measurement of muzzle velocity by the two devices.

    (c) $\bar{d} \pm t_{0.005} \cdot \dfrac{s_d}{\sqrt{n}} = 0.117 \pm 3.106 \cdot \dfrac{0.475}{\sqrt{12}} = 0.117 \pm 0.426 = (-0.309, 0.543)$. We are 99%

    confident that the true mean difference
    in measured muzzle velocity is be-
    tween –0.309 and 0.543 feet per sec-
    ond.

    (d) Since a difference of 0 is centrally
    located, the boxplot supports the con-
    clusion in **(b)**.

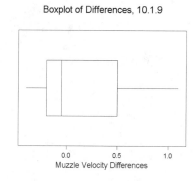

Boxplot of Differences, 10.1.9

11. **(a)** Using technology, $\bar{d} = 0.093$ and $s_d = 0.174$, where we measure differences as Blue
    – Red. The hypotheses are $H_0 : \mu_d = 0$, $H_1 : \mu_d \neq 0$. Since this is a two-tailed test
    with 5 df, the critical values are $\pm t_{0.005} = \pm 4.032$. The test statistic is

    $$t = \frac{\bar{d}}{s_d / \sqrt{n}} = \frac{0.093}{0.174 / \sqrt{6}} = 1.309,$$ which is not in the critical region and so we do not

    reject H_0. There is not enough evidence to show that there is a difference in reaction
    times.

(b) $\bar{d} \pm t_{0.01} \cdot \dfrac{s_d}{\sqrt{n}} = 0.093 \pm 3.365 \cdot \dfrac{0.174}{\sqrt{6}} = 0.093 \pm 0.239 = (-0.146, 0.332)$. We are 98%

confident that the true mean difference in reaction times is between –0.146 and 0.332 seconds. Note that this confidence interval would match a two-tailed test of significance at the 0.02 level of significance.

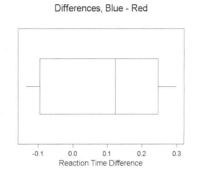

Differences, Blue - Red

Reaction Time Difference

(c) Since a difference of 0 is located in the middle 50%, the boxplot supports the conclusion in **(b)**.

13. (a) Using technology, $\bar{d} = 5.125$ and $s_d = 6.081$, where we measure differences as 5 years later – initial clarity. The hypotheses are $H_0 : \mu_d = 0$, $H_1 : \mu_d > 0$. Since this is a right-tailed test with 7 df, the critical value is $t_{0.05} = 1.895$. The test statistic is

$$t = \frac{\bar{d}}{s_d / \sqrt{n}} = \frac{5.125}{6.081 / \sqrt{8}} = 2.384,$$ which is in the critical region and so we reject H_0.

There is enough evidence to show that the clarity of the lake has improved.

(b) $\bar{d} \pm t_{0.01} \cdot \dfrac{s_d}{\sqrt{n}} = 5.125 \pm 2.365 \cdot \dfrac{6.081}{\sqrt{8}} = 5.125 \pm 5.085 = (0.04, 10.21)$. We are 95% con-

fident that the true mean improvement in clarity is between 0.04 inches and 10.21 inches. Note that this confidence interval corresponds to a one-tailed test at the 0.025 level of significance.

15. (a) Using technology, $\bar{d} = 118.75$ and $s_d = 544.02$, where we measure differences as costs for a Neon – costs for a Civic. The hypotheses are $H_0 : \mu_d = 0$, $H_1 : \mu_d \neq 0$. Since this is a two-tailed test with 3 df, the critical values are $\pm t_{0.025} = \pm 3.182$. The

test statistic is $t = \dfrac{\bar{d}}{s_d / \sqrt{n}} = \dfrac{118.75}{544.02 / \sqrt{4}} = 0.437$, which is not in the critical region

and so we do not reject H_0. There is not enough evidence to show that repair costs differ.

(b) $\bar{d} \pm t_{0.05} \cdot \dfrac{s_d}{\sqrt{n}} = 118.75 \pm 2.353 \cdot \dfrac{544.02}{\sqrt{4}} = 118.75 \pm 640.04 = (-521, 759)$. We are 90%

confident that the true mean difference in repair cost is between –\$521 and \$759. Note that this confidence interval corresponds to a two-tailed test at the 0.10 level of significance.

17. (a) Using technology, $\bar{d} = 0.259$ and $s_d = 9.202$, where we measure differences as Thrifty – Hertz. The hypotheses are $H_0 : \mu_d = 0$, $H_1 : \mu_d < 0$. Since $\bar{d} > 0$ and the alternative hypothesis is that $\mu_d < 0$, there is **no** evidence to support the alternative hypothesis (we don't need to even carry out the mechanics of the hypothesis test) and so we do not reject H_0. There is no evidence to show that Thrifty is less expensive than Hertz.

(b) $\bar{d} \pm t_{0.025} \cdot \dfrac{s_d}{\sqrt{n}} = 0.259 \pm 1.833 \cdot \dfrac{9.202}{\sqrt{10}} = 0.259 \pm 5.334 = (-5.08, 5.59)$. We are 90% confident that the true mean difference in rental costs is between –\$5.08 and \$5.59 points. Note that this confidence interval corresponds to a one-tailed test at the 0.05 level of significance.

19. (a) The hypotheses are $H_0 : \mu_d = 0$, $H_1 : \mu_d \neq 0$.

(b) The sample data must be matched-pairs data (which it is) from samples obtained one by simple random sampling and the other by matching pairs and the differences must be normally distributed since the sample size is not large ($n < 30$).

(c) Since $P = 0.001 < 0.05$ we reject the null hypothesis and so it does appear that space flight affected the red blood count of the rats.

10.2 Inference about Two Means: Independent Samples

10.2   Concepts and Vocabulary

1. The samples must be independent, must have been obtained by simple random sampling and must either come from a normal population or must be large samples ($n_1 \geq 30$ and $n_2 \geq 30$).

10.2   Exercises: Skill Building

1. (a) This is a two-tailed test, σ unknown, with df $= 15-1 = 14$. The critical t-values are $\pm t_{0.025} = \pm 2.145$. The test statistic is:

$$t = \frac{(\bar{x}_1 - \bar{x}_2) - (\mu_1 - \mu_2)}{\sqrt{s_1^2 / n_1 + s_2^2 / n_2}} = \frac{(15.3 - 14.2) - 0}{\sqrt{3.2^2 / 15 + 3.5^2 / 15}} = 0.898$$

which is not in the rejection region and so we do not reject H_0.

(b) For a 95% confidence interval we use $\pm t_{0.025} = \pm 2.145$, giving bounds of:

$$(\bar{x}_1 - \bar{x}_2) \pm t_{\alpha/2} \cdot \sqrt{\frac{s_1^2}{n_1} + \frac{s_2^2}{n_2}} = (15.3 - 14.2) \pm 2.145 \cdot \sqrt{\frac{3.2^2}{15} + \frac{3.5^2}{15}} = 1.1 \pm 2.63 = (-1.53, 3.73)$$

3. **(a)** If the hypotheses are $H_0: \mu_1 - \mu_2 = 0$, $H_1: \mu_1 - \mu_2 > 0$ then this is a right-tailed test, σ unknown, with df $= 18-1 = 17$. The critical t-value is $t_{0.10} = 1.333$. The test statistic is:

$$t = \frac{(\bar{x}_1 - \bar{x}_2) - (\mu_1 - \mu_2)}{\sqrt{s_1^2/n_1 + s_2^2/n_2}} = \frac{(50.2 - 42.0) - 0}{\sqrt{6.4^2/25 + 9.9^2/18}} = 3.081$$

which is in the rejection region and so we reject H_0.

(b) For a 90% confidence interval we use $\pm t_{0.05} = \pm 1.740$, giving bounds of:

$$(\bar{x}_1 - \bar{x}_2) \pm t_{\alpha/2} \cdot \sqrt{\frac{s_1^2}{n_1} + \frac{s_2^2}{n_2}} = (50.2 - 42.0) \pm 1.740 \cdot \sqrt{\frac{6.4^2}{25} + \frac{9.9^2}{18}} = 8.2 \pm 4.63 = (3.57, 12.83)$$

Note that this confidence interval corresponds to a one-tailed test at 5% significance.

5. **(a)** If the hypotheses are $H_0: \mu_1 - \mu_2 = 0$, $H_1: \mu_1 - \mu_2 < 0$ then this is a left-tailed test, σ unknown, with df $= 25-1 = 24$. The critical t-value is $-t_{0.02} = -2.172$. The test statistic is:

$$t = \frac{(\bar{x}_1 - \bar{x}_2) - (\mu_1 - \mu_2)}{\sqrt{s_1^2/n_1 + s_2^2/n_2}} = \frac{(103.4 - 114.2) - 0}{\sqrt{12.3^2/32 + 13.2^2/25}} = -3.158$$

which is in the rejection region and so we reject H_0.

(b) For a 90% confidence interval we use $\pm t_{0.05} = \pm 1.711$, giving bounds of:

$$(\bar{x}_1 - \bar{x}_2) \pm t_{\alpha/2} \cdot \sqrt{\frac{s_1^2}{n_1} + \frac{s_2^2}{n_2}} = (103.4 - 114.2) \pm 1.711 \cdot \sqrt{\frac{12.3^2}{32} + \frac{13.2^2}{25}}$$
$$= -10.8 \pm 5.85 = (-16.65, -4.95)$$

Note that this confidence interval corresponds to a one-tailed test at 5% significance.

10.2 Exercises: Applying the Concepts

7. **(a)** With $\mu_1 =$ mean improvement for the treatment group and $\mu_2 =$ mean improvement for the control group we test the hypotheses $H_0: \mu_1 - \mu_2 = 0$, $H_1: \mu_1 - \mu_2 > 0$. This is a right-tailed test, σ unknown, with df $= 55-1 = 54$, which we approximate by 50 df. The critical t-value is $t_{0.01} = 2.403$. The test statistic is:

$$t = \frac{(\bar{x}_1 - \bar{x}_2) - (\mu_1 - \mu_2)}{\sqrt{s_1^2/n_1 + s_2^2/n_2}} = \frac{(14.8 - 8.1) - 0}{\sqrt{12.5^2/55 + 12.7^2/60}} = 2.849$$

which is in the rejection region and so we reject H_0. There is enough evidence to conclude that the treatment group experienced a larger mean improvement than the control group.

(b) For a 95% confidence interval we use $\pm t_{0.025} = \pm 2.009$, giving bounds of:

$$(\bar{x}_1 - \bar{x}_2) \pm t_{\alpha/2} \cdot \sqrt{\frac{s_1^2}{n_1} + \frac{s_2^2}{n_2}} = (14.8 - 8.1) \pm 2.009 \cdot \sqrt{\frac{12.5^2}{55} + \frac{12.7^2}{60}} = 6.7 \pm 4.72 = (1.98, 11.42)$$

We are 95% confident that the true mean difference in improvement (treatment – control) is between 1.98 and 11.42 on the Young-Mania Rating Scale. Note that this confidence interval corresponds to a one-tailed test at 2.5% significance.

9. **(a)** Yes, Welch's t-test is appropriate since the data are obtained from simple random samples that are independent and appear to come from normal populations.

(b) With μ_{400} = mean strength of mixture 67-0-400 and μ_{301} = mean strength of mixture 67-0-301, we test the hypotheses $H_0 : \mu_{400} - \mu_{301} = 0$, $H_1 : \mu_{400} - \mu_{301} > 0$. This is a right-tailed test, σ unknown, with df = 9–1 = 8. The critical t-value is $t_{0.05} = 1.860$. Using technology, the summary statistics are $\bar{x}_{400} = 4483$, $s_{400} = 474$, $n_{400} = 10$ and $\bar{x}_{301} = 3669$, $s_{301} = 459$, $n_{301} = 9$. The test statistic is:

$$t = \frac{(\bar{x}_{400} - \bar{x}_{301}) - (\mu_{400} - \mu_{301})}{\sqrt{s_{400}^2 / n_{400} + s_{301}^2 / n_{301}}} = \frac{(4483 - 3669) - 0}{\sqrt{474^2 / 10 + 459^2 / 9}} = 3.800$$

which is in the rejection region and so we reject H_0. There is enough evidence to conclude that mixture 67-0-400 is stronger than mixture 67-0-301.

(c) For a 90% confidence interval we use $\pm t_{0.05} = \pm 1.860$, giving bounds of:

$$(\bar{x}_{400} - \bar{x}_{301}) \pm t_{\alpha/2} \cdot \sqrt{\frac{s_{400}^2}{n_{400}} + \frac{s_{301}^2}{n_{301}}} = (4483 - 3669) \pm 1.860 \cdot \sqrt{\frac{474^2}{10} + \frac{459^2}{9}}$$
$$= 814 \pm 398 = (416, 1212)$$

We are 90% confident that the true mean difference in strength (mixture 67-0-301 minus mixture 67-0-400) is between 416 and 1212 pounds per square inch.

(d) From the boxplot, mixture 67-0-400 clealrly appears to be stronger than mixture 67-0-301.

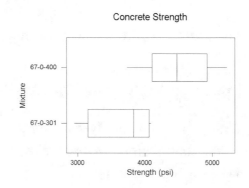

11. (a) The normal probability plots both show a linear pattern with all points within the bounds. The boxplots show that there are no outliers. The conditions for Welch's t-test are satisfied.

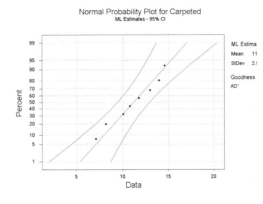

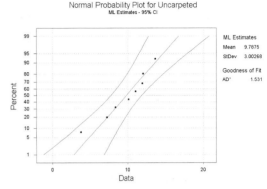

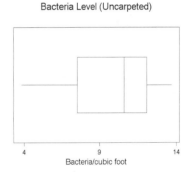

(b) With μ_1 = mean bacteria level for carpeted rooms and μ_2 = mean bacteria level for uncarpeted rooms, we test the hypotheses $H_0: \mu_1 - \mu_2 = 0$, $H_1: \mu_1 - \mu_2 > 0$. This is a right-tailed test, σ unknown, with df = 8–1 = 7. The critical t-value is $t_{0.05} = 1.895$. Using technology, the summary statistics are $\bar{x}_1 = 11.20$, $s_1 = 2.677$, $n_1 = 8$ and $\bar{x}_2 = 9.79$, $s_2 = 3.21$, $n_2 = 8$. The test statistic is:

$$t = \frac{(\bar{x}_1 - \bar{x}_2) - (\mu_1 - \mu_2)}{\sqrt{s_1^2 / n_1 + s_2^2 / n_2}} = \frac{(11.20 - 9.79) - 0}{\sqrt{2.677^2 / 8 + 3.21^2 / 8}} = 0.954$$

which is not in the rejection region and so we do not reject H_0. There is not enough evidence to conclude that carpeted rooms have higher bacteria levels than uncarpeted rooms.

(c) For a 95% confidence interval we use $\pm t_{0.025} = \pm 2.365$, giving bounds of:

$$(\bar{x}_1 - \bar{x}_2) \pm t_{\alpha/2} \cdot \sqrt{\frac{s_1^2}{n_1} + \frac{s_2^2}{n_2}} = (11.20 - 9.79) \pm 2.365 \cdot \sqrt{\frac{2.677^2}{8} + \frac{3.21^2}{8}}$$

$$= 1.41 \pm 3.49 = (-2.08, 4.90)$$

We are 95% confident that the true mean difference bacteria in per cubic foot (carpeted – uncarpeted) is between –2.08 and 4.90. Note that this confidence interval corresponds to a one-tailed test at 2.5% significance.

13. **(a)** With μ_1 = mean house price in Lemont and μ_2 = mean house price in Naperville, we test the hypotheses $H_0: \mu_1 - \mu_2 = 0$, $H_1: \mu_1 - \mu_2 < 0$. This is a left-tailed test, σ unknown, with df = 32–1 = 31. The critical t-value is $-t_{0.05} = -1.696$. The test statistic is:

$$t = \frac{(\bar{x}_1 - \bar{x}_2) - (\mu_1 - \mu_2)}{\sqrt{s_1^2/n_1 + s_2^2/n_2}} = \frac{(253.6 - 310.3) - 0}{\sqrt{106.9^2/44 + 153.9^2/32}} = -1.793$$

which is in the rejection region and so we reject H_0. There is enough evidence to conclude that housing is less expensive in Lemont than in Naperville.

(b) For a 90% confidence interval we use $\pm t_{0.05} = \pm 1.696$, giving bounds of:

$$(\bar{x}_1 - \bar{x}_2) \pm t_{\alpha/2} \cdot \sqrt{\frac{s_1^2}{n_1} + \frac{s_2^2}{n_2}} = (253.6 - 310.3) \pm 1.696 \cdot \sqrt{\frac{106.9^2}{44} + \frac{153.9^2}{32}}$$

$$= -56.7 \pm 53.63 = (-110.33, -3.07)$$

We are 90% confident that the true mean difference in the mean house price (Lemont – Naperville) is between –$110,330 and –$3070.

(c) It is very likely that the distribution of house prices is not normal, but is skewed to the right, and so large samples are necessary to use Welch's t-test.

15. **(a)** This is a randomized, double-blind study with treatment being medication, and two levels of treatment (combined drug therapy or placebo).

(b) With μ_1 = mean HDL increase for the treatment group and μ_2 = mean HDL increase for the control group, we test the hypotheses $H_0: \mu_1 - \mu_2 = 0$, $H_1: \mu_1 - \mu_2 > 0$. This is a right-tailed test, σ unknown, with df = 29–1 = 28. The critical t-value is $t_{0.01} = 2.467$. The test statistic is:

$$t = \frac{(\bar{x}_1 - \bar{x}_2) - (\mu_1 - \mu_2)}{\sqrt{s_1^2/n_1 + s_2^2/n_2}} = \frac{(8.1 - 2.4) - 0}{\sqrt{10.5^2/30 + 4.3^2/29}} = 2.745$$

which is in the rejection region and so we reject H_0. There is enough evidence to conclude that the mean increase in HDL was greater for the treatment group than for the control group.

(c) For a 95% confidence interval we use $\pm t_{0.025} = \pm 2.048$, giving bounds of:

$$(\bar{x}_1 - \bar{x}_2) \pm t_{\alpha/2} \cdot \sqrt{\frac{s_1^2}{n_1} + \frac{s_2^2}{n_2}} = (8.1 - 2.4) \pm 2.048 \cdot \sqrt{\frac{10.5^2}{30} + \frac{4.3^2}{29}}$$

$$= 5.7 \pm 4.25 = (1.45, 9.95)$$

We are 95% confident that the true mean difference in the increase in HDL (treatment – placebo) is between 1.45 and 9.95. Note that this confidence interval corresponds to a one-tailed test at 2.5% significance.

17. (a) The hypotheses are $H_0 : \mu_{men} - \mu_{women} = 0$, $H_1 : \mu_{men} - \mu_{women} < 0$.

(b) $P = 0.0051 < 0.01$ and so the researcher will reject H_0. There is enough evidence to conclude that men have a lower mean step pulse rate than women.

(c) The 95% confidence interval is $(-10.7, -1.5)$. We are 95% confident that the true mean difference in mean step pulse rates (men – women) is between –10.7 and –1.5.

10.3 Inference about Two Population Proportions

10.3 Concepts and Vocabulary

1. Under the null hypothesis, $p_1 = p_2$ and we should use the best estimate of this common value, which is obtained by pooling the data from both samples.

3. A difference is statistically significant if it is great enough to justify that we reject the null hypothesis (of no difference). However, a difference that is statistically significant may still not be great enough to have any practical significance.

10.3 Exercises: Skill Building

1. (a) The hypotheses are $H_0 : p_1 = p_2$ and $H_1 : p_1 > p_2$.

(b) The two sample estimates are $\hat{p}_1 = \dfrac{x_1}{n_1} = \dfrac{368}{541} = 0.6802$, $\hat{p}_2 = \dfrac{x_2}{n_2} = \dfrac{351}{593} = 0.5919$ and

the pooled estimate is $\hat{p} = \dfrac{x_1 + x_2}{n_1 + n_2} = \dfrac{368 + 351}{541 + 593} = 0.6340$. The test statistic is

$$Z = \dfrac{\hat{p}_1 - \hat{p}_2}{\sqrt{\hat{p}(1-\hat{p})}\sqrt{1/n_1 + 1/n_2}} = \dfrac{0.6802 - 0.5919}{\sqrt{0.634(1-0.634)}\sqrt{1/541 + 1/593}} = 3.08.$$

(c) This is a right-tailed test and so the critical value is $z_\alpha = z_{0.05} = 1.645$. Since the test statistic is in the rejection region, we reject H_0. There is enough evidence to support the claim that $p_1 > p_2$.

(d) $P = P(Z \geq 3.08) = 1 - 0.9990 = 0.0010$.

3. **(a)** The hypotheses are $H_0 : p_1 = p_2$ and $H_1 : p_1 \neq p_2$.

(b) The two sample estimates are $\hat{p}_1 = \dfrac{x_1}{n_1} = \dfrac{28}{254} = 0.1102$, $\hat{p}_2 = \dfrac{x_2}{n_2} = \dfrac{36}{301} = 0.1196$ and

the pooled estimate is $\hat{p} = \dfrac{x_1 + x_2}{n_1 + n_2} = \dfrac{28 + 36}{254 + 301} = 0.1153$. The test statistic is

$$Z = \frac{\hat{p}_1 - \hat{p}_2}{\sqrt{\hat{p}(1 - \hat{p})}\sqrt{1/n_1 + 1/n_2}} = \frac{0.1102 - 0.1196}{\sqrt{0.1153(1 - 0.1153)}\sqrt{1/254 + 1/301}} = -0.34.$$

(c) This is a two-tailed test and so the critical values are $\pm z_{0.025} = \pm 1.96$. Since the test statistic is not in the rejection region, we do not reject H_0. There is not enough evidence to support the claim that $p_1 \neq p_2$.

(d) $P = 2 \cdot P(Z \leq -0.34) = 2 \cdot 0.3669 = 0.7338$.

5. For a 90% confidence interval we use $\pm z_{0.05} = \pm 1.645$. We have $\hat{p}_1 = \dfrac{x_1}{n_1} = \dfrac{368}{541} = 0.6802$

and $\hat{p}_2 = \dfrac{x_2}{n_2} = \dfrac{351}{593} = 0.5919$. The bounds are:

$$(\hat{p}_1 - \hat{p}_2) \pm z_{\alpha/2} \cdot \sqrt{\frac{\hat{p}_1(1 - \hat{p}_1)}{n_1} + \frac{\hat{p}_2(1 - \hat{p}_2)}{n_2}}$$

$$= (0.6802 - 0.5919) \pm 1.645 \cdot \sqrt{\frac{0.6802(1 - 0.6802)}{541} + \frac{0.5919(1 - 0.5919)}{593}}$$

$$= 0.088 \pm 0.047 = (0.04, 0.14).$$

7. For a 95% confidence interval we use $\pm z_{0.025} = \pm 1.96$. We have $\hat{p}_1 = \dfrac{x_1}{n_1} = \dfrac{28}{254} = 0.1102$

and $\hat{p}_2 = \dfrac{x_2}{n_2} = \dfrac{36}{301} = 0.1196$. The bounds are:

$$(\hat{p}_1 - \hat{p}_2) \pm z_{\alpha/2} \cdot \sqrt{\frac{\hat{p}_1(1 - \hat{p}_1)}{n_1} + \frac{\hat{p}_2(1 - \hat{p}_2)}{n_2}}$$

$$= (0.1102 - 0.1196) \pm 1.96 \cdot \sqrt{\frac{0.1102(1 - 0.1102)}{254} + \frac{0.1196(1 - 0.1196)}{301}}$$

$$= -0.009 \pm 0.053 = (-0.06, 0.04).$$

10.3   Exercises: Applying the Concepts

9. (a) The hypotheses are $H_0 : p_1 = p_2$ and $H_1 : p_1 > p_2$, where $p_1 =$ Group1 proportion.

The two sample estimates are $\hat{p}_1 = \dfrac{x_1}{n_1} = \dfrac{107}{710} = 0.1507$, $\hat{p}_2 = \dfrac{x_2}{n_2} = \dfrac{67}{611} = 0.1097$ and

the pooled estimate is $\hat{p} = \dfrac{x_1 + x_2}{n_1 + n_2} = \dfrac{107 + 67}{710 + 611} = 0.1317$. The test statistic is

$$Z = \frac{\hat{p}_1 - \hat{p}_2}{\sqrt{\hat{p}(1 - \hat{p})}\sqrt{1/n_1 + 1/n_2}} = \frac{0.1507 - 0.1097}{\sqrt{0.1317(1 - 0.1317)}\sqrt{1/710 + 1/611}} = 2.20.$$

This is a right-tailed test and so the critical value is $z_\alpha = z_{0.05} = 1.645$. Since the test statistic is in the rejection region, we reject H_0. There is enough evidence to support the claim that a higher percentage of subjects in Group 1 experience fever as a side effect than of subjects in Group 2. $P = P(Z \geq 2.20) = 1 - 0.9861 = 0.0139 < 0.05$.

(b) For a 90% confidence interval we use $\pm z_{0.05} = \pm 1.645$. The bounds are:

$$(\hat{p}_1 - \hat{p}_2) \pm z_{\alpha/2} \cdot \sqrt{\frac{\hat{p}_1(1 - \hat{p}_1)}{n_1} + \frac{\hat{p}_2(1 - \hat{p}_2)}{n_2}}$$

$$= (0.1507 - 0.1097) \pm 1.645 \cdot \sqrt{\frac{0.1507(1 - 0.1507)}{710} + \frac{0.1097(1 - 0.1097)}{611}}$$

$$= 0.041 \pm 0.030 = (0.01, 0.07).$$

11. (a) The hypotheses are $H_0 : p_1 = p_2$ and $H_1 : p_1 > p_2$, where $p_1 =$ proportion for individuals with at most an eighth-grade education.

The two sample estimates are $\hat{p}_1 = \dfrac{x_1}{n_1} = \dfrac{114}{320} = 0.3563$, $\hat{p}_2 = \dfrac{x_2}{n_2} = \dfrac{112}{350} = 0.3200$ and

the pooled estimate is $\hat{p} = \dfrac{x_1 + x_2}{n_1 + n_2} = \dfrac{114 + 112}{320 + 350} = 0.3373$. The test statistic is

$$Z = \frac{\hat{p}_1 - \hat{p}_2}{\sqrt{\hat{p}(1 - \hat{p})}\sqrt{1/n_1 + 1/n_2}} = \frac{0.3563 - 0.3200}{\sqrt{0.3373(1 - 0.3373)}\sqrt{1/320 + 1/350}} = 0.99.$$

This is a right-tailed test and so the critical value is $z_\alpha = z_{0.10} = 1.28$. Since the test statistic is not in the rejection region, we do not reject H_0. There is not enough evidence to support the claim that a higher percentage of individuals with at most an eighth-grade education consume too much cholesterol than of individuals with some college education. $P = P(Z \geq 0.99) = 1 - 0.8389 = 0.1611 > 0.10$.

(b) For a 95% confidence interval we use $\pm z_{0.025} = \pm 1.96$. The bounds are:

$$(\hat{p}_1 - \hat{p}_2) \pm z_{\alpha/2} \cdot \sqrt{\frac{\hat{p}_1(1 - \hat{p}_1)}{n_1} + \frac{\hat{p}_2(1 - \hat{p}_2)}{n_2}}$$

$$= (0.3563 - 0.3200) \pm 1.96 \cdot \sqrt{\frac{0.3563(1-0.3563)}{320} + \frac{0.3200(1-0.3200)}{350}}$$

$$= 0.036 \pm 0.072 = (-0.04, 0.11).$$

13. (a) The hypotheses are $H_0 : p_1 = p_2$ and $H_1 : p_1 < p_2$, where p_1 = proportion for 2000.

The two sample estimates are $\hat{p}_1 = \frac{x_1}{n_1} = \frac{257}{1028} = 0.2500$, $\hat{p}_2 = \frac{x_2}{n_2} = \frac{278}{1028} = 0.2704$ and

the pooled estimate is $\hat{p} = \frac{x_1 + x_2}{n_1 + n_2} = \frac{257 + 278}{1028 + 1028} = 0.2602$. The test statistic is

$$Z = \frac{\hat{p}_1 - \hat{p}_2}{\sqrt{\hat{p}(1-\hat{p})}\sqrt{1/n_1 + 1/n_2}} = \frac{0.2500 - 0.2704}{\sqrt{0.2602(1-0.2602)}\sqrt{1/1028 + 1/1028}} = -1.06.$$

This is a left-tailed test and so the critical value is $-z_\alpha = -z_{0.05} = -1.645$. Since the test statistic is not in the rejection region, we do not reject H_0. There is not enough evidence to support the claim that the percentage of adults who smoked in the last week decreased from 1990 to 2000. $P = P(Z \le -1.06) = 0.1446 > 0.05$.

(b) For a 95% confidence interval we use $\pm z_{0.025} = \pm 1.96$. The bounds are:

$$(\hat{p}_1 - \hat{p}_2) \pm z_{\alpha/2} \cdot \sqrt{\frac{\hat{p}_1(1-\hat{p}_1)}{n_1} + \frac{\hat{p}_2(1-\hat{p}_2)}{n_2}}$$

$$= (0.2500 - 0.2704) \pm 1.96 \cdot \sqrt{\frac{0.2500(1-0.2500)}{1028} + \frac{0.2704(1-0.2704)}{1028}}$$

$$= -0.020 \pm 0.038 = (-0.06, 0.02).$$

15. (a) The hypotheses are $H_0 : p_1 = p_2$ and $H_1 : p_1 < p_2$, where p_1 = proportion for the experimental group.

The sample estimates are $\hat{p}_1 = \frac{x_1}{n_1} = \frac{33}{200,000} = 0.0002$, $\hat{p}_2 = \frac{x_2}{n_2} = \frac{115}{200,000} = 0.0006$

and the pooled estimate is $\hat{p} = \frac{x_1 + x_2}{n_1 + n_2} = \frac{33 + 115}{200,000 + 200,000} = 0.0004$. The test statistic is

$$Z = \frac{\hat{p}_1 - \hat{p}_2}{\sqrt{\hat{p}(1-\hat{p})}\sqrt{1/n_1 + 1/n_2}} = \frac{0.0002 - 0.0006}{\sqrt{0.0004(1-0.0004)}\sqrt{1/200,000 + 1/200,000}} = -6.74.$$

This is a left-tailed test and so the critical value is $-z_\alpha = -z_{0.01} = -2.33$. Since the test statistic is in the rejection region, we reject H_0. There is enough evidence to support the claim that the percentage of subjects in the experimental group who contracted polio is less than the percentage in the control group.
$P = P(Z \le -6.74) < 0.0002 < 0.01$.

(b) For a 90% confidence interval we use $\pm z_{0.05} = \pm 1.645$. The bounds are:

$$(\hat{p}_1 - \hat{p}_2) \pm z_{\alpha/2} \cdot \sqrt{\frac{\hat{p}_1(1-\hat{p}_1)}{n_1} + \frac{\hat{p}_2(1-\hat{p}_2)}{n_2}}$$

$$= (0.0002 - 0.0004) \pm 1.645 \cdot \sqrt{\frac{0.0002(1-0.0002)}{200,000} + \frac{0.0004(1-0.0004)}{200,000}}$$

$$= -0.0004 \pm 0.0001 = (-0.0005, -0.0003).$$

17. (a) $n = n_1 = n_2 = \left[\hat{p}_1(1-\hat{p}_1) + \hat{p}_2(1-\hat{p}_2)\right]\left(\dfrac{z_{\alpha/2}}{E}\right)^2$

$$= \left[0.219(1-0.219) + 0.197(1-0.197)\right]\left(\frac{1.96}{0.03}\right)^2 = 1405.3 \text{ which we round up to } 1406.$$

(b) $n = n_1 = n_2 = 0.5\left(\dfrac{z_{\alpha/2}}{E}\right)^2 = 0.5\left(\dfrac{1.96}{0.03}\right)^2 = 2134.2$ which we round up to 2135.

19. Since $P = 0.672$ is large, the researchers will not reject the null hypothesis and so they will conclude that there is not enough evidence to support the claim that there is a difference between the two treatment modes in the percentage of patients that are healed.

21. At a 5% level of significance, there is enough evidence to conclude that caffeine citrate is more effective than placebo in reducing sleep apnea episodes by at least 50% in six days.

Review Exercises

1. Dependent, since the members of the two samples are matched by diagnosis.

3. Independent because the subjects are randomly selected from two distinct populations.

5. (a)

Observation	1	2	3	4	5	6
X_1	34.2	32.1	39.5	41.8	45.1	38.4
X_2	34.9	31.5	39.5	41.9	45.5	38.8
$X_1 - X_2$	-0.7	0.6	0.0	-0.1	-0.4	-0.3

(b) Using technology, $\bar{d} = -0.167$ and $s_d = 0.450$.

(c) The hypotheses are $H_0 : \mu_d = 0$, $H_1 : \mu_d < 0$. Since this is a left-tailed test with 5 df,

the critical value is $-t_{0.05} = -2.015$. Then $t = \dfrac{\bar{d}}{s_d / \sqrt{n}} = \dfrac{-0.167}{0.450 / \sqrt{6}} = -0.909$, which is

not in the critical region and so we do not reject H_0.

(d) $\bar{d} \pm t_{0.01} \cdot \dfrac{s_d}{\sqrt{n}} = -0.167 \pm 3.365 \cdot \dfrac{0.450}{\sqrt{6}} = -0.167 \pm 0.618 = (-0.79, 0.45)$. Note that this

confidence interval would match a one-tailed test of significance at the 0.01 level.

7. (a) This is a two-tailed test, σ unknown, with df $= 8{-}1 = 7$ (the lesser of $n_1 - 1$ and
$n_2 - 1$). The critical t-values are $\pm t_{0.05} = \pm 1.895$. The test statistic is:

$$t = \frac{(\bar{x}_1 - \bar{x}_2) - (\mu_1 - \mu_2)}{\sqrt{s_1^2 / n_1 + s_2^2 / n_2}} = \frac{(32.4 - 28.2) - 0}{\sqrt{4.5^2 / 13 + 3.8^2 / 8}} = 2.290$$

which is in the rejection region and so we reject H_0.

(b) For a 90% confidence interval we use $\pm t_{0.05} = \pm 1.895$, giving bounds of:

$$(\bar{x}_1 - \bar{x}_2) \pm t_{\alpha/2} \cdot \sqrt{\frac{s_1^2}{n_1} + \frac{s_2^2}{n_2}} = (32.4 - 28.2) \pm 1.895 \cdot \sqrt{\frac{4.5^2}{13} + \frac{3.8^2}{8}} = 4.2 \pm 3.47 = (0.73, 7.67).$$

9. (a) This is a right-tailed test, σ unknown, with df $= 41{-}1 = 40$ (the lesser of $n_1 - 1$ and
$n_2 - 1$). The critical t-value is $t_{0.01} = 2.423$. The test statistic is:

$$t = \frac{(\bar{x}_1 - \bar{x}_2) - (\mu_1 - \mu_2)}{\sqrt{s_1^2 / n_1 + s_2^2 / n_2}} = \frac{(48.2 - 45.2) - 0}{\sqrt{8.4^2 / 45 + 10.3^2 / 41}} = 1.472$$

which is not in the rejection region and so we do not reject H_0.

(b) For a 90% confidence interval we use $\pm t_{0.05} = \pm 1.684$, giving bounds of:

$$(\bar{x}_1 - \bar{x}_2) \pm t_{\alpha/2} \cdot \sqrt{\frac{s_1^2}{n_1} + \frac{s_2^2}{n_2}} = (48.2 - 45.2) \pm 1.684 \cdot \sqrt{\frac{8.4^2}{45} + \frac{10.3^2}{41}}$$

$$= 3.0 \pm 3.43 = (-0.43, 6.43).$$

Note that this confidence interval would match a one-tailed test of significance at the
0.05 level.

11. (a) The hypotheses are $H_0 : p_1 = p_2$ and $H_1 : p_1 \neq p_2$.

(b) The two sample estimates are $\hat{p}_1 = \dfrac{x_1}{n_1} = \dfrac{451}{555} = 0.8126$, $\hat{p}_2 = \dfrac{x_2}{n_2} = \dfrac{510}{600} = 0.8500$ and

the pooled estimate is $\hat{p} = \dfrac{x_1 + x_2}{n_1 + n_2} = \dfrac{451 + 510}{555 + 600} = 0.8320$. The test statistic is

$$Z = \frac{\hat{p}_1 - \hat{p}_2}{\sqrt{\hat{p}(1 - \hat{p})} \sqrt{1/n_1 + 1/n_2}} = \frac{0.8126 - 0.8500}{\sqrt{0.832(1 - 0.832)} \sqrt{1/555 + 1/600}} = -1.70.$$

(c) This is a two-tailed test and so the critical values are $\pm z_{0.025} = \pm 1.96$. Since the test statistic is not in the rejection region, we do not reject H_0. There is not enough evidence to support the claim that $p_1 \neq p_2$.

(d) $P = 2 \cdot P(Z \leq -1.70) = 2 \cdot 0.0446 = 0.0892$.

13. (a) Yes, Welch's t-test is appropriate since the data are obtained from simple random samples that are independent and appear to come from normal populations.

(b) With μ_f = reaction time of females and μ_m = reaction time of males, we test the hypotheses $H_0 : \mu_f - \mu_m = 0$, $H_1 : \mu_f - \mu_m \neq 0$. This is a two-tailed test, σ unknown, with df = 12–1 = 11. The critical t-values are $\pm t_{0.025} = \pm 2.201$. Using technology, the summary statistics are $\bar{x}_f = 0.6117$, $s_f = 0.1737$, $n_f = 16$ and $\bar{x}_m = 0.6675$, $s_m = 0.1882$, $n_m = 12$. The test statistic is:

$$t = \frac{(\bar{x}_f - \bar{x}_m) - (\mu_f - \mu_m)}{\sqrt{s_f^2 / n_f + s_m^2 / n_m}} = \frac{(0.6117 - 0.6675) - 0}{\sqrt{0.1737^2 / 16 + 0.1882^2 / 12}} = -0.802$$

which is not in the rejection region and so we do not reject H_0. There is not enough evidence to conclude that there is a difference in reaction time between females and males.

(c) For a 95% confidence interval we use $\pm t_{0.025} = \pm 2.201$, giving bounds of:

$$(\bar{x}_f - \bar{x}_m) \pm t_{\alpha/2} \cdot \sqrt{\frac{s_f^2}{n_f} + \frac{s_m^2}{n_m}} = (0.6117 - 0.6675) \pm 2.201 \cdot \sqrt{\frac{0.1737^2}{16} + \frac{0.1882^2}{12}}$$

$$= -0.0558 \pm 0.1531 = (-0.21, 0.10)$$

We are 95% confident that the true mean difference in reaction time (female – male) is between –0.21 and 0.10 seconds.

(d) From the boxplot, there does not appear to be a lot of difference in the reaction times of the two groups.

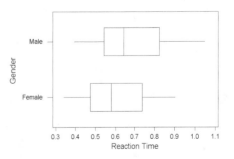

Reaction Time to a "Choice" Stimulus

15. (a) This is independent sampling since the pennies come from different populations.

(b) With μ_1 = weight of wheat pennies and μ_2 = weight of modern pennies, we test the hypotheses $H_0 : \mu_1 - \mu_2 = 0$, $H_1 : \mu_1 - \mu_2 < 0$. This is a left-tailed test, σ unknown, with df = 19–1 = 18. The critical t-value is $-t_{0.05} = -1.734$. Using technology, the summary statistics are $\bar{x}_1 = 3.0259$, $s_1 = 0.0295$, $n_1 = 22$ and $\bar{x}_2 = 3.0553$, $s_2 = 0.0324$, $n_2 = 19$. The test statistic is:

$$t = \frac{(\bar{x}_1 - \bar{x}_2) - (\mu_1 - \mu_2)}{\sqrt{s_1^2/n_1 + s_2^2/n_2}} = \frac{(3.0259 - 3.0553) - 0}{\sqrt{0.0295^2/22 + 0.0324^2/19}} = -3.019$$

which is in the rejection region and so we reject H_0. There is enough evidence to conclude that wheat pennies weigh less than modern pennies.

(c) For a 95% confidence interval for $\mu_2 - \mu_1$ we use $\pm t_{0.025} = \pm 2.101$, giving bounds of:

$$(\bar{x}_2 - \bar{x}_1) \pm t_{\alpha/2} \cdot \sqrt{\frac{s_1^2}{n_1} + \frac{s_2^2}{n_2}} = (3.0553 - 3.0259) \pm 2.101 \cdot \sqrt{\frac{0.0295^2}{22} + \frac{0.0324^2}{19}}$$

$$= 0.0294 \pm 0.0205 = (0.009, 0.050)$$

We are 95% confident that the true mean difference in weight is between 0.009 and 0.050 grams.

(d) The wheat pennies, having been in circulation for longer, will on average be more worn than modern pennies and so weigh less.

17. (a) The hypotheses are $H_0 : p_1 = p_2$ and $H_1 : p_1 < p_2$, where p_1 = proportion of women in the experimental group who experienced a bone fracture. The two sample estimates are $\hat{p}_1 = \frac{x_1}{n_1} = \frac{27}{696} = 0.0388$, $\hat{p}_2 = \frac{x_2}{n_2} = \frac{49}{678} = 0.0723$ and the pooled estimate is

$\hat{p} = \frac{x_1 + x_2}{n_1 + n_2} = \frac{27 + 49}{696 + 678} = 0.0553$. The test statistic is

$$Z = \frac{\hat{p}_1 - \hat{p}_2}{\sqrt{\hat{p}(1 - \hat{p})}\sqrt{1/n_1 + 1/n_2}} = \frac{0.0388 - 0.0723}{\sqrt{0.0553(1 - 0.0553)}\sqrt{1/696 + 1/678}} = -2.71.$$

This is a left-tailed test and so the critical value is $-z_\alpha = -z_{0.01} = -2.33$. Since the test statistic is in the rejection region, we reject H_0. There is enough evidence to support the claim that the percentage of women taking Actonel who experience fractures is lower than the percentage of women taking a placebo.

(b) For a 95% confidence interval we use $\pm z_{0.025} = \pm 1.96$. The bounds are:

$$(\hat{p}_1 - \hat{p}_2) \pm z_{\alpha/2} \cdot \sqrt{\frac{\hat{p}_1(1 - \hat{p}_1)}{n_1} + \frac{\hat{p}_2(1 - \hat{p}_2)}{n_2}}$$

$$= (0.0388 - 0.0723) \pm 1.96 \cdot \sqrt{\frac{0.0388(1 - 0.0388)}{696} + \frac{0.0723(1 - 0.0723)}{678}}$$

$$= -0.033 \pm 0.024 = (-0.06, -0.01).$$

(c) This is a completely randomized design. The treatment is medication which has two levels (Actonel and placebo).

19. (a) $n = n_1 = n_2 = \left[\hat{p}_1(1-\hat{p}_1) + \hat{p}_2(1-\hat{p}_2)\right]\left(\frac{z_{\alpha/2}}{E}\right)^2$

$= \left[0.188(1-0.188) + 0.205(1-0.205)\right]\left(\frac{1.645}{0.02}\right)^2 = 2135.3$ which we round up to 2136.

(b) $n = n_1 = n_2 = 0.5\left(\frac{z_{\alpha/2}}{E}\right)^2 = 0.5\left(\frac{1.645}{0.02}\right)^2 = 3382.5$ which we round up to 3383.

21. The matched-pairs t-test should be used when the two samples are dependent. A paired samples test has the advantage of greater precision because the pairing reduces confounding effects (i.e. the influence of other factors) which might obscure the difference that is being investigated in the experiment.

Chapter 11. Additional Inferential Procedures

11.1 Chi-Square Goodness-of-Fit Test

11.1 Concepts and Vocabulary

1. These procedures are for testing whether sample data are a good fit with a hypothesized distribution.

3. The sample data must be obtained one by random sampling, all expected frequencies must be greater than or equal to 1, and no more than 20% of the expected frequencies should be less than 5.

11.1 Exercises: Skill Building

1. Each expected count is $n \cdot p_i$ where $n = 500$. This gives expected counts of 100, 50, 225 and 125 respectively.

3. (a)

Observed (O_i)	Expected (E_i)	$(O_i - E_i)^2$	$(O_i - E_i)^2 / E_i$
30	25	25	1
20	25	25	1
28	25	9	0.36
22	25	9	0.36
		$\chi^2 =$	2.72

(b) df $= 4 - 1 = 3$
(c) $\chi^2_{0.05} = 7.815$
(d) The test statistic is not in the (right-tailed) critical region and so we do not reject H_0.

5. (a)

Observed (O_i)	Expected (E_i)	$(O_i - E_i)^2$	$(O_i - E_i)^2 / E_i$
1	1.6	0.36	0.225
38	25.6	153.76	6.006
132	153.6	466.56	3.038
440	409.6	924.16	2.256
389	409.6	424.36	1.036
		$\chi^2 =$	12.561

(b) df $= 5 - 1 = 4$

(c) $\chi^2_{0.05} = 9.488$

(d) The test statistic is in the (right-tailed) critical region and so we reject H_0.

11.1   Exercises: Applying the Concepts

7.

Observed Count (O_i)	Expected %	Expected Count (E_i)	$(O_i - E_i)^2$	$(O_i - E_i)^2 / E_i$
125	30%	120	25	0.208
77	20%	80	9	0.113
90	20%	80	100	1.250
31	10%	40	81	2.025
42	10%	40	4	0.100
35	10%	40	25	0.625
			$\chi^2 =$	4.321

The critical value, with df $= 6 - 1 = 5$, is $\chi^2_{0.05} = 11.071$. Since the test statistic is not in the critical region, we do not reject H_0. There is not enough evidence to support the claim that the distribution of colors of plain M&M's differs from that claimed by M&M/Mars.

9.

Observed Count (O_i)	Expected Rel. Freq.	Expected Count (E_i)	$(O_i - E_i)^2$	$(O_i - E_i)^2 / E_i$
19	0.112	44.8	665.64	14.858
20	0.071	28.4	70.56	2.485
42	0.092	36.8	27.04	0.735
34	0.061	24.4	92.16	3.777
39	0.061	24.4	213.16	8.736
98	0.123	49.2	2381.44	48.403
101	0.255	102	1	0.010
47	0.225	90	1849	20.544
			$\chi^2 =$	99.548

The critical value, with df = 8 – 1 = 7, is $\chi^2_{0.05} = 14.067$. Since the test statistic is in the critical region, we reject H_0. There is enough evidence to support the claim that the distribution of pedestrian deaths by time of day differs from the distribution of bicycle deaths by time of day.

11.

Observed Count (O_i)	Expected Count (E_i)	$(O_i - E_i)^2$	$(O_i - E_i)^2 / E_i$
52	$500/12 = 41.67$	106.78	2.563
35	41.67	44.44	1.067
44	41.67	5.44	0.131
42	41.67	0.11	0.003
42	41.67	0.11	0.003
36	41.67	32.11	0.771
44	41.67	5.44	0.131
34	41.67	58.78	1.411
36	41.67	32.11	0.771
46	41.67	18.78	0.451
48	41.67	40.11	0.963
41	41.67	0.44	0.011
		$\chi^2 =$	8.272

The critical value, with df = 12 – 1 = 11, is $\chi^2_{0.05} = 19.675$. Since the test statistic is not in the critical region, we do not reject H_0. There is not enough evidence to support the claim that the distribution of births by month is not uniform.

13.

Observed Count (O_i)	Expected Count (E_i)	$(O_i - E_i)^2$	$(O_i - E_i)^2 / E_i$
39	$300/7 = 42.86$	14.88	0.347
40	42.86	8.16	0.190
30	42.86	165.31	3.857
40	42.86	8.16	0.190
41	42.86	3.45	0.080
49	42.86	37.73	0.880
61	42.86	329.16	7.680
		$\chi^2 =$	13.227

The critical value, with df $= 7 - 1 = 6$, is $\chi^2_{0.05} = 12.592$. Since the test statistic is in the critical region, we reject H_0. There is enough evidence to support the claim that the distribution of pedestrian deaths by day of the week is not uniform.

15. **(a)** Results will vary.
   (b) Each of the five numbers should be equally likely and so the proportions should all be 20%.
   (c) Results will vary.

17. **(a), (b)**

Observed Count (O_i)	Expected Rel. Freq.	Expected Count (E_i)	$(O_i - E_i)^2$	$(O_i - E_i)^2 / E_i$
11	0.071	8.52	6.1504	0.722
109	0.929	111.48	6.1504	0.055
120			$\chi^2 =$	0.777

The critical value, with df $= 2 - 1 = 1$, is $\chi^2_{0.05} = 3.841$. Since the test statistic is not in the critical region, we do not reject H_0. There is not enough evidence to support the claim that the percentage of low-birth-weight babies is higher for mothers 35–39 years old.
   (c) The hypotheses are $H_0 : p = 0.071$, $H_1 : p > 0.071$. From the sample data,

   $\hat{p} = \dfrac{11}{120} = 0.0917$. The test statistic is $Z = \dfrac{\hat{p} - p_0}{\sqrt{p_0(1-p_0)/n}} = \dfrac{0.0917 - 0.071}{\sqrt{0.071(1-0.071)/120}}$

   $= 0.88$. This is a right-tailed test and so the critical value is $z_{0.05} = 1.645$. The test statistic is not in the critical region and so we do not reject the null hypothesis.

19. The sum is 0, as shown below. The observed frequencies and the expected frequencies must both sum to $n = 100$, in this example, and so the sum of their differences must be 0.

Observed (O_i)	Expected (E_i)	$O_i - E_i$
30	25	5
20	25	−5
28	25	3
22	25	−3
Total =		0

11.2 Chi-Square Test for Independence; Homogeneity of Proportions

11.2 Concepts and Vocabulary

1. The chi-square test for independence is a test of a single population and is to determine if there is an association between two characteristics of that population. The chi-square test for homogeneity is a test to determine if two distinct populations are the same with respect to a single characteristic, i.e. if that characteristic is exhibited by the same percentage of the two populations.

11.2 Exercises: Basic Skills

1. **(a)** $\chi^2 = \sum \dfrac{(O_i - E_i)^2}{E_i} = \dfrac{(34-36.26)^2}{36.26} + \cdots + \dfrac{(17-20.89)^2}{20.89} = 1.701$

   (b) df $= (2-1)(3-1) = 2$ and so the critical value is $\chi^2_{0.05} = 5.991$. The test statistic is less than the critical value and so we do not reject H_0. There is not enough evidence to support the claim that the two variables are dependent.

   (c) Using technology we get $P = 0.428$. (Answers may vary due to rounding.)

3. The hypotheses are $H_0 : p_1 = p_2 = p_3$ and H_1 : at least one proportion differs from the others. df $= (2-1)(3-1) = 2$ and so the critical value is $\chi^2_{0.01} = 9.210$. The expected counts are calculated as $\dfrac{(\text{row total}) \cdot (\text{column total})}{(\text{table total})} = \dfrac{229 \cdot 120}{363} = 75.70$ (for the first cell) and so on. The observed and expected counts are shown in the table below. The test statistic is $\chi^2 = \sum \dfrac{(O_i - E_i)^2}{E_i} = \dfrac{(76-75.70)^2}{75.70} + \cdots + \dfrac{(49-43.56)^2}{43.56} = 1.988$ which is less than the critical value and so we do not reject H_0. Using technology we get $P = 0.370$.

	Category 1	Category 2	Category 3	Total
Success	76	84	69	229
	(75.70)	(78.86)	(74.44)	
Failure	44	41	49	134
	(44.30)	(46.14)	(43.56)	
Total	120	125	118	363

11.2   Exercises: Applying the Concepts

5. **(a)** The expected counts are calculated as $\dfrac{\text{(row total)} \cdot \text{(column total)}}{\text{(table total)}} = \dfrac{199 \cdot 150}{380} = 78.55$

   (for the first cell) and so on, giving the following table of observed and expected counts:

Sexual Activity	Family Structure				Total
	Both Parents	One Parent	Parent/ Stepparent	Nonparental Guardian	
Had inter-course	64	59	44	32	199
	(78.55)	(52.37)	(41.89)	(26.18)	
Did not have	86	41	36	18	181
	(71.45)	(47.63)	(38.11)	(23.82)	
Total	150	100	80	50	380

   (b) All expected frequencies are greater than 5 and so all requirements for a chi-square test are satisfied.

   (c) $\chi^2 = \sum \dfrac{(O_i - E_i)^2}{E_i} = \dfrac{(64 - 78.55)^2}{78.55} + \cdots + \dfrac{(18 - 23.82)^2}{23.82} = 10.357$

   (d) $df = (2-1)(4-1) = 3$ and so the critical value is $\chi^2_{0.05} = 7.815$. The test statistic is greater than the critical value and so we reject H_0. There is enough evidence to support the claim that family structure and sexual activity are dependent.

   (e) From the calculations we find that the cell that contributed the most to the test statistic was for the family structure with both parents present, and the females did not have sexual intercourse. The expected frequency was lower than the observed frequency suggesting that the presence of both parents in the home influences the daughter not to have sexual intercourse.

   (f) The conditional frequencies and bar chart show that sexual activity varies by family structure.

	Both Parents	One Parent	Parent/ Stepparent	Nonparental Guardian
Had inter-course	64/150 = 0.427	0.590	0.550	0.640
Did not have	0.573	0.410	0.450	0.360

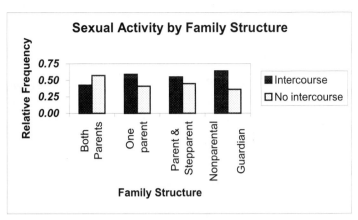

(g) Using technology we get that $P = 0.016$.

7. (a) The expected counts and observed counts are shown in the table:

Area	Level of Education				Total
	Not HS Graduate	**HS Graduate**	**Some College**	**Graduated College**	
Northeast	52	123	70	94	339
	(66.90)	(108.80)	(80.99)	(82.31)	
Midwest	123	146	102	96	467
	(92.16)	(149.89)	(111.57)	(113.38)	
South	119	204	148	144	615
	(121.36)	(197.39)	(146.93)	(149.32)	
West	62	106	111	104	383
	(75.58)	(122.93)	(91.50)	(92.99)	
Total	356	579	431	438	1804

All expected frequencies are greater than 5 and so all requirements for a chi-square test are satisfied. Using technology we calculate $\chi^2 = 32.926$. df $= (4-1)(4-1) = 9$ and so the critical value is $\chi^2_{0.05} = 16.919$. The test statistic is greater than the critical value and so we reject H_0. There is enough evidence to support the claim that level of education and region of the United States are dependent.

(b) From the calculations we find that the cell that contributed the most to the test statistic is the cell corresponding to "Midwest" and "Not a HS Graduate". The expected frequency was lower than the observed frequency suggesting that the Midwest has a higher proportion than other regions of people who are not high-school graduates.

(c) The conditional frequencies and bar chart show that the amount of education varies by region of the United States.

	Not HS Graduate	HS Graduate	Some College	Graduated College
Northeast	0.146	0.212	0.162	0.215
Midwest	0.346	0.252	0.237	0.219
South	0.334	0.352	0.343	0.329
West	0.174	0.183	0.258	0.237

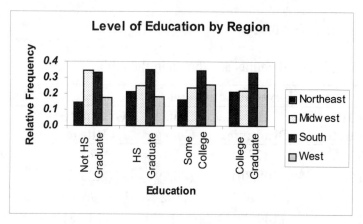

9. (a) The expected counts and observed counts are shown in the table:

Opinion	Age Group			Total
	18–29 Years	30–49 Years	> 49 Years	
For	172	313	258	743
	(163.65)	(303.92)	(275.43)	
Against	52	103	119	274
	(60.35)	(112.08)	(101.57)	
Total	224	416	377	1017

All expected frequencies are greater than 5 and so all requirements for a chi-square test are satisfied. Using technology we calculate $\chi^2 = 6.681$. df $= (2-1)(3-1) = 2$ and so the critical value is $\chi^2_{0.05} = 5.991$. The test statistic is greater than the critical value and so we reject H_0. There is enough evidence to support the claim that opinion about the limited legalization of marijuana and age are dependent.

(b) Using technology we get $P = 0.035$.

(c) The conditional frequencies and bar chart show that the percentage in favor of limited legalization of marijuana declines with age.

	18–29 Years	30–49 Years	> 49 Years
For	0.768	0.752	0.684
Against	0.232	0.248	0.316

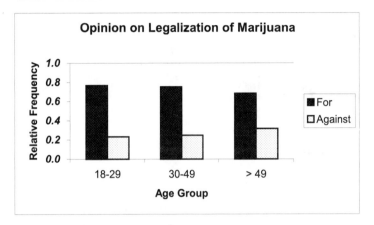

11. (a) The expected counts and observed counts are shown in the table:

Gender	Delinquency				Total
	Person	**Property**	**Drugs**	**Public Order**	
Female	24	85	7	28	144
	(23.23)	(86.78)	(8.83)	(25.15)	
Male	97	367	39	103	606
	(97.77)	(365.22)	(37.17)	(105.85)	
Total	121	452	46	131	750

All expected frequencies are greater than 5 and so all requirements for a chi-square test are satisfied. Using technology we calculate $\chi^2 = 0.946$. df $= (2-1)(4-1) = 3$ and so the critical value is $\chi^2_{0.05} = 7.815$. The test statistic is less than the critical value and so we do not reject H_0. There is not enough evidence to support the claim that type of delinquency and gender are dependent.

(b) Using technology we get $P = 0.814$.

(c) The conditional frequencies and bar chart show that the distribution of genders is very similar for all offenses.

	Person	Property	Drugs	Public Order
Female	0.198	0.188	0.152	0.214
Male	0.802	0.812	0.848	0.786

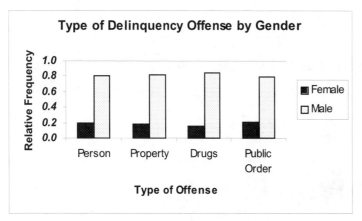

13. **(a)** The expected counts and observed counts are shown in the table:

Smoking Status	Age				Total
	18–29 Years	30–49 Years	50–64 Years	> 64 Years	
Smoked	24 (20.00)	21 (20.00)	23 (20.00)	12 (20.00)	80
Did not smoke	56 (60.00)	59 (60.00)	57 (60.00)	68 (60.00)	240
Total	80	80	80	80	320

All expected frequencies are greater than 5 and so all requirements for a chi-square test are satisfied. Using technology we calculate $\chi^2 = 6.000$. df $= (2-1)(4-1) = 3$ and so the critical value is $\chi^2_{0.05} = 7.815$. The test statistic is less than the critical value and so we do not reject H_0. There is not enough evidence to support the claim that the proportion of smokers differs by age group.

(b) Using technology we get $P = 0.112$.

(c) The conditional frequencies and bar chart show that the distribution of smokers is very similar for all age groups, except perhaps the over 64 years group.

	18–29 Years	30–49 Years	50–64 Years	> 64 Years
Smoked	0.300	0.263	0.288	0.150
Did not smoke	0.700	0.738	0.713	0.850

15. (a) The expected counts and observed counts are shown in the table:

Side Effect	Treatment					Total
	Placebo	Celebrex 50 mg	Celebrex 100 mg	Celebrex 200 mg	Naproxen 500 mg	
Ulcer	5	8	7	13	34	67
	(13.12)	(14.09)	(13.73)	(13.36)	(12.70)	
No Ulcer	212	225	220	208	176	1041
	(203.88)	(218.91)	(213.27)	(207.64)	(197.30)	
Total	217	233	227	221	210	1108

All expected frequencies are greater than 5 and so all requirements for a chi-square test are satisfied. Using technology we calculate $\chi^2 = 49.703$. df $= (2-1)(5-1) = 4$ and so the critical value is $\chi^2_{0.01} = 13.277$. The test statistic is greater than the critical value and so we reject H_0. There is enough evidence to support the claim that the incidence of ulcers varies by treatment.

(b) Using technology we get $P = 0.000$, to three decimal places.

(c) The conditional frequencies and bar chart show that the percentage of subjects suffering ulcers varies by treatment.

	Placebo	Celebrex 50 mg	Celebrex 100 mg	Celebrex 200 mg	Naproxen 500 mg
Ulcer	0.023	0.034	0.031	0.059	0.162
No Ulcer	0.977	0.966	0.969	0.941	0.838

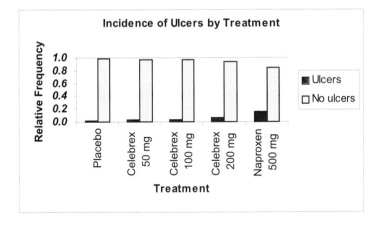

17. (a) The expected counts and observed counts are shown in the table. Since there were no individuals who gave "career" as a reason for dropping, we have omitted that category from the analysis.

Gender	Drop Reason			Total
	Personal	**Work**	**Course**	
Female	5	3	13	21
	(4.62)	(6.72)	(9.66)	
Male	6	13	10	29
	(6.38)	(9.28)	(13.34)	
Total	11	16	23	50

(b) All expected frequencies are greater than 1 and only one (out of six) expected frequency is less than 5. All requirements for a chi-square test are satisfied. Using technology we calculate $\chi^2 = 5.595$. df $= (2-1)(3-1) = 2$ and so the critical value is $\chi^2_{0.10} = 4.605$. The test statistic is greater than the critical value and so we reject H_0. There is enough evidence to support the claim that reason for dropping and gender are dependent.

(c) Using technology we get $P = 0.061$.

(d) The conditional frequencies and bar chart show that the distribution of genders varies by reason for dropping.

	Personal	**Work**	**Course**
Female	0.455	0.188	0.565
Male	0.545	0.813	0.435

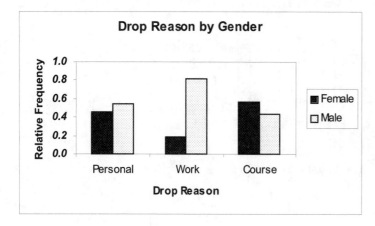

19. (a) The expected and observed counts are shown in the table.

Smoking Status	Year		Total
	1990	**2000**	
Smoked	278	257	535
	(267.50)	(267.50)	
Did not smoke	750	771	1521
	(760.50)	(760.50)	
Total	1028	1028	2056

(b) All expected frequencies are greater than 5 and so the requirements for a chi-square test are satisfied. Using technology we calculate $\chi^2 = 1.114$.

(c) df $= (2-1)(2-1) = 1$ and so the critical value is $\chi^2_{0.10} = 3.841$. The test statistic is less than the critical value and so we do not reject H_0. There is not enough evidence to support the claim that the percentage of smokers changed from 1990 to 2000.

(d) The two sample estimates of percentage of smokers are $\hat{p}_1 = \frac{x_1}{n_1} = \frac{278}{1028} = 0.2704$,

$\hat{p}_2 = \frac{x_2}{n_2} = \frac{257}{1028} = 0.25$. The pooled estimate is $\hat{p} = \frac{x_1 + x_2}{n_1 + n_2} = \frac{278 + 257}{1028 + 1028} = 0.2602$.

The test statistic is

$$Z = \frac{\hat{p}_1 - \hat{p}_2}{\sqrt{\hat{p}(1-\hat{p})}\sqrt{1/n_1 + 1/n_2}} = \frac{0.2704 - 0.25}{\sqrt{0.2602(1-0.2602)}\sqrt{1/1028 + 1/1028}} = 1.054$$

and $Z^2 = 1.111 = \chi^2$ up to rounding.

11.3 Inference about the Least-Squares Regression Model

11.3   Concepts and Vocabulary

1. The requirements are that the sample was obtained by random sampling, and that the residuals are normally distributed with constant variance. We check the latter two assumptions by doing both a normal probability plot of the residuals, and a plot of the residuals against the values of the predictor variable. The errors in the residual plot should be evenly spread about a horizontal line drawn at 0 error.

3. The y-coordinates on the regression line represent the predicted mean value of the response variable for any given value of the predictor variable.

5. If we do not reject $H_0 : \beta_1 = 0$ then the best point estimate of y is just $\bar{y}$.

11.3   Exercises: Skill Building

1. **(a)** Using technology, we get: $b_0 = -2.3256$ is the unbiased estimate of β_0 and $b_1 = 2.0233$ is the unbiased estimate of β_1. (Note that in the notation of Chapter 4, $b_0 = a$ and $b_1 = b$.)

   (b) We calculate $\hat{y} = 2.0233x - 2.3256$ to generate the following table:

x	y	$\hat{y}$	$y - \hat{y}$	$(y - \hat{y})^2$	$(x - \bar{x})^2$
3	4	3.74	0.26	0.0654	5.76
4	6	5.77	0.23	0.0541	1.96
5	7	7.79	-0.79	0.6252	0.16
7	12	11.84	0.16	0.0265	2.56
8	14	13.86	0.14	0.0195	6.76
			Sum:	0.7907	17.20

$$s_e = \sqrt{\frac{\sum (y - \hat{y})^2}{n - 2}} = \sqrt{\frac{0.7907}{5 - 2}} = 0.5134$$

   (c) $s_{b_1} = \dfrac{s_e}{\sqrt{\sum (x - \bar{x})^2}} = \dfrac{0.5134}{\sqrt{17.20}} = 0.1238$

   (d) The hypotheses are $H_0 : \beta_1 = 0$, $H_1 : \beta_1 \neq 0$. df $= n - 2 = 5 - 2 = 3$ and so the critical values are $\pm t_{0.025} = \pm 3.182$. The test statistic is $t = \dfrac{b_1}{s_{b_1}} = \dfrac{2.0233}{0.1238} = 16.345$, which is in the critical region and so we reject H_0.

3. **(a)** Using technology, we get: $b_0 = 1.2$ and $b_1 = 2.2$.

   (b) We calculate $\hat{y} = 2.2x + 1.2$ to generate the following table:

x	y	$\hat{y}$	$y - \hat{y}$	$(y - \hat{y})^2$	$(x - \bar{x})^2$
-2	-4	-3.20	-0.80	0.6400	4
-1	0	-1.00	1.00	1.0000	1
0	1	1.20	-0.20	0.0400	0
1	4	3.40	0.60	0.3600	1
2	5	5.60	-0.60	0.3600	4
			Sum	2.4000	10

$$s_e = \sqrt{\frac{\sum (y - \hat{y})^2}{n - 2}} = \sqrt{\frac{2.4}{5 - 2}} = 0.8944$$

   (c) $s_{b_1} = \dfrac{s_e}{\sqrt{\sum (x - \bar{x})^2}} = \dfrac{0.8944}{\sqrt{10}} = 0.2828$

(d) The hypotheses are $H_0 : \beta_1 = 0$, $H_1 : \beta_1 \neq 0$. df $= n - 2 = 5 - 2 = 3$ and so the critical values are $\pm t_{0.025} = \pm 7.453$. The test statistic is $t = \dfrac{b_1}{s_{b_1}} = \dfrac{2.2}{0.2828} = 7.778$, which is in the critical region and so we reject H_0.

5. **(a)** Using technology, we get: $b_0 = 116.6$ and $b_1 = -0.72$.

   (b) We calculate $\hat{y} = -0.72x + 116.6$ to generate the following table:

x	y	$\hat{y}$	$y - \hat{y}$	$(y - \hat{y})^2$	$(x - \bar{x})^2$
20	100	102.20	-2.20	4.8400	400
30	95	95.00	0.00	0.0000	100
40	91	87.80	3.20	10.2400	0
50	83	80.60	2.40	5.7600	100
60	70	73.40	-3.40	11.5600	400
			Sum	32.4000	1000

$$s_e = \sqrt{\frac{\sum (y - \hat{y})^2}{n - 2}} = \sqrt{\frac{32.4}{5 - 2}} = 3.2863$$

   (c) $s_{b_1} = \dfrac{s_e}{\sqrt{\sum (x - \bar{x})^2}} = \dfrac{3.2863}{\sqrt{1000}} = 0.1039$

   (d) The hypotheses are $H_0 : \beta_1 = 0$, $H_1 : \beta_1 \neq 0$. df $= n - 2 = 5 - 2 = 3$ and so the critical values are $\pm t_{0.025} = \pm 7.453$. The test statistic is $t = \dfrac{b_1}{s_{b_1}} = \dfrac{-0.72}{0.1039} = -6.928$, which is not in the critical region and so we do not reject H_0.

11.3 Exercises: Applying the Concepts

7. **(a)** Using technology, we get: $b_0 = 12.4932$ and $b_1 = 0.1827$.

   (b) Using technology, we calculate $\hat{y} = 0.1827x + 12.4932$ to generate the table:

x	y	$\hat{y}$	$y - \hat{y}$	$(y - \hat{y})^2$	$(x - \bar{x})^2$
27.75	17.5	17.5640	-0.0640	0.0041	1.6782
24.50	17.1	16.9701	0.1299	0.0169	3.8202
25.50	17.1	17.1528	-0.0528	0.0028	0.9112
26.00	17.3	17.2442	0.0558	0.0031	0.2066
25.00	16.9	17.0615	-0.1615	0.0261	2.1157
27.75	17.6	17.5640	0.0360	0.0013	1.6782
26.50	17.3	17.3356	-0.0356	0.0013	0.0021
27.00	17.5	17.4269	0.0731	0.0053	0.2975

26.75	17.3	17.3813	-0.0813	0.0066	0.0873
26.75	17.5	17.3813	0.1187	0.0141	0.0873
27.50	17.5	17.5183	-0.0183	0.0003	1.0930
			Sum	0.0819	11.9773

$$s_e = \sqrt{\frac{\sum(y-\hat{y})^2}{n-2}} = \sqrt{\frac{0.0819}{11-2}} = 0.0954$$

(c) A normal probability plot shows that the residuals are normally distributed.

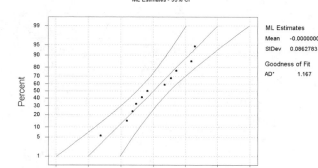

Normal Probability Plot for Residuals
ML Estimates - 95% CI

(d) $s_{b_1} = \dfrac{s_e}{\sqrt{\sum(x-\bar{x})^2}} = \dfrac{0.0954}{\sqrt{11.9773}} = 0.0276$

(e) The hypotheses are $H_0 : \beta_1 = 0$, $H_1 : \beta_1 \neq 0$. df $= n-2 = 11-2 = 9$ and so the critical values are $\pm t_{0.005} = \pm 3.250$. The test statistic is $t = \dfrac{b_1}{s_{b_1}} = \dfrac{0.1827}{0.0276} = 6.630$, which is in the critical region and so we reject H_0. There is enough evidence to support the claim of a linear relationship between height and head circumference.

(f) For a 95% confidence interval we use $t_{0.025} = 2.262$ and get bounds:

$b_1 \pm t_{\alpha/2} \cdot s_{b_1} = 0.1827 \pm 2.262 \cdot 0.0276 = 0.1827 \pm 0.0624 = (0.1204, 0.2451)$.

(g) We can use the regression equation to give the best guess of:
$\hat{y} = 0.1827x + 12.4932 = 0.1827 \cdot 26.5 + 12.4932 = 17.3$ inches.

9. (a) Using technology, we get: $b_0 = 1.1140$ and $b_1 = 1.3902$.

(b) Using technology, we calculate $\hat{y} = 1.3902x + 1.1140$ to generate the table:

x	y	$\hat{y}$	$y-\hat{y}$	$(y-\hat{y})^2$	$(x-\bar{x})^2$
24.80	36.05	35.59	0.4598	0.2114	0.2916
24.59	35.57	35.30	0.2717	0.0738	0.5625
24.59	35.57	35.30	0.2717	0.0738	0.5625
24.29	34.58	34.88	-0.3012	0.0907	1.1025
23.81	34.20	34.21	-0.0139	0.0002	2.3409

24.87	34.73	35.69	-0.9575	0.9169	0.2209
25.90	37.38	37.12	0.2606	0.0679	0.3136
26.11	37.96	37.41	0.5487	0.3010	0.5929
26.63	37.46	38.13	-0.6742	0.4546	1.6641
26.31	37.75	37.69	0.0606	0.0037	0.9409
26.84	38.50	38.43	0.0738	0.0055	2.2500
			Sum	2.1995	10.8424

$$s_e = \sqrt{\frac{\sum(y-\hat{y})^2}{n-2}} = \sqrt{\frac{2.1995}{11-2}} = 0.4944$$

(c) A normal probability plot shows that the residuals are normally distributed.

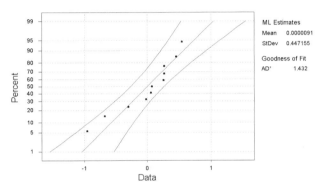

Normal Probability Plot for Residuals
ML Estimates - 95% CI

ML Estimates
Mean   0.0000091
StDev   0.447155

Goodness of Fit
AD*   1.432

(d) $s_{b_1} = \dfrac{s_e}{\sqrt{\sum(x-\bar{x})^2}} = \dfrac{0.4944}{\sqrt{10.8424}} = 0.1501$

(e) The hypotheses are $H_0 : \beta_1 = 0$, $H_1 : \beta_1 \neq 0$. df $= n-2 = 11-2 = 9$ and so the critical values are $\pm t_{0.005} = \pm 3.250$. The test statistic is $t = \dfrac{b_1}{s_{b_1}} = \dfrac{1.3902}{0.1501} = 9.260$, which is in the critical region and so we reject H_0. There is enough evidence to support the claim of a linear relationship between right humerus length and right tibia length.

(f) For a 99% confidence interval we use $t_{0.005} = 3.250$ and get bounds:
$$b_1 \pm t_{\alpha/2} \cdot s_{b_1} = 1.3902 \pm 3.250 \cdot 0.1501 = 1.3902 \pm 0.4879 = (0.902, 1.878).$$

(g) We can use the regression equation to calculate the mean length of the right tibia:
$$\hat{y} = 1.3902x + 1.1140 = 1.3902 \cdot 25.93 + 1.1140 = 37.16 \text{ mm.}$$

11. (a) Using technology, we get: $b_0 = 2.0336$ and $b_1 = 1.6363$.

(b) Using technology, we calculate $\hat{y} = 1.6363x + 2.0336$ to generate the table:

x	y	$\hat{y}$	$y-\hat{y}$	$(y-\hat{y})^2$	$(x-\bar{x})^2$
-2.9	1.1	-2.7118	3.8118	14.5299	13.463
6.3	7.9	12.3425	-4.4425	19.7361	30.589

1.9	2.1	5.1426	-3.0426	9.2576	1.279
5.8	20.1	11.5244	8.5756	73.5416	25.309
-5.1	2.2	-6.3118	8.5118	72.4500	34.448
-2	20.7	-1.2391	21.9391	481.3240	7.669
9.7	17	17.9061	-0.9061	0.8210	79.759
-3.1	-10.3	-3.0391	-7.2609	52.7211	14.971
-2.2	-17.9	-1.5664	-16.3336	266.7876	8.816
2.4	11.6	5.9608	5.6392	31.8006	2.659
-1.6	2.9	-0.5846	3.4846	12.1422	5.613
6.1	4.9	12.0153	-7.1153	50.6270	28.417
-5.3	-19.5	-6.6390	-12.8610	165.4047	36.836
			Sum	1251.1432	289.828

$$s_e = \sqrt{\frac{\sum (y - \hat{y})^2}{n-2}} = \sqrt{\frac{1251.1432}{13-2}} = 10.6649$$

(c) A normal probability plot shows that the residuals are normally distributed.

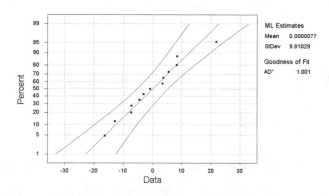

(d) $s_{b_1} = \dfrac{s_e}{\sqrt{\sum (x - \bar{x})^2}} = \dfrac{10.6649}{\sqrt{289.828}} = 0.6265$

(e) The hypotheses are $H_0 : \beta_1 = 0$, $H_1 : \beta_1 \neq 0$. df $= n - 2 = 13 - 2 = 11$ and so the critical values are $\pm t_{0.005} = \pm 1.796$. The test statistic is $t = \dfrac{b_1}{s_{b_1}} = \dfrac{1.6363}{0.6265} = 2.612$, which is in the critical region and so we reject H_0. There is enough evidence to support the claim of a linear relationship between the monthly rate of return on the S&P 500 and the monthly rate of return of Cisco Systems.

(f) For a 99% confidence interval we use $t_{0.005} = 3.106$ and get bounds:

$b_1 \pm t_{\alpha/2} \cdot s_{b_1} = 1.6363 \pm 3.106 \cdot 0.6265 = 1.6363 \pm 1.9459 = (-0.309, 3.582)$.

(g) We can use the regression equation to calculate the mean rate of return:
$\hat{y} = 1.6363x + 2.0336 = 1.6363 \cdot 4.2 + 2.0336 = 8.91$ mg.

13. (a) There does not appear to be much of a relationship between calories and sugar:

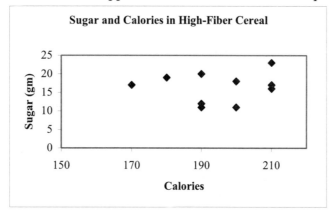

(b) Using technology, we get $\hat{y} = 0.0821x + 0.929$.

(c)

x	y	$\hat{y}$	$y - \hat{y}$	$(y - \hat{y})^2$	$(x - \bar{x})^2$
200	18	17.3571	0.6429	0.4133	11
210	23	18.1786	4.8214	23.2462	178
170	17	14.8929	2.1071	4.4401	711
190	20	16.5357	3.4643	12.0013	44
200	18	17.3571	0.6429	0.4133	11
180	19	15.7143	3.2857	10.7959	278
210	23	18.1786	4.8214	23.2462	178
210	16	18.1786	-2.1786	4.7462	178
210	17	18.1786	-1.1786	1.3890	178
190	12	16.5357	-4.5357	20.5727	44
190	11	16.5357	-5.5357	30.6441	44
200	11	17.3571	-6.3571	40.4133	11
			Sum	172.3214	1867

$$s_e = \sqrt{\frac{\sum(y - \hat{y})^2}{n - 2}} = \sqrt{\frac{172.3214}{12 - 2}} = 4.151$$

(d) A normal probability plot shows that the residuals are normally distributed.

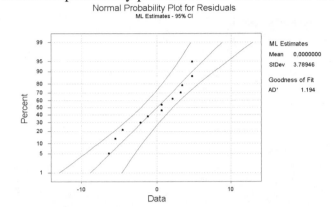

(e) $s_{b_1} = \dfrac{s_e}{\sqrt{\sum (x-\bar{x})^2}} = \dfrac{4.151}{\sqrt{1867}} = 0.0961$

(f) The hypotheses are $H_0 : \beta_1 = 0$, $H_1 : \beta_1 \neq 0$. df $= n-2 = 12-2 = 10$ and so the critical values are $\pm t_{0.005} = \pm 3.169$. The test statistic is $t = \dfrac{b_1}{s_{b_1}} = \dfrac{0.0821}{0.0961} = 0.855$, which is not in the critical region and so we do not reject H_0. There is not enough evidence to support the claim of a linear relationship between calories and sugar content.

(g) For a 95% confidence interval we use $t_{0.025} = 2.228$ and get bounds:

$b_1 \pm t_{\alpha/2} \cdot s_{b_1} = 0.0821 \pm 2.228 \cdot 0.0961 = 0.0821 \pm 0.2141 = (-0.132, 0.296)$.

(h) The scatter plot and hypothesis test show that there is not a sufficiently strong linear relationship to warrant using the regression equation and so we should just use $\bar{y} = 17.1$ gm as our best estimate of the sugar content.

11.4 Confidence and Prediction Intervals

11.4   Concepts and Vocabulary

1. A confidence interval is an interval that, for a given value of x, contains the mean value of the response variable, y, with some given probability—it is an interval estimate of the mean response. A prediction interval is an interval that, for a given value of x, contains the value of the response variable for an individual, with some given probability—it is an interval estimate of an individual response. Since there is more variability in individuals than in means, for the same probability the prediction interval will always be wider than the confidence interval.

11.4 Exercises: Skill Building

1. **(a)** From 11.3.1, the regression equation is $\hat{y} = 2.0233x - 2.3256$ and so the predicted mean value of y when $x = 7$ is $\hat{y} = 2.0233 \cdot 7 - 2.3256 = 11.84$.

   (b) From 11.3.1 we have that $n = 5$, $s_e = 0.5134$, $\bar{x} = 5.4$ and $\sum (x - \bar{x})^2 = 17.20$. For a 95% confidence interval with df $= n - 2 = 3$, we use $t_{0.025} = 3.182$. The bounds are:

   $$\hat{y} \pm t_{\alpha/2} \cdot s_e \sqrt{\frac{1}{n} + \frac{(x^* - \bar{x})^2}{\sum (x - \bar{x})^2}} = 11.84 \pm 3.182 \cdot 0.5134 \cdot \sqrt{\frac{1}{5} + \frac{(7 - 5.4)^2}{17.20}}$$

   $$= 11.84 \pm 0.96 = (10.87, 12.80).$$

   (c) The predicted value of y is also 11.84.

   (d) The bounds are:

   $$\hat{y} \pm t_{\alpha/2} \cdot s_e \sqrt{1 + \frac{1}{n} + \frac{(x^* - \bar{x})^2}{\sum (x - \bar{x})^2}} = 11.84 \pm 3.182 \cdot 0.5134 \cdot \sqrt{1 + \frac{1}{5} + \frac{(7 - 5.4)^2}{17.20}}$$

   $$= 11.84 \pm 1.90 = (9.94, 13.74).$$

   (e) In (a) and (b) we are predicting the mean response (a point estimate and an interval estimate) for the population of individuals with $x = 7$. In (c) and (d) we are predicting the response (a point estimate and an interval estimate) for a single individual with $x = 7$.

3. **(a)** From 11.3.3, the regression equation is $\hat{y} = 2.2x + 1.2$ and so the predicted mean value of y when $x = 1.4$ is $\hat{y} = 2.2 \cdot 1.4 + 1.2 = 4.28$.

   (b) From 11.3.3 we have that $n = 5$, $s_e = 0.8944$, $\bar{x} = 0$ and $\sum (x - \bar{x})^2 = 10$. For a 95% confidence interval with df $= n - 2 = 3$, we use $t_{0.025} = 3.182$. The bounds are:

   $$\hat{y} \pm t_{\alpha/2} \cdot s_e \sqrt{\frac{1}{n} + \frac{(x^* - \bar{x})^2}{\sum (x - \bar{x})^2}} = 4.28 \pm 3.182 \cdot 0.8944 \cdot \sqrt{\frac{1}{5} + \frac{(1.4 - 0)^2}{10}}$$

   $$= 4.28 \pm 1.79 = (2.49, 6.07).$$

   (c) The predicted value of y is also 4.28.

   (d) The bounds are:

   $$\hat{y} \pm t_{\alpha/2} \cdot s_e \sqrt{1 + \frac{1}{n} + \frac{(x^* - \bar{x})^2}{\sum (x - \bar{x})^2}} = 4.28 \pm 3.182 \cdot 0.8944 \cdot \sqrt{1 + \frac{1}{5} + \frac{(1.4 - 0)^2}{10}}$$

   $$= 4.28 \pm 3.36 = (0.92, 7.64).$$

11.4   Exercises: Applying the Concepts

5. (a) From 11.3.7, the regression equation is $\hat{y}=0.1827x+12.4932$ and so the predicted mean value of y when $x=25.75$ is $\hat{y}=0.1827\cdot25.75+12.4932=17.20$ inches.

(b) Using technology we get a 95% confidence interval of (17.12,17.28) inches.

(c) The predicted value of y is also 17.20 inches.

(d) Using technology we get a 95% prediction interval of (16.97,17.43) inches.

(e) In (a) and (b) we are predicting the mean head circumference (a point estimate and an interval estimate) for the population of children who are 25.75 inches tall. In (c) and (d) we are predicting the head circumference (a point estimate and an interval estimate) for a single child with a height of 25.75 inches.

7. (a) From 11.3.9, the regression equation is $\hat{y}=1.3902x+1.1140$ and so the predicted mean value of y when $x=25.83$ is $\hat{y}=1.3902\cdot25.83+1.1140=37.02$ mm.

(b) Using technology we get a 95% confidence interval of (36.65,37.40) mm.

(c) The predicted value of y is also 37.02 mm.

(d) Using technology we get a 95% prediction interval of (35.84,38.20) mm.

(e) The best point estimate for the length of the right tibia of an individual whose humerus measures 25.83 mm is the population mean (of all individuals with humerus measuring 25.83 mm). However the interval estimates will differ because the variability of individuals will be greater than the variability of sample means.

9. (a) From 11.3.11, the predicted mean value of y when $x=4.2$ is given by $\hat{y}=1.6363x+2.0336=1.6363\cdot4.2+2.0336=8.91\%$ return.

(b) Using technology we get a 90% confidence interval of (2.34%,15.47%) return.

(c) The predicted value of y is also 8.91%.

(d) Using technology we get a 90% prediction interval of (−11.34%,29.15%) return.

(e) The best point estimate for the return on Cisco Systems stock in an individual month when the return on the S&P 500 is 4.2% is the population mean (of all months when the return on the S&P 500 is 4.2%). However the interval estimates will differ because the variability of individuals will be greater than the variability of sample means.

11. (a) We showed in 11.3.13 there was not a significant linear relationship between sugar content and calories in high-fiber cereals and so we should not use the regression equation.

(b) For a 95% confidence interval for the mean sugar content we just use the y-values in our sample. The summary statistics are $n=12$, $\bar{y}=17.08$ and $s_y=4.100$. For 95% confidence with df $=n-1=11$, we use $t_{.025}=2.201$ and get:

$$\bar{y}\pm t_{0.025}\cdot\frac{s_y}{\sqrt{n}}=17.08\pm2.201\cdot\frac{4.100}{\sqrt{12}}=17.08\pm2.61=(14.5,19.7).$$

Review Exercises

1.

Observed Count (O_i)	Expected Rel. Freq.	Expected Count (E_i)	$(O_i - E_i)^2$	$(O_i - E_i)^2 / E_i$
233	18/38	236.84	14.76	0.062
237	18/38	236.84	0.02	0.000
30	2/38	26.32	13.57	0.516
500		500	$\chi^2 =$	0.578

The critical value, with df $= 3 - 1 = 2$, is $\chi^2_{0.05} = 5.991$. Since the test statistic is less than the critical value, we do not reject H_0. There is not enough evidence to support the claim that the roulette wheel is out of balance.

3.

Observed Count (O_i)	Expected Rel. Freq.	Expected Count (E_i)	$(O_i - E_i)^2$	$(O_i - E_i)^2 / E_i$
89	0.191	95.50	42.25	0.442
152	0.344	172.00	400.00	2.326
83	0.174	87.00	16.00	0.184
39	0.07	35.00	16.00	0.457
93	0.147	73.50	380.25	5.173
44	0.075	37.50	42.25	1.127
500		500	$\chi^2 =$	9.709

The critical value, with df $= 6 - 1 = 5$, is $\chi^2_{0.10} = 9.236$. Since the test statistic is greater than the critical value, we reject H_0. There is enough evidence to support the claim that the distribution of educational attainment has changed since 1994.

5. (a) The expected counts are calculated as
$$\frac{(\text{row total}) \cdot (\text{column total})}{(\text{table total})} = \frac{1{,}016 \cdot 732}{2{,}033} = 365.82 \text{ (for the first cell)}$$
and so on, giving the following table of observed and expected counts:

Date	Belief				Total
	God Guiding	God had no Part	God Created	Other	
February 2001	376	122	457	61	1,016
	(365.82)	(116.94)	(467.27)	(65.97)	
June 1993	356	112	478	71	1,017
	(366.18)	(117.06)	(467.73)	(66.03)	
Total	732	234	935	132	2,033

(b) All expected frequencies are greater than 5 and so all requirements for a chi-square test are satisfied.

(c) $\chi^2 = \sum \dfrac{(O_i - E_i)^2}{E_i} = \dfrac{(376 - 365.82)^2}{365.82} + \cdots + \dfrac{(71 - 66.03)^2}{66.03} = 2.203$

(d) df $= (2-1)(4-1) = 3$ and so the critical values is $\chi^2_{0.05} = 7.815$. The test statistic is less than the critical value and so we do not reject H_0. There is not enough evidence to support the claim that these beliefs are dependent on the date of the survey.

(e) From the calculations we find that all of the cells contributed about the same to the test statistic and none of them made a large contribution. No particular conclusion can be drawn.

(f) The conditional frequencies and bar chart show that beliefs appear not to have changed very much.

	God Guiding	God had no Part	God Created	Other
February 2001	0.370	0.120	0.450	0.060
June 1993	0.350	0.110	0.470	0.070

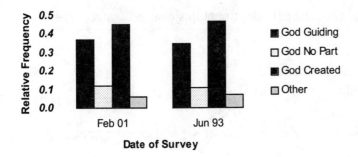

(g) Using technology we get that $P = 0.531$.

7. The expected counts and observed counts are shown in the table:

Race	Region				Total
	Not HS Graduate	HS Graduate	Some College	Graduated College	
White	421	520	656	400	1997
	(405.65)	(459.03)	(690.83)	(441.49)	
Black	56	57	158	28	299
	(60.74)	(68.73)	(103.43)	(66.10)	
American Indian etc	2	4	6	9	21
	(4.27)	(4.83)	(7.26)	(4.64)	
Asian	13	8	11	40	72
	(14.63)	(16.55)	(24.91)	(15.92)	
Hispanic	38	17	68	101	224
	(45.50)	(51.49)	(77.49)	(49.52)	
Other	17	8	24	50	99
	(20.11)	(22.76)	(34.25)	(21.89)	
Total	532	602	906	579	2619

All expected frequencies are greater than 1 and 3 out of 24 (which is less than 20%) of them are less than 5 and so all requirements for a chi-square test are satisfied. Using technology we calculate $\chi^2 = 242.829$. df $= (6-1)(4-1) = 15$ and so the critical value is $\chi^2_{0.01} = 30.578$. The test statistic is greater than the critical value and so we reject H_0. There is enough evidence to support the claim that race and region of the United States are dependent.

9. The expected counts and observed counts are shown in the table:

Symptoms	Region				Total
	Northeast	Midwest	South	West	
Within Last Year	26	31	23	35	115
	(28.75)	(28.75)	(28.75)	(28.75)	
Not Within Last Year	94	89	97	85	365
	(91.25)	(91.25)	(91.25)	(91.25)	
Total	120	120	120	120	480

All expected frequencies are greater than 5 and so all requirements for a chi-square test are satisfied. Using technology we calculate $\chi^2 = 3.877$. df $= (2-1)(4-1) = 3$ and so the critical value is $\chi^2_{0.05} = 7.815$. The test statistic is less than the critical value and so we do not reject H_0. There is not enough evidence to support the claim that the proportion of people who have had colds in the last year varies by region.

11. (a) Using the results from Chapter 4 we have: $b_0 = 32.12$ and $b_1 = -3.5339$. We use the regression equation to calculate the mean mpg for cars with 3.8-liter engines:
$\hat{y} = -3.5339 \cdot 3.8 + 32.12 = 18.7$ mpg.

(b) Using technology, we calculate $\hat{y} = -3.5339x + 32.12$ to generate the table:

x	y	$\hat{y}$	$y - \hat{y}$	$(y - \hat{y})^2$	$(x - \bar{x})^2$
3.1	20	21.165	-1.165	1.357	0.002
3.8	19	18.691	0.309	0.095	0.427
4.6	16	15.864	0.136	0.018	2.112
3.8	19	18.691	0.309	0.095	0.427
2.2	24	24.345	-0.345	0.119	0.896
3.1	23	21.165	1.835	3.368	0.002
3.5	18	19.751	-1.751	3.067	0.125
2.7	19	22.578	-3.578	12.806	0.200
4.6	17	15.864	1.136	1.290	2.112
2	28	25.052	2.948	8.689	1.315
3.8	20	18.691	1.309	1.713	0.427
3.5	19	19.751	-0.751	0.565	0.125
2.4	22	23.639	-1.639	2.685	0.558
2.2	23	24.345	-1.345	1.810	0.896
1.9	28	25.406	2.594	6.731	1.554
			Sum	44.409	11.177

$$s_e = \sqrt{\frac{\sum (y - \hat{y})^2}{n - 2}} = \sqrt{\frac{44.409}{15 - 2}} = 1.8483$$

(c) A normal probability plot shows that the residuals are normally distributed.

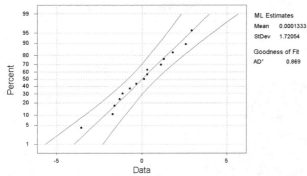

Normal Probability Plot for Residuals
ML Estimates - 95% CI

ML Estimates
Mean   0.0001333
StDev   1.72054

Goodness of Fit
AD*   0.869

(d) $s_{b_1} = \dfrac{s_e}{\sqrt{\sum(x-\bar{x})^2}} = \dfrac{1.8483}{\sqrt{11.177}} = 0.5528$

(e) The hypotheses are $H_0 : \beta_1 = 0$, $H_1 : \beta_1 \neq 0$. df $= n-2=15-2=13$ and so the critical values are $\pm t_{0.025} = \pm 2.160$. The test statistic is $t = \dfrac{b_1}{s_{b_1}} = \dfrac{-3.5339}{0.5528} = -6.392$, which

is in the critical region and so we reject H_0. There is enough evidence to support the claim of a linear relationship between engine displacement and mpg.

(f) For a 95% confidence interval we use $t_{0.025} = 2.160$ and get bounds:

$b_1 \pm t_{\alpha/2} \cdot s_{b_1} = -3.5339 \pm 2.160 \cdot 0.5528 = -3.5339 \pm 1.1940 = (-4.7279, -2.3399)$.

(g) We have $n=15$, $s_e = 1.8483$, $\bar{x} = 3.147$ and $\sum(x-\bar{x})^2 = 11.177$. For a 90% confidence interval with df $= n-2=13$, we use $t_{0.05} = 1.771$. The bounds are:

$$\hat{y} \pm t_{\alpha/2} \cdot s_e \sqrt{\dfrac{1}{n} + \dfrac{(x^*-\bar{x})^2}{\sum(x-\bar{x})^2}} = 18.7 \pm 1.771 \cdot 1.8483 \cdot \sqrt{\dfrac{1}{15} + \dfrac{(3.8-3.147)^2}{11.177}}$$

$$= 18.7 \pm 1.1 = (17.6, 19.8).$$

(h) The predicted value of y is also 18.7.

(i) The bounds are:

$$\hat{y} \pm t_{\alpha/2} \cdot s_e \sqrt{1 + \dfrac{1}{n} + \dfrac{(x^*-\bar{x})^2}{\sum(x-\bar{x})^2}} = 18.7 \pm 1.771 \cdot 1.8483 \cdot \sqrt{1 + \dfrac{1}{15} + \dfrac{(3.8-3.147)^2}{11.177}}$$

$$= 18.7 \pm 3.4 = (15.3, 22.1).$$

(j) The best point estimate for the mpg of an individual car with engine displacement of 3.8 liters is the population mean (of all cars with 3.8-liter engine displacement). However the interval estimates will differ because the variability of individuals will be greater than the variability of sample means.

13. (a) Using technology we get: $b_0 = -132.57$ and $b_1 = 1.1702$. We use the regression equation to calculate the mean rent of a 900-square-foot apartment:
$\hat{y} = 1.1702 \cdot 900 - 132.57 = 920.61$ \$/month.

(b) Using technology, we calculate $\hat{y} = 1.1702\,x - 132.57$ to generate the table:

x	y	$\hat{y}$	$y - \hat{y}$	$(y - \hat{y})^2$	$(x - \bar{x})^2$
1161	1265	1225.98	39.02	1522.80	39024.2
1000	1050	1037.58	12.42	154.21	1335.6
1034	915	1077.37	-162.37	26363.13	4976.7
910	1003	932.27	70.73	5003.00	2857.4
934	920	960.35	-40.35	1628.27	867.6
860	890	873.76	16.24	263.73	10702.8
1056	1035	1103.11	-68.11	4639.06	8564.7

1000	1190	1037.58	152.42	23231.24	1335.6
784	730	784.83	-54.83	3006.18	32203.9
962	1005	993.12	11.88	141.23	2.1
897	940	917.06	22.94	526.42	4416.2
			Sum	66479.27	106286.7

$$s_e = \sqrt{\frac{\sum(y-\hat{y})^2}{n-2}} = \sqrt{\frac{66479.27}{11-2}} = 85.9452$$

(c) A normal probability plot shows that the residuals are normally distributed.

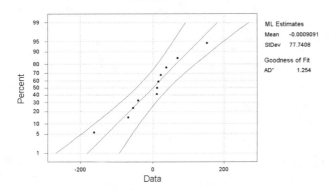

(d) $s_{b_1} = \dfrac{s_e}{\sqrt{\sum(x-\bar{x})^2}} = \dfrac{85.9452}{\sqrt{106286.7}} = 0.2636$

(e) The hypotheses are $H_0: \beta_1 = 0$, $H_1: \beta_1 \neq 0$. df $= n - 2 = 11 - 2 = 9$ and so the critical values are $\pm t_{0.025} = \pm 2.262$. The test statistic is $t = \dfrac{b_1}{s_{b_1}} = \dfrac{1.1702}{0.2636} = 4.439$, which is in the critical region and so we reject H_0. There is enough evidence to support the claim of a linear relationship between size and rent.

(f) For a 95% confidence interval we use $t_{0.025} = 2.262$ and get bounds:

$b_1 \pm t_{\alpha/2} \cdot s_{b_1} = 1.1702 \pm 2.262 \cdot 0.2636 = 1.1702 \pm 0.5963 = (0.5739, 1.7665)$.

(g) We have $n = 11$, $s_e = 85.9452$, $\bar{x} = 963.45$ and $\sum(x-\bar{x})^2 = 106286.7$. For a 90% confidence interval with df $= n - 2 = 9$, we use $t_{0.05} = 1.833$. The bounds are:

$$\hat{y} \pm t_{\alpha/2} \cdot s_e \sqrt{\frac{1}{n} + \frac{(x^*-\bar{x})^2}{\sum(x-\bar{x})^2}} = 920.61 \pm 1.833 \cdot 85.9452 \cdot \sqrt{\frac{1}{11} + \frac{(900-963.45)^2}{106286.7}}$$

$$= 920.61 \pm 56.54 = (\$864.07, \$977.15).$$

(h) The predicted value of y is also $920.61.

(i) The bounds are:

$$\hat{y} \pm t_{\alpha/2} \cdot s_e \sqrt{1 + \frac{1}{n} + \frac{(x^*-\bar{x})^2}{\sum(x-\bar{x})^2}} = 920.61 \pm 1.833 \cdot 85.9452 \cdot \sqrt{1 + \frac{1}{11} + \frac{(900-963.45)^2}{106286.7}}$$

$$= 920.61 \pm 167.37 = (\$753.24, \$1087.98).$$

(j) The best point estimate for the rent of a 900-square-foot apartment is the population mean (of all 900-square-foot apartments). However the interval estimates will differ because the variability of individuals will be greater than the variability of sample means.

15. (a) Using technology we get: $b_0 = 67.388$ and $b_1 = -0.2632$.

(b) Using technology, we calculate $\hat{y} = -0.2632x + 67.388$ to generate the table:

x	y	$\hat{y}$	$y - \hat{y}$	$(y - \hat{y})^2$	$(x - \bar{x})^2$
15	65	63.440	1.560	2.433	598.81
16	60	63.177	-3.177	10.093	550.87
28	58	60.019	-2.019	4.076	131.57
61	60	51.334	8.666	75.101	463.52
53	46	53.439	-7.439	55.344	183.04
43	66	56.071	9.929	98.582	12.46
16	56	63.177	-7.177	51.509	550.87
25	75	60.808	14.192	201.403	209.40
28	46	60.019	-14.019	196.527	131.57
34	45	58.440	-13.440	180.627	29.93
37	58	57.650	0.350	0.122	6.10
41	70	56.597	13.403	179.627	2.34
43	73	56.071	16.929	286.587	12.46
49	45	54.492	-9.492	90.099	90.81
53	60	53.439	6.561	43.042	183.04
61	56	51.334	4.666	21.772	463.52
68	30	49.492	-19.492	379.924	813.93
			Sum	1876.869	4434.24

$$s_e = \sqrt{\frac{\sum (y - \hat{y})^2}{n - 2}} = \sqrt{\frac{1876.869}{17 - 2}} = 11.1859$$

(c) A normal probability plot shows that the residuals are normally distributed.

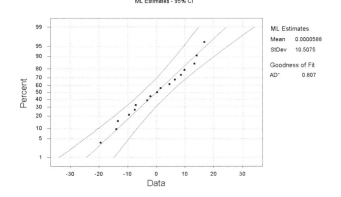

Normal Probability Plot for Residuals
ML Estimates - 95% CI

ML Estimates
Mean   0.0000588
StDev   10.5075

Goodness of Fit
AD*   0.807

(d) $s_{b_1} = \dfrac{s_e}{\sqrt{\sum(x-\bar{x})^2}} = \dfrac{11.1859}{\sqrt{4434.24}} = 0.1680$

(e) The hypotheses are $H_0 : \beta_1 = 0$, $H_1 : \beta_1 \neq 0$. df $= n-2 = 17-2 = 15$ and so the critical values are $\pm t_{0.025} = \pm 2.131$. The test statistic is $t = \dfrac{b_1}{s_{b_1}} = \dfrac{-0.2632}{0.1680} = -1.567$, which

is not in the critical region and so we do not reject H_0. There is not enough evidence to support the claim of a linear relationship between age and grip strength.

(f) Since there is no significant linear relationship, the best estimate is the sample mean grip strength, which is 57 psi.